CONNECTED MATHEMATICS® 3

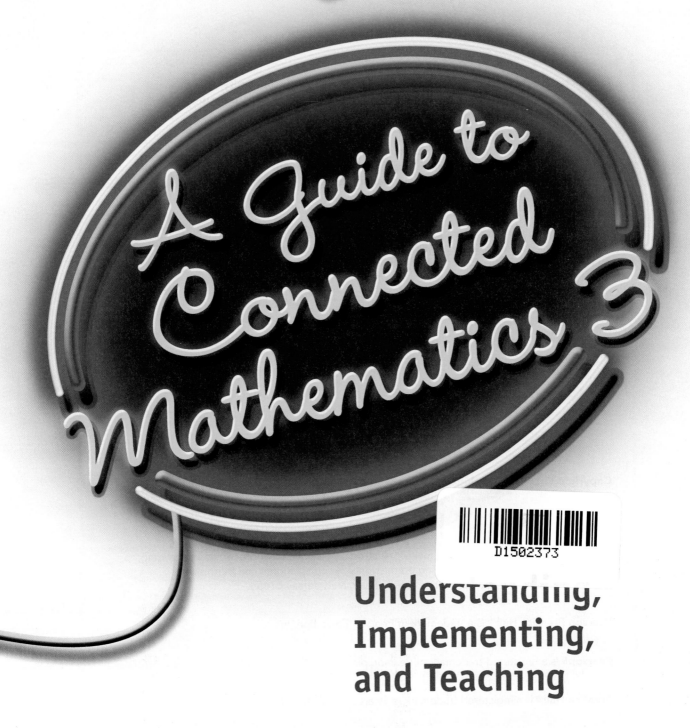

A Guide to Connected Mathematics 3

Understanding, Implementing, and Teaching

Glenda Lappan, Elizabeth Difanis Phillips,
James T. Fey, Susan N. Friel

D1502373

PEARSON

Boston, Massachusetts • Chandler, Arizona • Glenview, Illinois • Upper Saddle River, New Jersey

Connected Mathematics™ was developed at Michigan State University with financial support from the Michigan State University Office of the Provost, Computing and Technology, and the College of Natural Science.

 This material is based upon work supported by the National Science Foundation under Grant No. MDR 9150217 and Grant No. ESI 9986372. Opinions expressed are those of the authors and not necessarily those of the Foundation.

As with prior editions of this work, the authors and administration of Michigan State University preserve a tradition of devoting royalties from this publication to support activities sponsored by the MSU Mathematics Education Enrichment Fund.

13-digit ISBN 978-0-13-327421-9
10-digit ISBN 0-13-327421-7
5 6 7 8 9 10   V011   17 16 15 14

PEARSON

A Team of Experts

Glenda Lappan is a University Distinguished Professor in the Program in Mathematics Education (PRIME) and the Department of Mathematics at Michigan State University. Her research and development interests are in the connected areas of students' learning of mathematics and mathematics teachers' professional growth and change related to the development and enactment of K–12 curriculum materials.

Elizabeth Difanis Phillips is a Senior Academic Specialist in the Program in Mathematics Education (PRIME) and the Department of Mathematics at Michigan State University. She is interested in teaching and learning mathematics for both teachers and students. These interests have led to curriculum and professional development projects at the middle school and high school levels, as well as projects related to the teaching and learning of algebra across the grades.

James T. Fey is a Professor Emeritus at the University of Maryland. His consistent professional interest has been development and research focused on curriculum materials that engage middle and high school students in problem-based collaborative investigations of mathematical ideas and their applications.

Susan N. Friel is a Professor of Mathematics Education in the School of Education at the University of North Carolina at Chapel Hill. Her research interests focus on statistics education for middle-grade students and, more broadly, on teachers' professional development and growth in teaching mathematics K–8.

With... Yvonne Grant and Jacqueline Stewart

Yvonne Grant teaches mathematics at Portland Middle School in Portland, Michigan. Jacqueline Stewart is a recently retired high school teacher of mathematics at Okemos High School in Okemos, Michigan. Both Yvonne and Jacqueline have worked on all aspects of the development, implementation, and professional development of the CMP curriculum from its beginnings in 1991.

CMP3 Authors

Glenda Lappan, University Distinguished Professor, Michigan State University

Elizabeth Difanis Phillips, Senior Academic Specialist, Michigan State University

James T. Fey, Professor Emeritus, University of Maryland

Susan N. Friel, Professor, University of North Carolina – Chapel Hill

With...

Yvonne Grant, Portland Middle School, Michigan

Jacqueline Stewart, Mathematics Consultant, Mason, Michigan

In Memory of... William M. Fitzgerald, Professor (Deceased), Michigan State University, who made substantial contributions to conceptualizing and creating CMP1.

Administrative Assistant

Michigan State University
Judith Martus Miller

Support Staff

Michigan State University
Undergraduate Assistants:
Bradley Robert Corlett, Carly Fleming,
Erin Lucian, Scooter Nowak

Development Assistants

Michigan State University
Graduate Research Assistants:
Richard "Abe" Edwards, Nic Gilbertson,
Funda Gonulates, Aladar Horvath,
Eun Mi Kim, Kevin Lawrence, Jennifer Nimtz,
Joanne Philhower, Sasha Wang

Assessment Team

Maine
Falmouth Public Schools
Falmouth Middle School: Shawn Towle

Michigan
Ann Arbor Public Schools
Tappan Middle School:
Anne Marie Nicoll-Turner

Portland Public Schools
Portland Middle School:
Holly DeRosia, Yvonne Grant

Traverse City Area Public Schools
Traverse City East Middle School:
Jane Porath, Mary Beth Schmitt

Traverse City West Middle School:
Jennifer Rundio, Karrie Tufts

Ohio
Clark-Shawnee Local Schools
Rockway Middle School: Jim Mamer

Content Consultants

Michigan State University
Peter Lappan, Professor Emeritus,
Department of Mathematics

Normandale Community College
Christopher Danielson, Instructor,
Department of Mathematics & Statistics

University of North Carolina – Wilmington
Dargan Frierson, Jr., Professor,
Department of Mathematics & Statistics

Student Activities
Michigan State University
Brin Keller, Associate Professor,
Department of Mathematics

Consultants

Indiana
Purdue University
Mary Bouck, Mathematics Consultant

Michigan
Oakland Schools
Valerie Mills, Mathematics Education Supervisor

Mathematics Education Consultants: Geraldine Devine, Dana Gosen

Ellen Bacon, Independent Mathematics Consultant

New York
University of Rochester
Jeffrey Choppin, Associate Professor

Ohio
University of Toledo
Debra Johanning, Associate Professor

Pennsylvania
University of Pittsburgh
Margaret Smith, Professor

Texas
University of Texas at Austin
Emma Trevino, Supervisor of Mathematics Programs, The Dana Center

Mathematics for All Consulting
Carmen Whitman, Mathematics Consultant

Reviewers

Michigan
Ionia Public Schools
Kathy Dole, Director of Curriculum and Instruction

Grand Valley State University
Lisa Kasmer, Assistant Professor

Portland Public Schools
Teri Keusch, Classroom Teacher

Minnesota
Hopkins School District 270
Michele Luke, Mathematics Coordinator

Field Test Sites for CMP3

Michigan
Ann Arbor Public Schools
Tappan Middle School: Anne Marie Nicoll-Turner*

Portland Public Schools
Portland Middle School: Mark Braun, Angela Buckland, Holly DeRosia, Holly Feldpausch, Angela Foote, Yvonne Grant*, Kristin Roberts, Angie Stump, Tammi Wardwell

Traverse City Area Public Schools
Traverse City East Middle School
Ivanka Baic Berkshire, Brenda Dunscombe, Tracie Herzberg, Deb Larimer, Jan Palkowski, Rebecca Perreault, Jane Porath*, Robert Sagan, Mary Beth Schmitt*

Traverse City West Middle School
Pamela Alfieri, Jennifer Rundio, Maria Taplin, Karrie Tufts*

Maine
Falmouth Public Schools
Falmouth Middle School: Sally Bennett, Chris Driscoll, Sara Jones, Shawn Towle*

Minnesota
Minneapolis Public Schools
Jefferson Community School:
Leif Carlson*,
Katrina Hayek Munsisoumang*

Ohio
Clark-Shawnee Local Schools
Reid School: Joanne Gilley
Rockway Middle School: Jim Mamer*
Possum School: Tami Thomas

*Indicates a Field Test Site Coordinator

Part I
Overview

Part II
Components

Part III
The CMP Classroom

Part IV

A Curriculum for All Students

Part V

Implementing CMP

Part VI
Unifying Themes and Mathematical Strands

CMP is a coherent problem-centered curriculum that promotes an inquiry-based teaching-learning classroom environment. Important mathematical ideas are identified and the essential understandings of these ideas are embedded in a carefully-sequenced set of problems. The curriculum helps students grow in their ability to reason effectively with information represented in verbal, numeric, graphic and symbolic forms and to move flexibly among these representations to produce fluency in both conceptual and procedural knowledge.

The *Connected Mathematics Project* was funded by the National Science Foundation between 1991 and 1997 to develop a mathematics curriculum for grades 6, 7, and 8. The result was *Connected Mathematics*, a complete mathematics curriculum that helps students develop understanding of important concepts, skills, procedures, and ways of thinking and reasoning in number, geometry, measurement, algebra, probability, and statistics.

In 2000, the National Science Foundation funded a revision of the *Connected Mathematics* materials, *Connected Mathematics 2*, to take advantage of what was learned in the six years that the first edition of *Connected Mathematics* was used in schools. In 2010, with support from both the University of Maryland and Michigan State University, a third iteration, *Connected Mathematics 3*, was started.

Purpose of the Guide

This Guide elaborates the goals of *Connected Mathematics 3*, the process used for the revision, the scope of the curriculum, and a process for implementation that will support student and teacher learning. The Guide also describes digital enhancements specific to *Connected Mathematics 3*. Following is a brief description of the purpose of each part of the Guide.

Overview

The Overview provides insights into the history and philosophy of *Connected Mathematics* (CMP), including the rationale for problem-centered curriculum and inquiry-based teaching and learning, as well as principles of design that were used to develop both the student and teacher materials. The Overview also includes a description of CMP's development of procedural and conceptual understanding.

Components

Components of CMP3 details the components of the student materials, teacher materials, and assessments, including the digital support for these components.

The CMP Classroom

In The CMP Classroom, teachers will find useful information on how to set up a classroom environment that promotes mathematical discourse around problem solving and reasoning. There are suggestions for planning and implementing the Launch, Explore, and Summarize phase for each lesson.

A Curriculum for All Students

To find suggestions for working with diverse student populations, see A Curriculum for All Students.

Implementing CMP

Implementing CMP is particularly helpful for administrators, teacher leaders, and coaches. It provides important information needed to prepare the school and community to implement CMP and to conduct long-term professional development. Most importantly, the information is designed to produce collaborative and productive planning that leads to more effective teaching and learning for all teachers and students.

Unifying Themes and Mathematical Strands

The last section describes concepts and skills developed in four mathematical strands and two unifying themes. There is a section for each strand to list the details of coverage throughout the progression of Units in CMP3.

Overarching Goal of Connected Mathematics

The CMP materials reflect the understanding that teaching and learning are not distinct—"what to teach" and "how to teach it" are inextricably linked. The circumstances in which students learn affect what is learned. The needs of both students and teachers are considered in the development of the CMP curriculum materials. This curriculum helps teachers and those who work to support teachers examine their expectations for students and analyze the extent to which classroom mathematics tasks and teaching practices align with their goals and expectations. In developing the CMP curriculum, we have taken the following words of Jerome Bruner to heart:

> If it (new curriculum) cannot change, move, perturb, inform teachers, it will have no effect on those they teach. It must first and foremost be a curriculum for teachers. If it has any effect on pupils, it will have it by virtue of having an effect on teachers.

(Bruner 1977, p. xv)

The overarching goal of CMP is to help students and teachers develop mathematical knowledge, understanding, and skill along with an awareness of and appreciation for the rich connections among mathematical strands and between mathematics and other disciplines. The CMP curriculum development has been guided by our single mathematical standard:

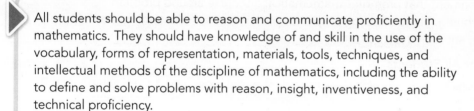

All students should be able to reason and communicate proficiently in mathematics. They should have knowledge of and skill in the use of the vocabulary, forms of representation, materials, tools, techniques, and intellectual methods of the discipline of mathematics, including the ability to define and solve problems with reason, insight, inventiveness, and technical proficiency.

History of Connected Mathematics

The CMP philosophy grew out of work in middle grades classrooms. With the aid of funds from several National Science Foundation (NSF) professional development grants, Glenda Lappan and Elizabeth Phillips, with their colleagues at Michigan State University, William Fitzgerald and Mary Winter, worked with experienced teachers to find new ways to engage students with mathematics. With pressure from teachers and funding from NSF, "we created five units that were published in 1985 for use by teachers to help make a transition from how they typically taught, 'show and practice,' to classrooms that required engagement in mathematical thinking, reasoning, solving, and proving. These units are known as the *Middle Grades Mathematics Project* (MGMP) materials. Each was focused on an important area of mathematical thinking and each was designed to engage students in important problem situations that were engaging, challenging, and educative. During this time our focus was on developing experienced teachers' knowledge of mathematics and their skill in engaging students in making sense of mathematics. It was due to these MGMP materials and their success that our group was asked to make substantial contributions to the development of the *Curriculum and Evaluation Standards for School*, published by the National Council of Teachers of Mathematics (NCTM, 1989). Lappan chaired the middle school writing group and reviewed the draft standards with teachers in our summer institutes. This document launched a new era of curriculum development in the US and our group was ready to act on our conviction that curriculum materials could make a difference" (Lappan & Phillips, 2009, p. 1).

For the next ten years, the MGMP units were used to provide professional development and leadership training for teachers and administrators in our Michigan State University summer institutes. Teachers and leaders who attended our summer institutes spread the units across the country through their local institutes. These NSF-funded activities created a rich school leadership base to support the subsequent development and use of the *Connected Mathematics Project* curriculum in school districts. The NSF funded *Connected Mathematics 1* (CMP1) in 1991. At this time, Professors James Fey from the University of Maryland and Susan Friel from the University of North Carolina joined the author team at Michigan State University for the development of CMP1. Both Fey and Friel had extensive curriculum and professional development experiences—Fey at the secondary level and Friel at the elementary level. This collaboration continues today. In 2000, NSF funded a revision of the materials, *Connected Mathematics 2* (CMP2), to take advantage of what was learned in the six years that the first edition of CMP had been used in schools. In 2010 the Common Core State Standards for Mathematics (CCSSM) were released at about the time a revision of CMP2 was being considered. With funding from the University of Maryland and Michigan State University, *Connected Mathematics 3* (CMP3) was developed. CMP3 builds on the unique strengths of the CMP philosophy and reflects the recommendations of CCSSM.

The Success of Connected Mathematics

The work of the authors with professional development and curriculum leading up to the development of CMP is a critical element in its success. Additionally, the professional development and outreach activities carried out by the CMP authors and teachers, beginning with the publication of CMP1 in 1996, are also very important. The CMP philosophy fosters a focus on isolating important mathematical ideas and embedding these ideas in carefully sequenced sets of contextual problems. These problems are developed and trialed in classrooms in different states over several years. Each revision of CMP has been extensively field-tested in its development phases. We solicited iterative and in-depth input and reviews from teachers, parents, administrators, mathematics educators, mathematicians, cognitive scientists, and experts in reading, special education, and English language learners. Our materials are created to support teachers in helping their students develop deeper mathematical understanding and reasoning. This stance is the foundation of the success of CMP, which has withstood the pressures of various political changes in the Nation over time.

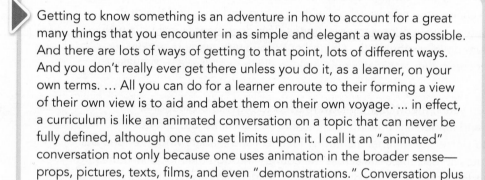

> Getting to know something is an adventure in how to account for a great many things that you encounter in as simple and elegant a way as possible. And there are lots of ways of getting to that point, lots of different ways. And you don't really ever get there unless you do it, as a learner, on your own terms. … All you can do for a learner enroute to their forming a view of their own view is to aid and abet them on their own voyage. … in effect, a curriculum is like an animated conversation on a topic that can never be fully defined, although one can set limits upon it. I call it an "animated" conversation not only because one uses animation in the broader sense— props, pictures, texts, films, and even "demonstrations." Conversation plus show-and-tell plus brooding on it all on one's own.
>
> Bruner (1992, p.5)[1]

For more information on the history of *Connected Mathematics*, see
http://www.educationaldesigner.org/ed/volume1/issue3/article11/index.htm.

---

[1] Bruner, Jerome. (1992). Science education and teachers: A Karplus lecture. Journal of Science Education and Technology; 1(1), 5–12.

The authors were guided by the following principles in the development of the CMP materials. These statements reflect both research and policy stances in mathematics education about what works to support students' learning of important mathematics.

Guiding Principles

- **CMP is problem-centered.** Mathematical tasks for students in class and in homework are the primary vehicle for student engagement with the mathematical concepts to be learned. The key mathematical goals are elaborated, exemplified, and connected through the Problems in an Investigation.

- **CMP identifies big ideas and goes for depth.** Ideas are explored through these mathematical tasks in the depth necessary to allow students to make sense of them. Superficial treatment of an idea produces shallow and short-lived understanding and does not support making connections among ideas.

- **CMP has coherence.** The underlying concepts, skills, or procedures supporting the development of a key idea are identified and included in an appropriate development sequence. The curriculum builds and connects from Problem to Problem, Investigation to Investigation, Unit to Unit and grade to grade.

- **CMP intertwines conceptual and procedural knowledge.** The curriculum helps students grow in their ability to reason effectively with information represented in graphic, numeric, symbolic, and verbal forms and to move flexibly among these representations to produce fluency in both conceptual and procedural knowledge.

- **CMP develops skills and concepts as needed.** Concepts and skills are developed, as appropriate, to solve interesting and challenging problems.

- **CMP promotes inquiry-based instruction.** Classroom instruction focuses on inquiry and investigation of mathematical ideas embedded in rich problem situations through rich classroom discourse and collaborations.

- **CMP promotes effective use of technology.** The curriculum reflects the information-processing and delivery capabilities of calculators and computers and the fundamental changes such tools are making in the way people learn mathematics and apply their knowledge of problem solving to new tasks.

- **CMP has high expectations of all students.** All students are asked sophisticated mathematical questions and are expected to persevere in their explorations to these questions, looking for patterns, generalizing, validating, and sharing and critiquing each others work.

Rationale for a Problem-Centered Curriculum

Students' perceptions about a discipline come from the tasks or problems with which they are asked to engage. For example, if students in a geometry course are asked to memorize definitions, they think geometry is about memorizing definitions. If students spend a majority of their mathematics time practicing paper-and-pencil computations, they come to believe that mathematics is about calculating answers to arithmetic problems as quickly as possible. They may become faster at performing specific types of computations, but they may not be able to apply these skills to other situations or to recognize problems that call for these skills. Formal mathematics begins with undefined terms, axioms, and definitions and deduces important conclusions logically from those starting points. However, mathematics is produced and used in a much more complex combination of exploration, experience-based intuition, and reflection. If the purpose of studying mathematics is to be able to solve a variety of problems, then students need to spend significant portions of their mathematics time solving problems that require thinking, planning, reasoning, computing, and evaluating.

A growing body of evidence from the cognitive sciences supports the theory that students can make more sense of mathematics if the concepts and skills are embedded within a context or problem. If time is spent exploring interesting mathematics situations, reflecting on solution methods, examining why the methods work, comparing methods, and relating methods to those used in previous situations, then students are likely to build more robust understanding of mathematical concepts and related procedures. This method is quite different from the assumption that students learn by observing a teacher as he or she demonstrates how to solve a problem and then practicing that method on similar problems. A problem-centered curriculum not only helps students to make sense of the mathematics, but also helps them to process the mathematics in a retrievable way.

Teachers of CMP report that students in succeeding grades remember and refer to a concept, technique, or problem-solving strategy by the name of the Problem in which they encountered the ideas. For example, the Basketball Problem from *What Do You Expect?* in grade 7 becomes a trigger for remembering the processes of finding compound probabilities and expected values.

Results from the cognitive sciences also suggest that learning is enhanced if it is connected to prior knowledge and is more likely to be retained and applied to future learning. Critically examining, refining, and extending conjectures and strategies are also important aspects of becoming reflective learners.

In CMP, important mathematical ideas are embedded in the context of interesting problems. As students explore a series of connected problems, they develop understanding of the embedded ideas and, with the aid of the teacher, abstract powerful mathematical ideas, problem-solving strategies, and ways of thinking. They learn mathematics and learn how to learn mathematics.

Criteria for a Mathematical Task

To be effective, problems must embody critical concepts and skills and have the potential to engage students in making sense of mathematics. And, since students build understanding by reflecting, connecting, and communicating, the problems need to encourage them to use these processes.

Each CMP Problem has some or all of the following characteristics:

- Embeds important, useful mathematics
- Promotes conceptual and procedural knowledge
- Builds on and connects to other important mathematical ideas
- Requires higher-level thinking, reasoning, and problem solving
- Engages students and promotes classroom discourse
- Allows for various solution strategies
- Creates an opportunity for teacher to assess student learning

Developing Mathematical Fluency

Students need to practice mathematical concepts, ideas, and procedures to reach a level of fluency that allows them to "think" with the ideas in new situations. To accomplish this, we were guided by the following principles related to skills practice.

- Immediate practice is related to the situations in which the ideas have been developed and learned.
- Continued practice uses reasoning, skills, and procedures in situations that connect to ideas that students have already encountered as well as to new situations.
- Practice is distributed over time to allow ideas, concepts and procedures to reach a level of fluency of use in familiar and unfamiliar situations and to allow connections to be made to other concepts and procedures.
- Students learn how to make judgments about what operation or combination of operations or representations is useful in a given situation, as well as becoming skillful in carrying out the needed computation(s); *knowing how to, but not when to, is insufficient.*

Rationale for Depth Versus Spiraling

The concept of a "spiraling" curriculum is philosophically appealing; but, too often, not enough time is spent initially with a new concept to build on it at the next stage of the spiral. This causes teachers to spend a great deal of time reteaching the same ideas over and over again. Without a deeper understanding of concepts and how they are connected, students come to view mathematics as a collection of different techniques and algorithms to be memorized.

Problem solving based on such learning becomes a search for the correct algorithm rather than seeking to make sense of the situation, considering the nature and size of a solution, putting together a solution path that makes sense, and examining the solution in light of the original question. Taking time for the ideas studied to be more carefully developed means that when these ideas are met in the future, students have a solid foundation on which to build. Rather than being caught in a cycle of relearning the same ideas at a superficial level, which are quickly forgotten, students are able to connect new ideas to previously learned knowledge and make substantive advances in learning.

With any important mathematical concept, there are many related ideas, procedures, and skills. At each grade level, a small, select set of important mathematical concepts, ideas, and related procedures are studied in depth rather than skimming through a larger set of ideas in a shallow manner. This means that time is allocated to develop understanding of key ideas in contrast to "covering" a book. The teacher support materials accompanying CMP were developed to support teachers to plan for and teach a problem-centered curriculum. Practice on related skills and algorithms is provided in a distributed fashion so that students not only practice these skills and algorithms to reach facility in carrying out computations, but they also learn to put their growing body of skills together to solve new problems.

Proportional Reasoning—Example of Depth and Connectedness

Through the process of field trials, we are able to develop content that results in student understanding of key ideas in depth. An example is illustrated in the way that CMP treats proportional reasoning, a fundamentally important topic for middle school mathematics and beyond. Conventional treatments of this central topic are often limited to a brief expository presentation of the ideas of ratio and proportion, followed by training in techniques for solving proportions. In contrast, the CMP curriculum materials develop core elements of proportional reasoning in a seventh-grade Unit, *Comparing and Scaling*, with the groundwork having been developed in four prior Units. Five succeeding Units build on and connect to students' understanding of proportional reasoning. These Units and their connections are summarized as follows:

Grade 6

Comparison statements are used to introduce ratios and rates in *Comparing Bits and Pieces*. Understanding of equivalent fractions is also extended and contrasted with equivalent ratios. In this Unit, ratios are not notated as fractions. The extensive work with equivalent forms of fractions builds the skills needed to work with ratio and proportion problems. These ideas are developed further in *Variables and Patterns* as rate reemerges in terms of rate tables and in graphs.

Grade 7

Stretching and Shrinking introduces proportionality concepts through the context of geometric Problems involving similarity. Students connect visual ideas about enlarging and reducing figures, numerical ideas about scale factors and ratios, and applications of similarity through work with problems focused around the question: "What would it mean to say two figures are similar?"

Next in the seventh grade is a core proportional reasoning Unit, *Comparing and Scaling*, which connects fractions, percents, and ratios through investigation of various situations in which the central question is: "What strategies make sense in describing how much greater one quantity is than another?" Through a series of problem-based Investigations, students explore the meaning of ratio comparison and through a progression of Problems that builds on intuition and moves to developing and articulating procedures, students develop a variety of techniques for dealing with questions that include unit rates and constants of proportionality.

Moving Straight Ahead follows *Comparing and Scaling* and is about linear relationships and equations. Proportional thinking is connected and extended to develop the core ideas of linearity (constant rate of change and slope), as well as recognizing the coefficients of x in $y = mx$ as the constant of proportionality. In *What Do You Expect?*, students use ratios to make comparisons of probabilities. In *Filling and Wrapping*, students investigate the effects on volume and surface area from scaling up the dimensions of prisms. Lastly, *Samples and Populations* uses proportional reasoning to compare data situations and to choose samples from populations.

Grade 8

Thinking With Mathematical Models; Looking For Pythagoras; Growing, Growing, Growing; and *Frogs, Fleas,* and *Painted Cubes* extend the understanding of proportional relationships in the eighth grade by investigating the contrast between linear relationships and inverse, exponential, and quadratic relationships.

This description of how CMP treats proportional reasoning shows two things about CMP: the in-depth development of fundamental ideas and the connected use of these important ideas throughout the program.

Instructional Phases

Problem-centered teaching opens the mathematics classroom to exploring, conjecturing, reasoning, and communicating. The CMP teacher materials are organized around an instructional model that supports this kind of "inquiry-based" teaching. This model is very different from the "transmission" or "direct instruction" model, in which teachers tell students facts and demonstrate procedures and then students memorize the facts and practice the procedures. The CMP model looks at instruction in three phases: launching, exploring, and summarizing.

The following text describes the three instructional phases and provides the general kinds of questions that are asked. Specific notes and questions for each Problem are provided in the teacher support.

Launch

In the first phase, the teacher launches the Problem with the whole class. Launches include connecting to prior knowledge, as well as presenting the challenge of the Problem.

Connecting to Prior Knowledge

First, the teacher helps position the new Problem within prior understandings and Problems. This is the time when the teacher clarifies prior definitions, reviews old concepts and connects the Problem to past experiences of the students. When planning for this part, teachers should ask themselves the following questions:

- What prior knowledge do my students need to build on?

- How can I use that information to support this Problem?

Presenting the Challenge

After connecting the Problem to prior knowledge, the teacher then helps students understand the Problem setting, the mathematical context, and the challenge.

The following questions can help the teacher prepare for the launch:

- What are students expected to do?

- What do the students need to know to understand the context of the story and the challenge of the Problem?

- What difficulties for students can I foresee?

- How can I help without giving away too much of the Problem solution?

It is critical that the teacher leaves the potential of the task intact, while giving students a clear picture of what is expected. He or she must be careful not to tell too much and consequently lower the challenge of the task to something routine, or to be so directive, that the rich array of strategies that may evolve from a more open launch of the Problem is lost.

Explore

For the Explore phase, the nature of the Problem suggests whether students work individually, in pairs, in small groups, or occasionally as a whole class to solve the Problem. The teacher support suggests an appropriate grouping. As students work, they gather data, share ideas, look for patterns, make conjectures, and develop problem-solving strategies. It is inevitable that students will exhibit variation in their progress. The teacher's role during this phase is twofold as described below:

Providing for Individual Needs

The Explore phase provides an opportunity for a teacher to observe and interact with individual and small groups. The teacher moves about the classroom, observing individual performance and encouraging on-task behavior. The teacher helps students persevere in their work by asking appropriate questions and providing confirmation and redirection where needed. For students who are interested in and capable of deeper investigation, the teacher may provide extra questions related to the Problem. These questions are called *Going Further* and are provided in the teacher support. Suggestions for helping students who may be struggling are also provided. The Explore is an appropriate time to attend to differentiated learning.

The following questions can help the teacher prepare for the Explore:

- How will I organize the students to explore this Problem? (Individuals? Pairs? Groups? Whole class?)

- What materials will students need?

- How should students record and report their work?

- What different strategies can I anticipate they might use?

- What questions can I ask to encourage student conversation, thinking, and learning?

- What questions can I ask to focus their thinking if they become frustrated or off-task?

- What questions can I ask to challenge students if the initial question is "answered"?

- What difficulties are students having?

- How can I help without giving away the solution?

- What strategies are students using? Are they correct?

- How will I use these strategies during the summary?

Planning for the Summary

As the teacher moves about the classroom during the Explore, she or he should attend to the following questions:

- What evidence do I have from the Explore that can be used to support student understanding of the Focus Question during the summary?

- How will I organize the discussion?

- What will I do if I have insufficient evidence to support the summary?

Summarize

It is during the Summarize phase that the teacher guides the students to reach the mathematical goals of the Problem and to connect their new understanding to prior mathematical goals and Problems in the Unit. The Summarize begins when most students have gathered sufficient data or made sufficient progress toward solving the Problem. In this phase, students present and discuss their solutions and the strategies they used to understand the Problem, organize the data, and find the solution. During the discussion, the teacher helps students enhance their conceptual understanding of the mathematics in the Problem and guides them in refining their strategies into efficient, effective, generalizable problem-solving techniques or algorithms.

Although the teacher leads the discussion in the Summarize, students play a significant role. Ideally, they pose conjectures, question each other, offer alternatives, provide reasons, refine their strategies and conjectures, and make connections. As a result of the discussion, students should become more skillful at using the ideas and techniques that come out of the experience with the Problem.

If it is appropriate, the Summarize can end by the teacher posing a question or two to check students' understanding of the mathematical goal(s) that have been developed at this point in time. Check for Understanding questions occur occasionally in the teacher support for the Summarize. These questions help the teacher to assess the degree to which students are developing and using their mathematical knowledge.

Orchestrating a Discussion

The following questions can help the teacher prepare for orchestrating a discussion during the summary.

- How can I help the students make sense of and appreciate the variety of methods that may be used?

- How can I orchestrate the discussion so that students summarize their thinking about the Problem?

- What questions can guide the discussion?

- What concepts or strategies need to be emphasized?

- What ideas do not need closure at this time?

- What definitions or strategies do we need to generalize?

- What connections and extensions can be made?

- What new questions might arise and how do I handle them?

- What can I do to follow up, practice, or apply the ideas after the summary?

Reflecting on Student Learning

The following questions can be used to assess student understanding at the end of the lesson.

- What evidence do I have that students understand the Focus Question?

  Where did my students get stuck?

  What strategies did they use?

  What breakthroughs did my students have today?

- How will I use this to plan for tomorrow? For the next time I teach this lesson?

- Where will I have the opportunity to reinforce these ideas as I continue through this Unit? The next Unit?

Teacher Roles

When mathematical ideas are embedded in problem-based investigations with rich context, the teacher has a critical responsibility for ensuring that students abstract and generalize the important mathematical concepts and procedures from their experiences with the problems. In a problem-centered classroom, teachers take on new roles. They move from always being the one who does the mathematics to being the one who guides, interrogates, and facilitates the learner to do and make sense of the mathematics. As teachers grow into their new roles, satisfaction comes from their increasing ability to recognize and use student thinking more effectively in developing deeper understanding, reasoning, and skills. Witnessing students collaborating, challenging each other, thinking in new ways, and communicating these ideas is worth the effort. Extensive help is provided in the teacher support. See Components and The CMP Classroom for more information about the teacher support.

The fundamental features of the CMP program reflect the authors' core beliefs about essential features of effective teaching and learning of mathematics. These features include, a focus on big ideas and the connections among them, teaching through student-centered exploration of mathematically rich problems, and using continuous assessment to inform instruction.

Through more than twenty years of CMP work, our personal knowledge and beliefs about mathematics and its teaching have been richly enhanced by advice from teachers and students who used field-test versions of the materials. We have gained valuable insights from mathematicians, teacher educators, and other curriculum developers. Our work has also been influenced in significant ways by insights from theoretical and empirical research in mathematics education, cognitive science, educational research about teaching and teacher development, and education policy implementation.

From the broad array of pertinent research findings seven major themes continue to influence development and implementation of the CMP curriculum and teaching resources. These themes are explored below.

Cooperative Learning and Classroom Discourse

We are in general agreement with constructivist explanations of the ways that knowledge is developed, especially the social constructivist ideas about the influence of discourse on learning.[2] There is a consistent and growing body of research indicating that when students engage in cooperative work on challenging problem solving tasks, their mathematical and social learning will be enhanced.[3] Recent research has also shown that the discourse of a classroom—the ways of representing, thinking, talking, agreeing and disagreeing—is central to what students learn about mathematics.[4] Effective teachers ask open-ended questions to elicit student thinking and ask students to explain their thinking and comment on one another's work.

This complex of related research findings is reflected in our decision to write materials that support student-centered investigation of mathematical problems and in our attempt to design problem content and formats that encourage student-student and student-teacher dialogue about the work.

Teaching Through Problem Solving

Mathematics education has always sought to develop student problem solving skills. But teaching mathematics *through problem solving* presents different challenges for both teachers and students.

Over the past several decades, researchers have engaged in extensive classroom studies to assess the effectiveness of problem-based learning[5] and the practices that make it effective. A summary of that research by Stein, Boaler, and Silver[6] identified five critical teacher actions: "(a) (appropriate) scaffolding of students' thinking; (b) a sustained press for students' explanations; (c) thoughtful probing of students' strategies and solutions; (d) helping students accept responsibility for, and gain facility with, learning in a more open way; and (e) attending to issues of equity in the classroom." The CMP instructional materials and teacher resources have been designed with the explicit aim of engaging and sustaining diverse groups of students in high-level thinking.

Equity and Motivation for Learning

In American schools, one of the greatest challenges for teachers is to provide learning tasks and supports that engage and sustain the interest and effort of students with very diverse background experiences, values, interests, and abilities. This challenge is especially acute for teachers who want their students to take principal responsibility for their own learning and to do so in collaboration with other students.

In designing the CMP instructional materials, we have paid careful attention to literature on extrinsic and intrinsic motivation, and we have done some informal developmental research of our own to explore aspects of mathematics and teaching that are most effective for engaging student attention and interest. We have also attended to research that explores the response of diverse students to teaching through problem solving.[7]

Conceptual and Procedural Knowledge

We have been influenced by theory and research indicating that mathematical understanding is fundamentally a web of logical and psychological connections among ideas. Knowledge that is rich in connections will be retained well and retrieved effectively for subsequent problem solving and reasoning tasks.[8] Furthermore, we have interpreted research on the interplay of conceptual and procedural knowledge to say that sound conceptual understanding is an important foundation for procedural skill, not an incidental and delayed consequence of repeated rote procedural practice.

These findings are reflected in the CMP instructional materials that are rich in connections between topics in the four major content strands of the curriculum— number and operations, geometry and measurement, data analysis and probability, and algebra—and in our careful attention to laying conceptual foundations for learning of mathematical procedures.

Formative Assessment

Extensive recent research has demonstrated convincingly that student learning improves significantly when teachers provide frequent feedback on their progress and when teachers use that assessment as a core input to their planning for instruction.[9] The CMP instructional resources provide a variety of classroom-tested tools for such helpful formative assessment.

Mathematical Knowledge for Teaching

Research over the past several decades has shown quite convincingly that effective mathematics teachers have a special kind of understanding of the subjects they teach—knowledge that includes ways of representing concepts and procedures in different forms and ways that students are likely to have difficulty in learning or to form misconceptions. This special kind of understanding of mathematics is often referred to as mathematical knowledge for teaching.[10] Some of the keys to this valuable teacher knowledge are generic—applying across all content strands of the subject—while others are particularly salient in specific topics.

In design and development of the CMP instructional materials, we have paid close attention to both general and specific kinds of mathematical knowledge for teaching. We have included tasks for students that will help them succeed when confronted by common obstacles to learning. We have included advice to teachers about those likely stumbling blocks and strategies for addressing or avoiding them. In particular, the research findings in the following content areas of mathematical reasoning have been incorporated into the student and teacher materials.

- **Multiple Representations** An important indication of students' connected mathematical knowledge is their ability to represent ideas in a variety of ways. We have interpreted this theory to imply that instructional materials should frequently provide and ask for knowledge representation using graphs, number patterns, written explanations, and symbolic expressions. Students also should be challenged to interpret information provided in one representational style through use of another representation.

- **Rational Numbers/Proportional Reasoning** The extensive psychological literature on the development of rational numbers and proportional reasoning has guided our development of curriculum materials to address this important middle school topic. Furthermore, the implementation of CMP materials in real classrooms has allowed us to contribute to that literature with research publications that show the effects of new teaching approaches to traditionally difficult topics.

- **Probability and Statistical Reasoning** The interesting research literature related to the development of and the cognitive obstacles to student learning of statistical concepts, such as mean and graphic displays, and probability concepts, such as the law of large numbers, has been used as we developed the statistics and probability Units for CMP3.

- **Algebraic Reasoning** The different conceptualizations of algebra described and studied in the research literature contributed to the treatment of algebra in CMP3. Various scholars describe algebra as a study of modeling, functions, generalized arithmetic, and/or as a problem-solving tool. CMP3 develops each of these foci for algebra, but attends more directly to functions and the effects of rates of change on representations.

  The research literature illuminates some of the cognitive complexities inherent in algebraic reasoning and offers suggestions for helping students overcome difficulties. We have drawn on that research in the design of our approach to concepts of equivalence, functions, the equal sign, algebraic variables, the use of graphs and other representations, and the role of technology.

- **Geometric/Measurement Reasoning** Results from national assessments show that achievement in geometry and measurement is weak among many American students. The theoretical ideas of the van Hieles and other specific studies about student understanding of shape and form, and learning of geometric/ measurement concepts, such as angle, area, perimeter, volume, and processes such as visualization, contributed to the development of geometry/measurement Units in CMP3 materials.

Teacher Development and School Change

Education is a social institution with traditional practices that are deeply resistant to change. Thus implementation of strikingly different curricular and instructional practices is a challenge for teachers and students and for the broader school community.

In the process of helping teachers through professional development, we have paid close attention to what is known about effective teacher professional development and the school strategies that seem to be most effective.[11] The sections of this guide reflect our reading of the research on teacher and school change and our experience over 20 years of work with teachers and schools introducing the CMP curriculum.

Conclusion

While each of the seven themes described above indicates influence of theory and research on design and development of the CMP curriculum, teacher, and assessment materials, it would be misleading to suggest that the influence is direct and controlling in all decisions. As the authors have read the research literature reporting empirical and theoretical work, research findings and new ideas have been absorbed and factored into the creative, deliberative, and experimental process that leads to a comprehensive mathematics program for schools.

A good reference book to consult for more insight into what research says in these areas is Kilpatrick, J., Martin, W. G., & Schifter, D. (Eds.) (2003) *A Research Companion to Principles and Standards for School Mathematics*, Reston, VA: National Council of Teachers of Mathematics.

Since it publication in 1996, a substantial number of research studies have been carried out in CMP classrooms. These studies have helped the field understand the conditions under which a problem-centered curriculum promotes students' and teachers' conceptual and procedural skills as well as their problem-solving and reasoning abilities.

[2] Yackel, E. and Cobb, P. (1996) Sociomathematical Norms, Argumentation, and Autonomy in Mathematics. *Journal for Research in Mathematics Education* (27), 458–477.

[3] Cohen, E. G. (1994). Restructuring the Classroom: Conditions for Productive Small Groups. Review of Educational Research, 64(1), pp. 1–35.

[4] Smith, M. S. and Stein, M. K. (2011) *5 Practices for Orchestrating Productive Mathematics Discussions*. Reston, VA: National Council of Teachers of Mathematics.

[5] Wirkala, C., & Kuhn, D. (2011). *Problem-based Learning in K-12 Education: Is it Effective and How Does it Achieve its Effects?* American Educational Research Journal, 48(5), pp. 1157–1186.

[6] Stein, M. K., Boaler, J., and Silver, E. A. (2003) Teaching Mathematics Through Problem Solving: Research Perspectives (p. 253). In H. L. Schoen and R. I. Charles (Eds.) *Teaching Mathematics through Problem Solving Grades 6–12*. Reston, VA: National Council of Teachers of Mathematics. pp. 245–256.

[7] Lubienski, S. T. and Stilwell, J. (2003). Teaching Low-SES Students Mathematics Through Problem Solving: Tough Issues, Promising Strategies, and Lingering Dilemmas. In H. L. Schoen and R. I. Charles, op cit.

[8] Hiebert, J. (Ed.) Conceptual and Procedural Knowledge: The Case of Mathematics. Hillsdale, NJ: Lawrence Erlbaum Associates (1986).

[9] Wiliam, D. (2007) *Keeping learning on track: classroom assessment and the regulation of learning*. In F. K. Lester Jr (Ed.), Second handbook of mathematics teaching and learning, Greenwich, CT: Information Age Publishing.

[10] Hill, H.C., Rowan, B., & Ball, D.L. (2005) Effects of teachers' mathematical knowledge for teaching on student achievement. *American Educational Research Journal* 42, 371–406.

[11] Borko, H. (2004) Professional Development and Teacher Learning: Mapping the Terrain. *Educational Researcher* (33) 3, pp. 3–15.

CMP and the Common Core Standards for Mathematical Content

The widespread adoption of the Common Core Standards for Mathematics called for thoughtful examination of the relationship of the Standards for Mathematical Content to CMP. This examination was central in guiding the authors in the development and placement of the mathematics in CMP3 in a way that aligns with the content standards while staying true to the CMP philosophy. As a result, CMP3 incorporates all of the Standards for Mathematical Content, as well as the Standards for Mathematical Practice. The details of the relationship of CMP3 content to the Mathematical Content standards are in Appendices C and D. At a broader level, Appendix E summarizes the changes in content from CMP2 to CMP3.

CMP and the Common Core Standards for Mathematical Practice

The Common Core Standards for Mathematical Practice come alive in the CMP classroom as students and teachers interact around a sequence of rich tasks to discuss, conjecture, validate, generalize, extend, connect, and communicate. As a result, students develop deep understanding of concepts and the inclination and ability to reason and make sense of new situations.

The heart and soul of the Mathematical Practices have been the foundation of the CMP classroom from its beginning, especially the practice "make sense of problems and persevere in solving them." In CMP, one additional practice has been critical in helping students develop new and deeper understandings and strategies. New knowledge is developed by connecting and building on prior knowledge. In the process, understanding of prior knowledge is extended and deepened. Thus, our additional practice is

> ▶ Build on and connect to prior knowledge in order to build deeper understandings and new insights.

Students use many of the Mathematical Practices each day in class. To enhance students' metacognition of the role of the Mathematical Practices in developing their understanding and reasoning, examples of student reasoning that reflect several of the Mathematical Practices are given at the end of each Investigation in the Student Edition. The teacher support offers additional examples of student reasoning. Below is an explanation of how CMP addresses mathematical practices throughout the student editions.

Make sense of problems and persevere in solving them

This mathematical practice comes alive in the *Connected Mathematics* classroom as students and teachers interact around a sequence of rich problems, to conjecture, validate, generalize, extend, connect, and communicate.

Reason abstractly and quantitatively

As students observe, experiment with, analyze, induce, deduce, extend, generalize, relate and manipulate information from problems, they develop the disposition to inquire, investigate, conjecture and communicate with others around mathematical ideas.

Construct viable arguments and critique the reasoning of others

The student and teacher materials support a pedagogy that focuses on explaining thinking and understanding the reasoning of others.

Model with mathematics

The student materials provide opportunities to construct, make inferences from, and interpret concrete, symbolic, graphic, verbal, and algorithmic models of quantitative, statistical, probabilistic and algebraic relationships.

Use appropriate tools strategically

Problem settings encourage the selection and intelligent use of calculators, computers, drawing and measuring tools, and physical models to measure attributes, and represent, simulate and manipulate relationships.

Attend to precision

Students are encouraged to decide whether an estimate or an exact answer for a calculation is called for, to compare estimates to computed answers, and to choose an appropriate measure or scale depending on the degree of accuracy needed.

Look for and make use of structure

Problems are deliberately designed and sequenced to prompt students to look for interrelated ideas, and take advantage of patterns that show how data points, numbers, shapes or algebraic expressions are related to each other.

Look for and express regularity in repeated reasoning

Students are encouraged to observe and explain patterns in computations or symbolic reasoning that lead to further insights and fluency with efficient algorithms.

Research, Field Tests, and Evaluation

The development of CMP3 was built on the extensive knowledge gained from the development, research and evaluation of CMP1 and CMP2. It is important to describe the development of CMP 1 and CMP 2 to gain insights into the important findings from a variety of experts, including extensive field testing that allowed the development of CMP3 to be smaller and more focused.

The Development of CMP1 and CMP2

Before starting the design phase for the CMP1 materials, we commissioned individual reviews of CMP material from 84 individuals in 17 states and comprehensive reviews from more than 20 schools in 14 states. Individual reviews focused on particular strands over all three grades (such as number, algebra, or statistics) on particular subpopulations (such as students with special needs or those who are commonly underserved), or on topical concerns (such as language use and readability). Comprehensive reviews were conducted in groups that included teachers, administrators, curriculum supervisors, mathematicians, experts in special education, language, and reading-level analyses, English language learners, issues of equity, and others. Each group reviewed an entire grade level of the curriculum. All responses were coded and entered into a database that allowed reports to be printed for any issue or combination of issues that would be helpful to an author or staff person in designing a Unit.

In addition, we made a call to schools to serve as pilot schools for the development of CMP2. We received 50 applications from districts for piloting. From these applications we chose 15 that included 49 school sites in 12 states and the District of Columbia. We received evaluation feedback from these sites over the five-year cycle of development.

Based on the reviews, what the authors had learned from CMP pilot schools over a six-year period, and input from our Advisory Board, the authors started with grades 6 and 7 and systematically revised and restructured the Units and their sequence for each grade level to create a first draft of the revision. These were sent to our pilot schools to be taught during the second year of the project. These initial grade-level Unit drafts were the basis for substantial feedback from our trial teachers.

Here are examples of the kinds of questions we asked classroom teachers following each revision of a Unit or grade level.

"Big Picture" Unit Feedback

- Is the mathematics important for students at this grade level? Explain.

- Are the mathematical goals clear to you?

- Overall, what are the strengths and weaknesses in this Unit?

- Please comment on your students' achievement of mathematics understanding at the end of this Unit. What concepts/skills did they "nail"? Which concepts/skills are still developing? Which concepts/skills need a great deal more reinforcement?

- Is there a flow to the sequencing of the Investigations? Does the mathematics develop smoothly throughout the Unit? Are there any big leaps where another Problem is needed to help students understand a big idea in an Investigation? What adjustments did you make in these rough spots?

Problem-by-Problem Feedback

- Are the mathematical goals of each Problem/Investigation clear to you?

- Is the language and wording of each Problem understandable to students?

- Are there any grammatical or mathematical errors in the Problems?

- Are there any Problems that you think can be deleted?

- Are there any Problems that needed serious revision?

Applications-Connections-Extensions

- Does the format of the ACE exercises work for you and your students? Why or why not?

- Which ACE exercises work well, which would you change, and why?

- What needs to be added to or deleted from the ACE exercises? Is there enough practice for students? How do you supplement and why?

- Are there sufficient ACE exercises that challenge your more interested and capable students? If not, what needs to be added and why?

- Are there sufficient ACE exercises that are accessible to and helpful to students that need more scaffolding for the mathematical ideas?

Mathematical Reflections and Looking Back/Ahead

- Are these reflections useful to you and your students in identifying and making more explicit the "big" mathematical ideas in the Unit? If not, how could they be improved?

Assessment Material Feedback

- Are the check-ups, quizzes, tests, and projects useful to you? If not, how can they be improved? What should be deleted and what should be added?

- How do you use the assessment materials? Do you supplement the materials? If so, how and why?

Teacher Content Feedback

- Is the teacher support useful to you? If not, what changes do you suggest and why?

- Which parts of the teacher support help you and which do you ignore or seldom use?

- What would be helpful to add or expand in the Teacher support?

Year-End Grade-Level Feedback

- Are the mathematical concepts, skills and processes appropriate for the grade level?

- Is the grade-level placement of Units optimal for your school district? Why or why not?

- Does the mathematics flow smoothly for the students over the year?

- Once an idea is learned, is there sufficient reinforcement and use in succeeding Units?

- Are connections made between Units within each grade level?

- Does the grade-level sequence of Units seem appropriate? If not, what changes would you make and why?

- Overall, what are the strengths and weaknesses in the Units for the year?

Final Big Question

- What three to five things would you have us seriously improve, change, or drop at each grade level?

Development Summary

CMP development followed the very rigorous design, field-test, evaluate loop pictured in the diagram below.

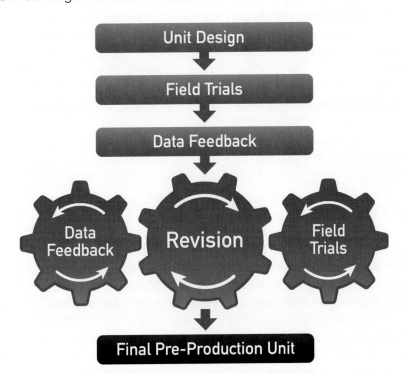

The Units for each grade level at CMP1 and CMP2 went through at least three cycles of field trials–data feedback–revision. If needed, Units had four rounds of field trials. This process of (1) commissioning reviews from experts, (2) using the field trials with feedback loops for the materials, (3) conducting key classroom observations by the CMP staff, and (4) monitoring student performance on state and local tests by trial schools comprises research-based development of curriculum. This process takes five years to produce the final drafts of Units that are sent to the publisher. Another 18 months is needed for editing, design, and layout for the published Units. This process produces materials that are cohesive and effectively sequenced.

The Development of CMP3

The development of CMP3 is built on the knowledge we have gained over the past 15 years of working with teachers and students who used CMP1 and CMP2. In addition, for the past 17 years we have solicited information from the field through our web site and CMP mailing list and through our annual CMP Users' Conference, the Getting to Know CMP workshops, and the CMP Teacher Leader/Coaches workshop. These extensive development processes for CMP1 and CMP2 and the ongoing gathering of information from teachers have resulted in a smaller but more focused development process for CMP3.

Therefore, the process of revision for CMP3 was similar to the preceding iterations except on a smaller scale. A group of field-test teachers from CMP2 trialed the versions of the Units for CMP3 that had substantive changes from CMP2. They also contributed to the development of the assessment items and suggested many of the new features in the student and teacher materials. They were influential in designing many new features such as the "focus questions" for each problem, a more streamlined set of mathematical goals, and Mathematical Reflections. Their feedback was invaluable in making sure that our adjustment for CCSSM resulted in materials from which students and teachers could learn. CMP3 is fully aligned with the CCSSM and Mathematical Practices and reflects the thoughtful concern and care of the authors and CMP3 trial teachers. This process has produced a mathematical experience that is highly educative for students and teachers in the middle grades.

Additional Evaluation Reports

CMP is a curriculum that mathematics education and policy researchers have found interesting to study. A substantial number of research studies have been carried out in CMP classrooms during the 17 years since the first iteration was available to the field. As a result, there is a growing body of published articles on efficacy, evaluation, classroom discourse, teacher knowledge, student reasoning, problem solving, and student understanding of geometry, algebra, probability, statistics, and number sense. These studies have been useful during revisions of CMP and have helped the field come to understand some of the conditions under which CMP and other "reform" curricula can support dramatic changes in what students know and are able to do in mathematics. These studies have also looked at teachers' learning and have confirmed that teachers learn from teaching the curriculum. CMP use in teacher education and professional development continues to grow. For more information on these studies, see www.connectedmath.msu.edu or www.connectedmathematics3.com.

Co-Development with Teachers and Students

Developing a curriculum with a complex set of interrelated goals takes time and input from many people. As authors, our work was based on a set of deep commitments we had to creating a more powerful way to engage students in making sense of mathematics. Our Advisory Boards took an active role in reading and critiquing Units in their various iterations. In order to enact our development principles, we found that three full years of field trials in schools for each development phase were essential.

This feedback from teachers and students across the country is the key element in the success of the CMP materials. The final materials comprised the ideas that stood the test of time in classrooms across the country. Nearly 200 teachers in 15 trial sites around the country (and their thousands of students) are a significant part of the team of professionals that made these materials happen. The interactions between teacher and students with the materials became the most compelling parts of the teacher support.

Without these teachers and their willingness to use materials that were never perfect in their first versions, CMP would have been a set of ideas that lived in the brains and imaginations of the author team. Instead, they are materials with classroom heart because our trial teachers and students made them so. We believe that such materials have the potential to dramatically change what students know and are able to do in mathematical situations. The emphasis on thinking and reasoning, on making sense of ideas, on making students responsible for both having and explaining their ideas, and on developing sound mathematical habits provides opportunities for students to learn in ways that can change how they think of themselves as learners of mathematics.

From the authors' perspectives, our hope has always been to develop materials that play out deeply held beliefs and firmly grounded theories about what mathematics is important for students to learn and how they should learn it. We hope that we have been a part of helping to challenge and change the curriculum landscape of our country. Our students are worth the effort.

In the following pages of Components, you will find a detailed discussion of the structure of the CMP3 student Units and the accompanying teacher support. This chart summarizes the components detailed.

Component	For Students	For Teachers
ACTIVe-book Student Edition	✔	
Printed Student Edition	✔	
Digital Teacher's Guide (Dash)		✔
Printed Teacher's Guides		✔
Printed Teacher's Resources		✔
Interactive Math Tools	✔	✔
Digital Student Activities	✔	✔
MathXL® for School	✔	✔
ExamView®		✔
Teacher Lesson Support CD-ROM		✔
Physical Manipulatives Kit	✔	✔

Connected Mathematics 3 provides seven student Units for grade six and eight Units each for grades 7 and 8. Each Unit is organized around an important mathematical idea or cluster of related ideas, such as area and perimeter, operations on fractions, ratio and proportion, linear relationships, or quadratic relationships. The format of the student material promotes student engagement with an exploration of important mathematical concepts and related skills and procedures. Students develop strategies and conceptual understanding by solving Problems and discussing their solutions in class.

The student materials include print student editions and Student Place. Student Place includes an ACTIVe-book for each Unit, which is an online version of the student edition with digital tools for students to be able to write and type right in the book. Student Place also includes digital math tools and student activities, as well as a digital version of the glossary with audio support.

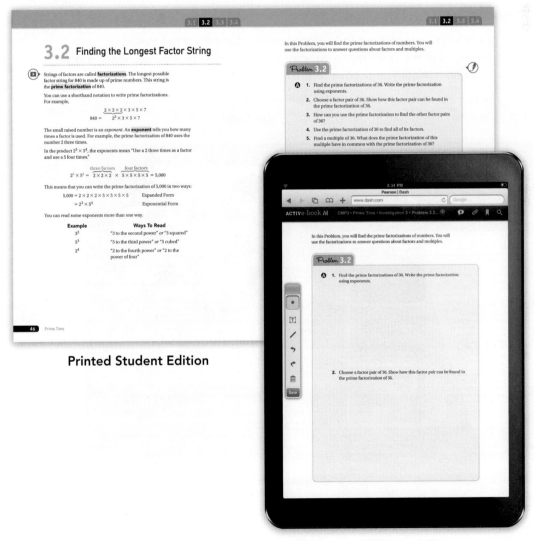

Printed Student Edition

ACTIVe-book

Organization of a Student Unit

The following sections are included in the student Units:

- **Looking Ahead**
- **Mathematical Highlights**
- **Mathematical Practices and Habits of Mind**
- **Unit Project**
- **Investigations**
- **Looking Back**
- **English/Spanish Glossary**

The following descriptions highlight the different sections of the student Units and the role each plays in student learning.

Looking Ahead

Each Unit opens with a set of three focusing questions that reflect the major mathematical goal(s) of the Unit. These questions are intended to draw students into the Unit, pique their curiosity, and point to the kinds of ideas they will investigate.

As the students move through the Unit they will encounter these questions either as a part of a Problem to explore in class or as ACE homework.

Mathematical Highlights

Mathematical Highlights are a set of student friendly goals that preview the important ideas of the Unit. The highlights help students track their progress through the Unit and provide parents and guardians with an overview of the mathematical concepts, processes, and ways of thinking developed in the Unit.

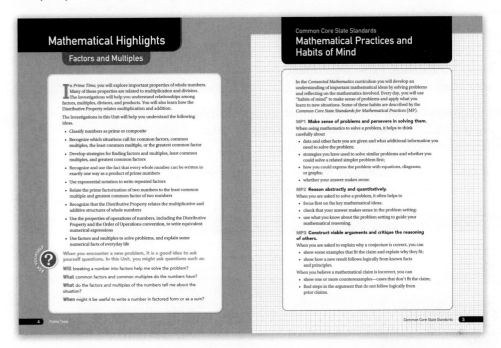

Investigations

The Investigations form the core of a Unit. Each Unit includes three to five Investigations with the following key elements:

- Problems
- Applications-Connections-Extensions
- Mathematical Reflections
- Mathematical Practices Reflections

Each Investigation builds toward the mathematical goals of the unit.

Problems

Problems start with an introduction. The introduction connects the Problem to prior knowledge, describes the context of the Problem, and provides the challenge. The connections in the introduction are often made with questions to guide the teacher and students. These questions are intended to be answered by students as part of the Launch.

When appropriate, the last one of the Launch questions is called out by an icon with a question mark and "boxed" because it captures the essence of the Problem and is answered during the Explore. Experienced teachers may use this boxed question to open up the Problem or to replace parts or all of the questions in the Problem.

Each Problem consists of a set of questions that students explore during class. As students solve the problem they uncover important mathematical relationships and develop problem-solving strategies and skills related to the goals of the Unit.

Occasionally, there is a Did You Know? feature within a Problem that presents interesting facts related to the context of an investigation.

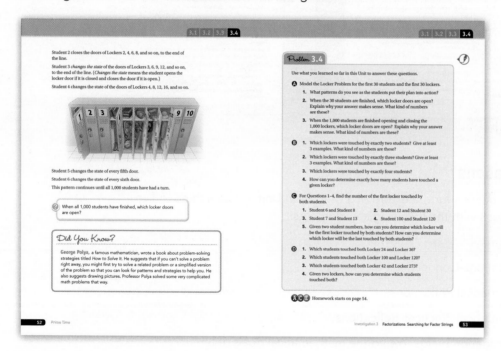

Applications-Connections-Extensions (ACE)

The last Problem in each Investigation is followed by a set of exercises meant to be used as homework. In the exercises, students are asked to compare, visualize, model, measure, count, reason, connect, and/or communicate their ideas in writing. To truly own an idea, strategy, or concept, a student must apply it, connect it to what he or she already knows or has experienced, and seek ways to extend or generalize it.

The exercises are categorized into Applications, Connections, and Extensions (ACE): The Applications help students solidify their understanding by providing practice with ideas and strategies that were in the Investigation. Applications contain contexts both similar to and different from those in the Investigation.

The Connections provide the opportunity for students to connect new knowledge to prior learning—a powerful learning strategy. This section also provides continued review of concepts and skills across the grades. For example, the Connections in *Covering and Surrounding*, a Unit on measurement, contain practice with operations on decimals and fractions for the most part without context. Connections can connect to "real-world problems." Often these are problems that contain original data sets. For example, in *Moving Straight Ahead*, a Unit on linear relationships, there are connections to sports records.

The Extensions may provide a challenge for students to think beyond what is covered in class, provide an interesting excursion "side ways" that looks at related mathematical ideas, foreshadow mathematics in future Units, or pursue an interesting application.

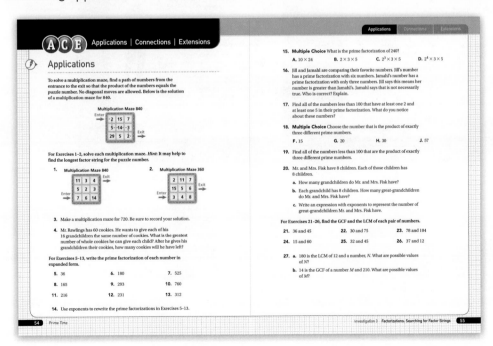

Mathematical Reflections

At the end of each Investigation, students reflect on what they have learned in the Mathematical Reflections. This set of questions helps students organize their thoughts and summarize important concepts and strategies. After thinking about the questions and sketching their own ideas, students discuss the questions with their teacher and their classmates and then write a summary of their findings. Reflection questions help teachers assess student understanding of the "big" ideas.

The Mathematical Reflections end with an example of student thinking for one of the Standards for Mathematical Practice. Students are asked to study the example and comment on other Mathematical Practices that are reflected in the example. Then they are asked to think of other examples they used during the Investigation.

These two features within the Mathematical Reflections encourage students to take ownership for their mathematical understanding and reasoning and recognize the role the Mathematical Practices play every day as they work on Problems.

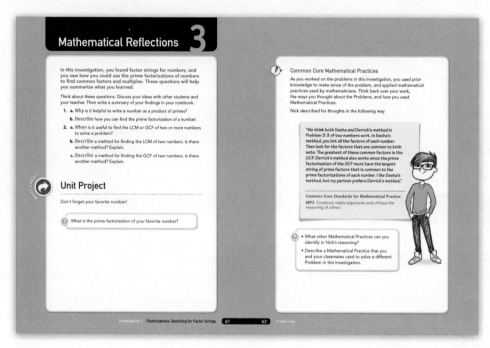

Unit Project

Each grade level includes three to four unit projects. Projects are typically introduced at the beginning of a Unit and formally assigned at the end of the Unit. Projects are open-ended tasks that provide opportunities for students to engage in independent work and to demonstrate their broad understanding of the mathematics in the Unit. A list of projects is given in Appendix H.

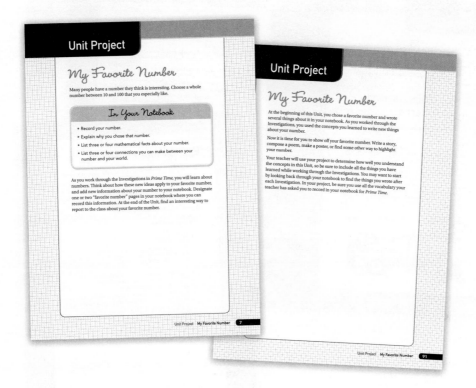

Looking Back

This feature provides a review of the "big ideas" and connections in the Unit. It includes questions that allow students to demonstrate their understanding, explain their reasoning, summarize, and connect what they have learned across the Unit.

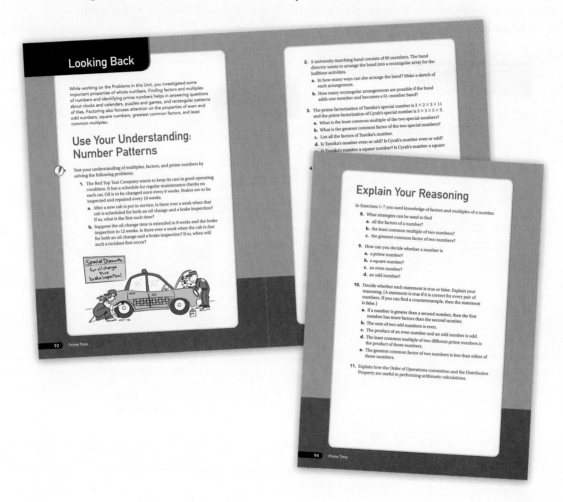

Glossary

Although students are encouraged to develop their own definitions and examples for key terms, each student edition includes an English/Spanish glossary. Student Place includes a digital glossary that also contains audio support for each term. Glossaries can serve as a guide for the student, the teacher, and parents, as students develop understanding of key ideas and strategies.

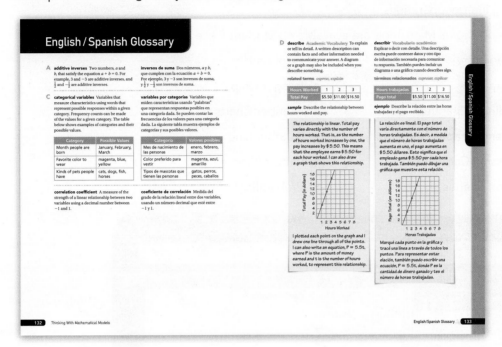

Digital Math Tools

Digital math tools are available via a menu on Student Place and Teacher Place. Students can use the digital tools at any time during their work on Problems or exercises. The teacher support will suggest when teachers may want to use a particular tool to facilitate the Problem or during the Summarize. For example, the integer chips tool can be used instead of physical chips during the Problems introducing integer operations.

The following Digital Math Tools are available on Student Place and Teacher Place:

- 3D Geometry
- Algebra Tiles
- Coordinate Grapher
- **Data and Graphs (shown)**
- Expression Calculator
- Fraction Shapes
- Geoboard
- Integer Chips
- Number Charts
- Number Line
- Pattern Blocks
- Probability

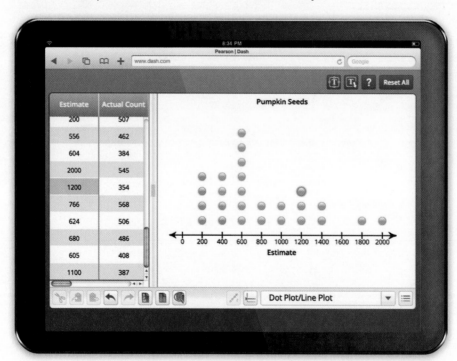

Student Activities

Although computers are not required for any of the Problems, Student Activities can be a time saver, as well as fun. Student Activites are mostly designed to be used during the Launches, but they are also available to teachers and students at all times through Teacher Place and Student Place. For example, while transformations can be done with paper and pencil, students need to see many examples before they can safely make conjectures about properties preserved under transformations. The Transformation Tool gives them the opportunity to create examples quickly. Lastly, many Student Activities help students form a proof of their conjectures.

The following Student Activities are available on Student Place and Teacher Place:

- Areas and Perimeters
- Bee Dance Activity
- Climbing Monkeys
- Factor Game
- Fraction Game
- Hubcap Maker
- Integer Product Game
- Interactive Pythagoras
- Locker Problem
- Mug Wumps
- Painted Cubes

- Paper Pool
- Pouring and Filling
- Product Game
- Quadrilateral Game
- Target Game
- Tessellations
- **Transformation Tool (shown)**
- Virtual Bridge Experiment
- Virtual Box
- Virtual Cylinder
- Virtual Polystrips

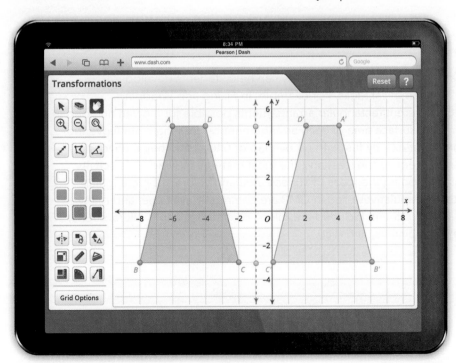

MathXL®

MathXL for School, developed by Pearson, is used in CMP3 to provide additional skills practice online, thereby replacing the CMP2 *Additional Practice and Skills Workbooks*. A link to MathXL is available via the Links menu in Student Place and Teacher Place. Teachers can assign skills practice by Unit to individuals or groups of students within MathXL. For each Unit, teachers also have the option of assigning students a short readiness test or a longer skills assessment at the conclusion of the Unit, which can inform the practice assignments. Thus, the student is only assigned practice on the skills the student has not yet mastered. MathXL is intended as a supplement and not as a replacement for the ACE in CMP3.

Calculators

Connected Mathematics (CMP) was developed with the belief that calculators should be available to students, and that students should know when and how to use them. Graphing calculators with table and statistical-display capabilities or similar digital tools, are used in all three grades.

In grade 6, students use calculators to simplify complicated calculations and explore patterns in computations. In grades 7 and 8, graphing calculators are used to investigate functions and as a tool for solving problems. Students use graphing calculators to explore the shape and features of graphs of linear, exponential, and quadratic functions as well as the patterns of change in the tables of such functions. Furthermore, in addition to using symbolic solution methods, students can use graphing-calculator tables and graphs to solve equations, as well as to display data and calculate statistical measures.

Manipulatives

In CMP, manipulatives are used only when they can help students develop understanding of mathematical ideas. For example, in *Filling and Wrapping*, students find all the different rectangular arrangements possible for a given number of cubes. They find the surface area of each arrangement by creating a net (covering) for the arrangement that exactly fits, with no overlap or underlap. They then identify the arrangements that require the least and the most material to wrap. This activity sets the stage for developing the ideas of surface area and volume of rectangular prisms. Most of the manipulatives used in CMP are commonly available, and many schools may already have them. Included are rulers, protractors, angle rulers, cubes, square tiles, counters, spinners, and dice.

The two manipulatives described below are unique to CMP.

Polystrips are plastic strips that can be pieced together with brass fasteners to form polygons. These manipulatives are used in grade 7 to investigate the relationship among the side lengths of triangles and quadrilaterals. They also are useful in the eighth grade geometry Unit, *Butterflies, Pinwheels and Wallpaper*. A digital version of polystrips is available in the Student Activities.

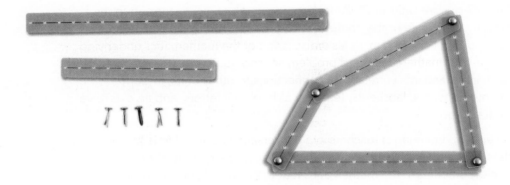

The CMP Shapes Set® is a set of polygons used in grade 7 to explore sides, angles, and tilings. Labsheets are provided for teachers who do not have polystrips or the Shapes Set.

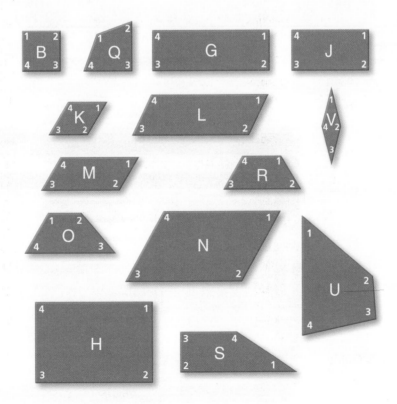

Teachers are an integral part of the learning process in *Connected Mathematics* (CMP). From the beginning, the authors have viewed CMP as a curriculum for both students and teachers. CMP provides teachers with ways to think about and enact problem-centered teaching and learning. The extensive field-testing of CMP has helped produce teacher materials that are rich with successful strategies, classroom dialogues and questions, and examples of student solutions and reasoning.

Each of the 23 student Units in CMP3 is accompanied by teacher support in the form of the Teacher Place or the printed Teacher Guides and Teacher Resources. The teacher support for each Unit includes a discussion of the mathematics underlying the Investigations, mathematical and problem-solving goals for each Investigation, planning charts, standards correlations, connections to other Units, in-depth teaching notes, answers, labsheets, teaching aids, parent letters, and an extensive assessment package.

The teacher support engages teachers in a conversation about what is possible in the classroom around a particular lesson. Suggestions are made about how to engage the students in the mathematics task in the *launch*, how to promote student thinking and reasoning during the *exploration* of the Problem, and how to *summarize* with the students the important mathematics embedded in the Problem. Support for this Launch–Explore–Summarize sequence occurs for each Problem in the curriculum.

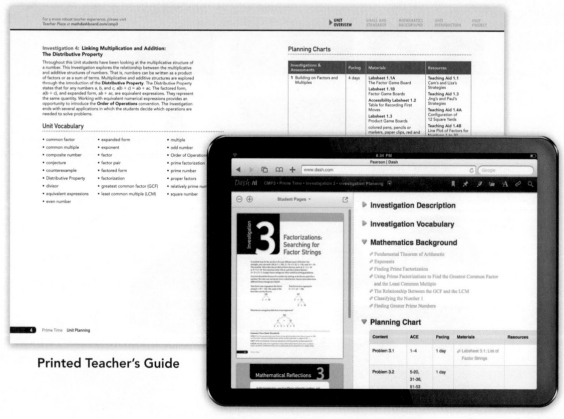

Printed Teacher's Guide

Teacher Place

Organization of the Teacher Support

The following categories of support are included in the teacher support:

- Unit/Investigation/Problem descriptions
- Unit/Investigation/Problem resources
- Vocabulary lists
- Planning charts
- Goals and Standards lists
- Mathematics Background
- Launch–Explore–Summarize suggestions

Some of the teacher support features are detailed below.

Planning Charts (Unit Level)

Each Unit includes a planning chart that provides an overview of the materials, labsheets, teaching aids, assessments, and pacing for the Unit. A block pacing chart is also included.

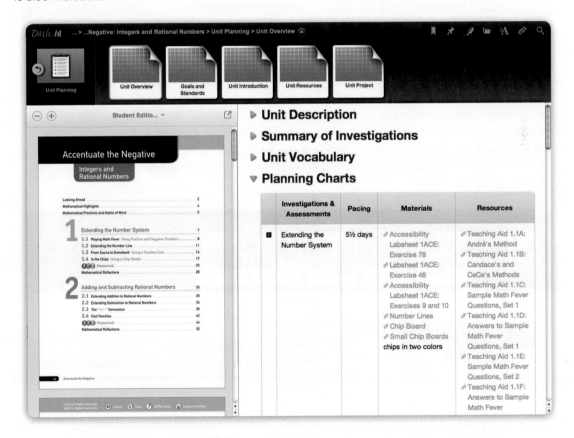

Goals (Unit level)

Two to four big concepts are identified for each Unit with an elaboration of the essential understandings for each. These goals are then listed at the beginning of each Investigation with the goals addressed in the Investigation highlighted.

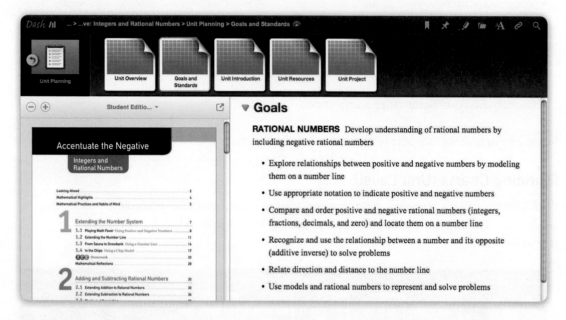

Standards

The Common Core Content Standards addressed in the Unit are listed, followed by a list of Investigations where they are addressed. The Common Core Standards for Mathematical Practice are also listed, with a few specific examples of where they play out in the Unit. Students will be using several Mathematical Practices each day as they explore Problems.

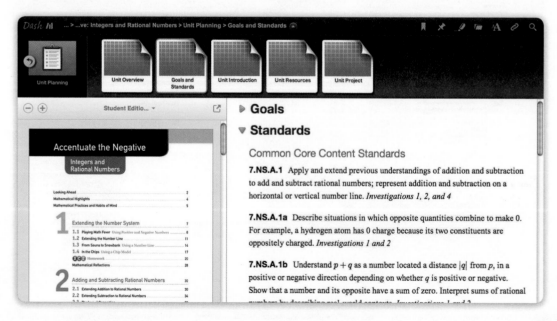

Mathematics Background

The Mathematics Background is an overview and elaboration of the mathematics of the Unit. It includes examples and a rationale for the models and procedures used in the Unit. This background helps a teacher stand above the Unit and see the mathematics from a perspective that includes the mathematics within the particular Unit, mathematical connections to earlier Units, mathematical connections to subsequent Units and courses.

In Teacher Place, the mathematics background is enhanced with videos, animations, and series of images to give teachers a more visual exposure to the mathematics involved.

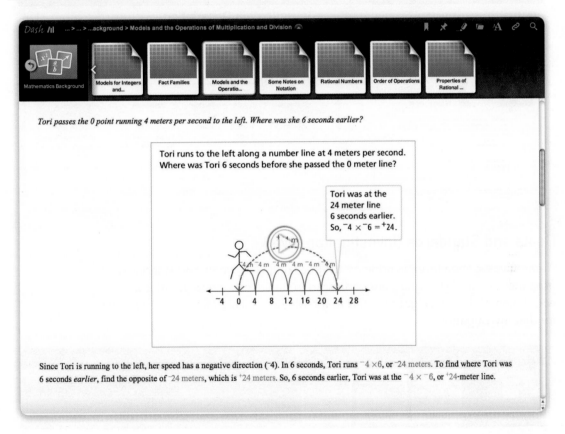

Planning Charts (Investigation Level)

Each Investigation includes a planning chart similar to the Unit planning chart. In addition to providing a list of Materials and Resources, the Investigation planning chart also includes the ACE homework assignments recommended at the conclusion of each Problem.

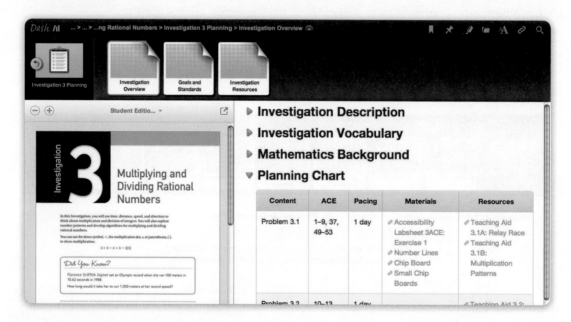

Goals and Standards (Investigation level)

At the Investigation level, in addition to specifying what goals and standards from the full list of Unit goals are addressed in the Investigation, there is a correlation of the Investigation goals to the Mathematical Reflections questions for that Investigation.

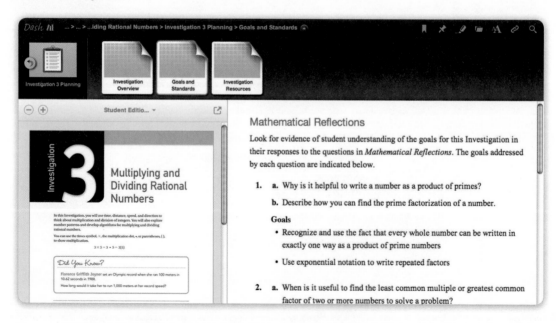

Focus Question (Problem level)

Each Problem has a focus question that the teacher can use to guide his/her instructional decisions throughout his/her planning, teaching, and reflections on student understanding. While these questions are intended for the teacher, some teachers do share them with their students as questions they will be able to answer at the end of the Problems. In Teacher Place, the focus question is repeated at the top of every Launch, Explore, and Summarize section.

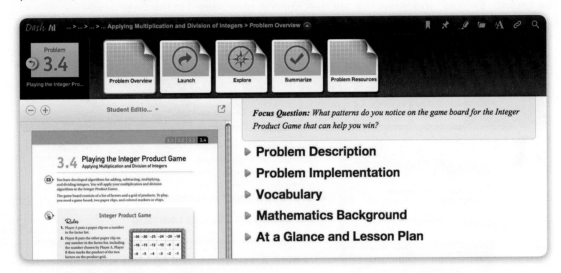

Problem Implementation

The Problem Implementation description includes recommendations on how the teacher can set up the groups of students and for how the teacher can break up Problem parts. In addition, the appropriate materials for the Problem, including optional technology, are listed, as well as vocabulary.

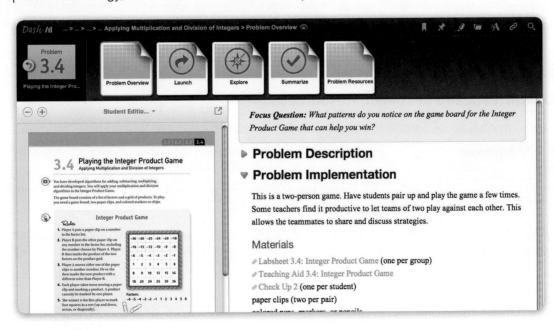

Launch–Explore–Summarize

Actual classroom scenarios and examples of student thinking are included in the Launch, Explore, and Summarize sections to help stimulate teachers' imaginations about what is possible.

Questions to ask students at all stages of the lesson are included to help teachers support student learning and support on-going formative assessment.

The Launch, Explore, and Summrize are described in more detail in the Overview. See pages 17–20.

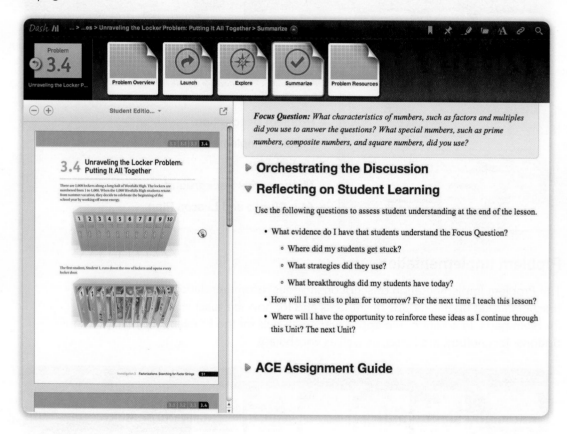

Unit/Investigation/Problem Resources

There are a full set of resources for each Unit. Resources include the following:

- At a Glances
- Labsheets
- Teaching Aids
- Assessments
- Answer Keys

At a Glance

The At a Glance provided for every Problem includes key pieces from the Launch, Explore, and Summarize teacher support which a teacher can use as a quick reference in class. Each At a Glance contains:

- The Focus Question

- A list of materials needed

- A list of vocabulary terms that need to be addressed before or within the Problem

- Key suggested questions

- A homework assignment guide

- Answers to the Problem

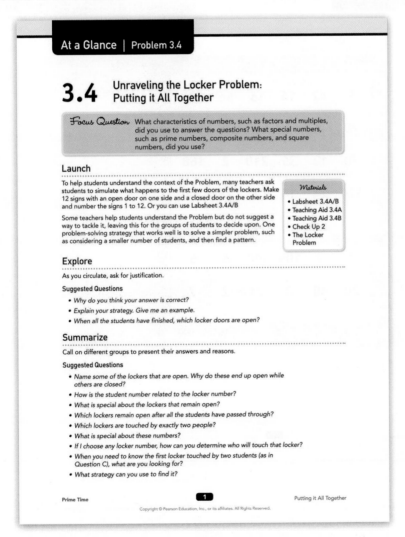

At a Glance | **Problem 3.4**

3.4 Unraveling the Locker Problem: Putting it All Together

Focus Question What characteristics of numbers, such as factors and multiples, did you use to answer the questions? What special numbers, such as prime numbers, composite numbers, and square numbers, did you use?

Launch

To help students understand the context of the Problem, many teachers ask students to simulate what happens to the first few doors of the lockers. Make 12 signs with an open door on one side and a closed door on the other side and number the signs 1 to 12. Or you can use Labsheet 3.4A/B

Some teachers help students understand the Problem but do not suggest a way to tackle it, leaving this for the groups of students to decide upon. One problem-solving strategy that works well is to solve a simpler problem, such as considering a smaller number of students, and then find a pattern.

Materials
- Labsheet 3.4A/B
- Teaching Aid 3.4A
- Teaching Aid 3.4B
- Check Up 2
- The Locker Problem

Explore

As you circulate, ask for justification.

Suggested Questions
- *Why do you think your answer is correct?*
- *Explain your strategy. Give me an example.*
- *When all the students have finished, which locker doors are open?*

Summarize

Call on different groups to present their answers and reasons.

Suggested Questions
- *Name some of the lockers that are open. Why do these end up open while others are closed?*
- *How is the student number related to the locker number?*
- *What is special about the lockers that remain open?*
- *Which lockers remain open after all the students have passed through?*
- *Which lockers are touched by exactly two people?*
- *What is special about these numbers?*
- *If I choose any locker number, how can you determine who will touch that locker?*
- *When you need to know the first locker touched by two students (as in Question C), what are you looking for?*
- *What strategy can you use to find it?*

Prime Time
1
Putting it All Together

A blank At a Glance template is also available to facilitate a teacher's personalization of the lesson plan.

Labsheets

Labsheets are black and white pages for a teacher to photocopy so that students can use them during the Explores. Many labsheets are time savers, repeating something as it is in the corresponding student edition so that students spend less time setting up the presentation of their strategies and more time thinking through their strategies. Other labsheets, are called "Accessibility Labsheets," although this designation is visible only to the teacher within teacher support. Accessibility labsheets can help provide for individual needs as they can include hints, prompts, partially filled in tables or graphs, and visuals to help students get started on a Problem or ACE exercise.

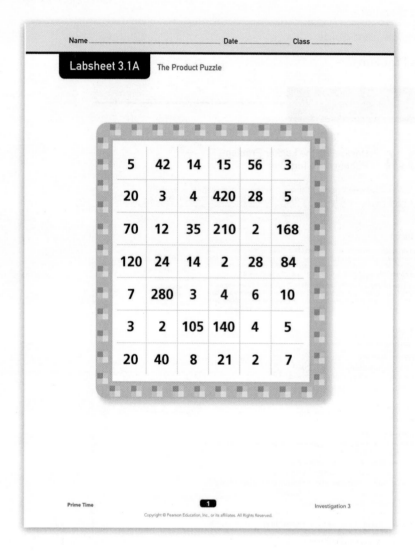

Teaching Aids

Teaching Aids are pages that a teacher may want to project during a Problem. In CMP2, Teaching Aids were called Transparencies. They include things like text showing different strategies and Check for Reasoning questions for the end of a Summarize. The purpose of Teaching Aids is also to save time. A teacher may also want to occasionally use Teaching Aids as labsheets.

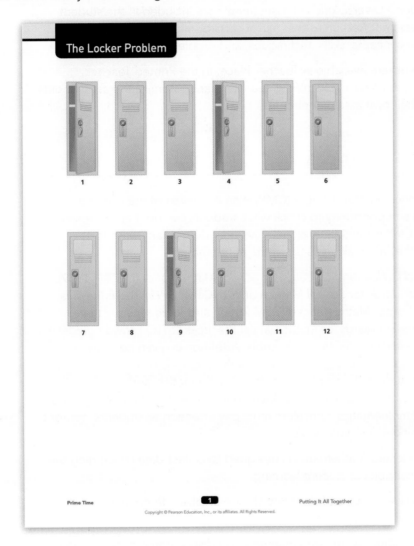

In addition to the Launch question and formative assessment that is provided throughout the Launch, Explore, and Summarize phases, multiple kinds of assessment are included in the program to help teachers see assessment and evaluation as a way to inform students of their progress, apprise parents of students' progress, and guide the decisions a teacher makes about lesson plans and classroom interactions. Diverse kinds of assessments are included in the student Units and the Assessment Resources that mirror classroom practices as well as highlight important concepts, skills, techniques, and problem-solving strategies.

All of the assessments are available in Teacher Place, in the Printed Teacher Resources, and in ExamView. In ExamView, teachers can customize the assessments, including writing their own assessment items.

Assessment Dimensions

Assessment in *Connected Mathematics* (CMP) is an extension of the learning process, as well as an opportunity to check what students can do. For this reason, the assessment in CMP is multidimensional, giving students many ways to demonstrate how they are making sense of the mathematics.

The *Curriculum and Evaluation Standards for School Mathematics* (NCTM, 1989), the *Assessment Standards for School Mathematics* (NCTM, 1995), the *Principles and Standards for School Mathematics* (NCTM 2000), and more recently the Common Core State Standards for Mathematical Practices (2010) provide guidelines that describe mathematics education in schools. Attention is given not only in terms of mathematical objectives, but in terms of the methods of instruction, the processes used by students in learning and doing mathematics, and students' dispositions towards mathematics. These documents suggest that the design and implementation of mathematics curriculum must pay attention to students' content knowledge, disposition, and work habits.

Assessment in *Connected Mathematics* is designed to collect data concerning the following three dimensions of student learning:

Content knowledge Assessing content knowledge involves determining what students know and what they are able to do.

Mathematical disposition A student's mathematical disposition is healthy when he or she responds well to mathematical challenges and sees himself or herself as a learner and inventor of mathematics. Disposition also includes confidence, expectations, and metacognition (reflecting on and monitoring one's own learning).

Work habits A student's work habits are good when he or she is willing to persevere, contribute to group tasks, and follow tasks to completion. These valuable skills are used in nearly every career. To assess work habits, it is important to ask questions, such as "Are the students able to organize and summarize their work?" and "Are the students progressing in becoming independent learners?"

Assessment Tools

CMP provides a variety of tools for student assessment. These assessments fall into the three broad categories of Checkpoints, Surveys of Knowledge, and Observations:

Checkpoints

Some of the assessment tools give teachers and students an opportunity to check student understanding at key points in the Unit. Checkpoints help students solidify their understanding, determine the areas that need further attention, and help teachers make decisions about whether students are ready to move on.

By assigning ACE exercises as homework, teachers can assess each student's developing knowledge of concepts and skills. Mathematical Reflections questions can help teachers assess students' developing conceptual knowledge and skills in the Investigation. The Looking Back can be used as a review, helping students to stand back and look at the "big" ideas and connections in the Unit. The "Check for Understanding" feature of some Summarizes provides students and teachers an additional checkpoint for students' progress.

Many teachers also require their students to keep organized notebooks, which include homework, notes from class, vocabulary, and assessments. Each Unit includes a checklist to help students organize these notebooks before they turn them in for teacher feedback. For classes using Student Place, homework, class notes, and vocabulary are all part of the ACTIVe-book. Teachers can also assess student understanding during their study of the Unit by examining their work or summaries for particular Problems.

Surveys of Knowledge

Check-ups, quizzes, tests, self-assessments, and projects provide teachers with a broad view of student knowledge both during a Unit and at the end of a Unit.

Check-ups

Check-ups are short, individual assessment instruments. Check-up questions tend to be less complex and more skill-oriented than questions on quizzes and Unit tests. These questions provide insight into student understanding of the baseline mathematical concepts and skills of the Unit. Student responses to Check-ups can help teachers plan further instruction for the Unit.

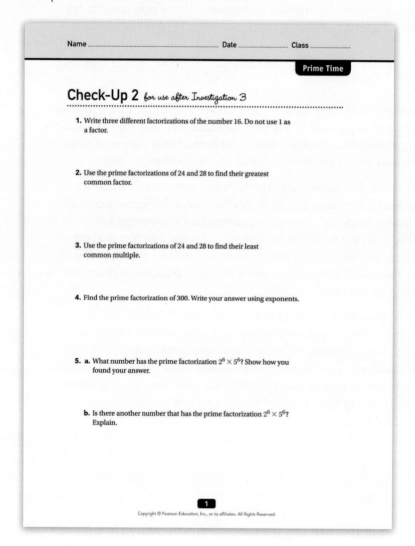

Name .... Date .... Class ....

Prime Time

Check-Up 2 *for use after Investigation 3*

1. Write three different factorizations of the number 16. Do not use 1 as a factor.

2. Use the prime factorizations of 24 and 28 to find their greatest common factor.

3. Use the prime factorizations of 24 and 28 to find their least common multiple.

4. Find the prime factorization of 300. Write your answer using exponents.

5. a. What number has the prime factorization $2^6 \times 5^6$? Show how you found your answer.

   b. Is there another number that has the prime factorization $2^6 \times 5^6$? Explain.

Partner Quizzes

Each Unit has at least one partner quiz. Quiz questions are richer and more challenging than checkup questions. Many quiz questions are extensions of ideas students explored in class. These questions provide insight into how students apply the ideas from the Unit to new situations. The quizzes were created with the following assumptions:

- Students work in pairs.

- Students are permitted to use their notebooks and any other appropriate materials, such as calculators.

- Pairs have an opportunity to submit a draft of the quiz for teacher input. They may then revise their work and turn in the finished product.

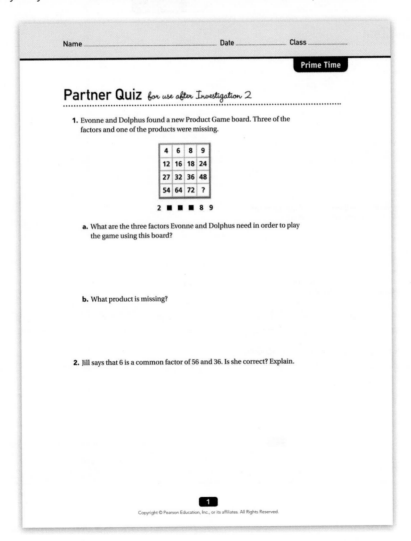

Name .... Date .... Class ....

Prime Time

Partner Quiz *for use after Investigation 2*

1. Evonne and Dolphus found a new Product Game board. Three of the factors and one of the products were missing.

4	6	8	9
12	16	18	24
27	32	36	48
54	64	72	?

2 ■ ■ 8 9

a. What are the three factors Evonne and Dolphus need in order to play the game using this board?

b. What product is missing?

2. Jill says that 6 is a common factor of 56 and 36. Is she correct? Explain.

1

Unit Tests

Each Unit includes a test that is intended to be an individual assessment. The test informs teachers about a student's ability to apply, refine, modify, and possibly extend the mathematical knowledge and skills acquired in the Unit. Some of the questions draw on ideas from the entire Unit, while others are smaller, focusing on a particular idea or concept. Some of the questions are skill oriented, while others require students to demonstrate problem-solving abilities and more in-depth knowledge of the Unit concepts. Teachers can use holistic scoring techniques and rubrics that take into account the many dimensions addressed by the test.

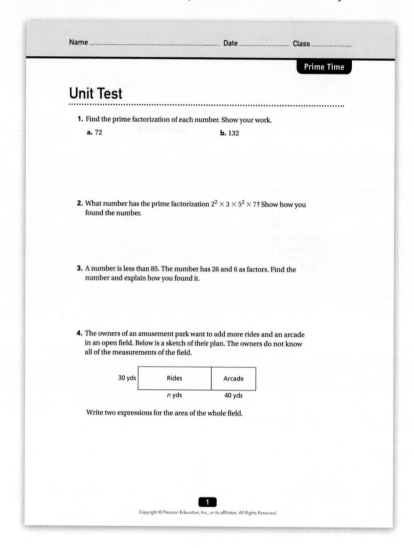

Name _____ Date _____ Class _____

Prime Time

Unit Test

1. Find the prime factorization of each number. Show your work.

   a. 72   **b.** 132

2. What number has the prime factorization $2^2 \times 3 \times 5^2 \times 7$? Show how you found the number.

3. A number is less than 85. The number has 26 and 6 as factors. Find the number and explain how you found it.

4. The owners of an amusement park want to add more rides and an arcade in an open field. Below is a sketch of their plan. The owners do not know all of the measurements of the field.

30 yds	Rides	Arcade
	n yds	40 yds

Write two expressions for the area of the whole field.

Self-Assessment

After every Unit, students complete a self-assessment, summarizing the mathematics they learned in the Unit and the ideas with which they are still struggling. The self-assessment also asks students to provide examples of what they did in class to add to the learning of the mathematics. The goal of this activity is to have students reflect on their learning. For many students, self-assessment is a new experience, and they may struggle with this at first. However, by receiving feedback from teachers and using other students' work as models, students can learn to reflect on their own progress in making sense of mathematics.

Unit Project

At least three Units in each grade include projects that can be used to replace or supplement the Unit test. Projects give teachers an opportunity to assign tasks that are more product/performance-based than those on traditional tests. Project tasks are typically open-ended and allow students to engage in independent work and to demonstrate broad understanding of ideas in the Unit. Through students' work on the projects, teachers can gather information about their disposition toward mathematics. Project guidelines, student examples, and scoring rubrics appear in the Unit Project section of the Teacher Support. The table on the next page gives locations and descriptions of projects by grade level.

Observations

The curriculum provides teachers with numerous opportunities to assess student understanding by observing students during group work and class discussions. Many Problems provide the opportunity to observe students as they "do mathematics," applying their knowledge, exhibiting their mathematical disposition, and displaying their work habits as they contribute to group tasks. The summary portion of each Problem and the Mathematical Reflections at the end of each Investigation provide ongoing opportunities to assess students' understanding through class discussions. This type of observation as a form of assessment is important, since some students are better able to show understanding in verbal situations than in formal, written assignments.

Teachers may also receive feedback from parents—who may comment on their child's enthusiasm or involvement with a particular Problem—and from students who may observe that another student's method is more efficient or useful, or who may offer an important observation, conjecture, or extension.

Summary of Assessment

The following chart summarizes the assessment tools just discussed and the dimensions addressed by each assessment item.

Assessment Tool	Assessment Dimension		
	Content Knowledge	Mathematical Disposition	Work Habits
Checkpoints			
ACE Exercises	✔	✔	✔
Notebook	✔	✔	✔
Mathematical Reflection	✔	✔	✔
Looking Back	✔	✔	✔
Surveys of Knowledge			
Check Up	✔		
Partner Quiz	✔	✔	✔
Unit Test	✔		
Self-Assessment	✔	✔	✔
Project	✔	✔	✔
Observations			
Group Work	✔	✔	✔
Class Discussions	✔	✔	✔
Students and Parents	✔	✔	✔

CMP Web Site

The Connected Mathematics (CMP) web site maintained by Michigan State University, **www.connectedmath.msu.edu**, contains additional support for teachers such as:

- CMP2 Classroom videos that can be used by individual teachers or in professional development. Each video comes with suggestions and questions for viewing the videos, student work, transcripts and professional development activities.

- Extensive Bibliography of research, evaluation and other articles related to the efficacy, evaluation, student learning, teaching and implementation of CMP. This list is updated periodically.

- Announcements of CMP conferences, workshops, news related to CMP and related activities.

- Suggestions for professional development

- Suggestions for enhancing teaching and classroom discourse

- Suggestions for parents

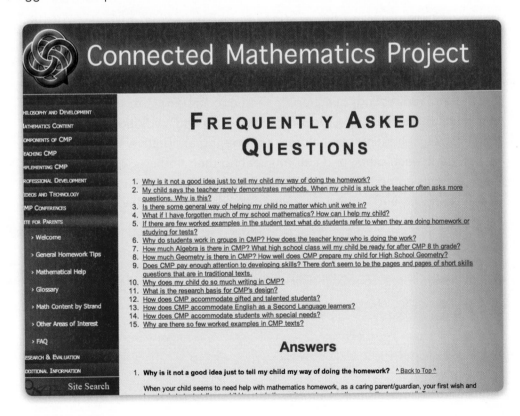

This section provides information to help in planning to teach *Connected Mathematics* (CMP) and gives suggestions for management. The discussion and suggestions come from our work with experienced CMP teachers. This material is intended to be read and used by teachers, so the text addresses teachers directly.

CMP may be very different from curricula with which you are familiar. Because important concepts are embedded within Problems rather than explicitly stated and demonstrated in the student text, you play a critical role in helping students develop appropriate understanding, strategies, and skills. Your thoughtful engagement with the curriculum and your reflections on student learning will create a productive classroom environment.

A typical CMP classroom has students and teachers actively working together in pursuit of an important and challenging mathematical task. The teacher provides the challenge. Students work together to solve the Problem as the teacher moves around the classroom observing, prompting, redirecting, questioning, and encouraging. Students are engaged in the challenge, working together to find a solution, making conjectures, validating conjectures, considering alternative strategies, questioning each other, and communicating their findings. The teacher and students come together at the end of the lesson to share, solidify, clarify, connect, and extend their understandings. The following sections will help you create these experiences for your students.

Contributor to The CMP Classroom
Mary Beth Schmitt, Traverse City East Middle School, Michigan

In planning to teach CMP, the most important thing you need to do is become familiar with the content and the way the concepts, reasoning, and skills are developed. As you prepare, try to anticipate your students' thinking and assess where difficulties might occur. The following section provides suggestions you can use as a guide as you plan to teach CMP.

As you prepare to begin your school year, setting the stage for a collaborative learning community of middle school mathematicians is crucial. Garnering student enthusiasm for their learning begins in the opening days of school. Posing the question, "What would make this an ideal class?" followed by, "How can we make it happen?" can set the stage for developing classroom norms for your school year. You can further foster that environment by creating a space that welcomes students and has plenty of room to display the products of their learning. Organizing your classroom space as well as preparing a plan for student organization and for your own organization is very important.

Preparing the Classroom Environment

This section provides suggestions for getting your physical environment set up in a way that enhances collaborative learning and student ownership. It also provides suggestions for student notebook organization, teacher material organization, and parent and family information distribution.

As you prepare your classroom space, consider the following questions:

- How can I foster opportunities for student collaboration by arranging their seating?

- How can I ensure that there is room for students to move comfortably in the classroom?

- Where can I place the tools that students may need so that they are easily accessible? (calculators, rulers, angle rulers, grid paper, technology applets, and so forth)

- What is the best location for student materials? (scissors, markers, colored pencils, glue sticks, construction paper, chart paper, and so forth)

- How can I use wall space to display artifacts of student learning that will foster continued growth in our knowledge of mathematics?

- Where can we keep a record of our learning and the unresolved questions posed for further thinking during a Unit? During the school year?

Suggestions for the Walls of a Classroom

- Post the Mathematical Goals and Problem Solving Goals so that students may refer to them as they work through a Unit.

- Post the Standards for Mathematical Practice for students to refer to during the Summarizes and during Mathematical Reflections.

- Add vocabulary terms to visual representations of student work as the terms are formally developed during class. For example, when students make a graph from the bike tour in *Variables and Patterns*, place the terms *independent variable* and *dependent variable* along the x-axis and the y-axis.

- Post vocabulary terms as they are introduced and developed, making a word wall poster for each Unit.

- Make a memory wall to display key visual displays of learning from each Unit. Post the questions What connections do you see? and How can you make use of them? (See description below.)

The idea behind a memory wall is that the classroom should reflect students' mathematical journey toward deeper understanding. Over the course of a Unit, students will benefit from having a visual reference. As the Unit draws to a close, students can select which visual display best represents their learning. Initially teachers may make those selections with the knowledge of what comes next.

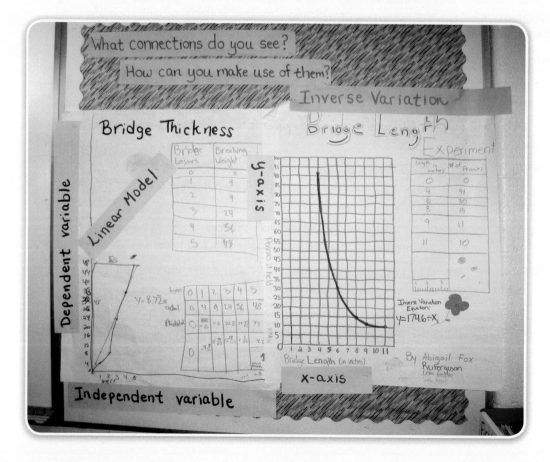

For example, during *Shapes* and *Designs*, the opening Unit of the seventh grade, students explore three questions What makes a polygon a polygon? Will any three side lengths create a triangle? and Which regular polygons will tile? You can post documentation on the walls of the sorting of polygons, data from testing triangle lengths with polystrips, and tiling designs showing those polygons that do and do not tile. Each of these Problems provides leverage for the upcoming Unit, *Stretching and Shrinking*. As students encounter rep-tiling in Investigation 3, they can compare and contrast tiling with rep-tiling. In *Shapes and Designs*, students make predictions about what makes a polygon a polygon and whether or not any three side lengths can form a triangle. In the *Stretching and Shrinking* Unit, students make predictions about which characters and which hats will be similar to the original figures. On the memory wall, students display their work from *Shapes and Designs*. This includes their predictions, testing, and data gathering to justify or contradict their predictions. Students later draw upon this work in *Stretching and Shrinking*.

As the memory wall becomes crowded, students can be asked to narrow down the artifacts to one display for each Unit after considering the question, Which Problem displayed shows the big ideas that you want to remember?

Suggestions for Seating Arrangements for Various Groupings

Arranging student seating so that learners can move freely in the classroom is helpful. Students should display their work, including their conjectures and evidence to support or contradict them. Students often explore daily Problems individually, with a partner, or with a small group of 3 or 4 students. Therefore, having flexible seating for ease in grouping is effective. As you determine where materials will be located, remember that students should be able to move freely and have the freedom to choose which tools and materials are used to delve into a Problem.

Preparing Communication and Organization Tools

Parent Letters

There is a Parent Letter available for each of the 23 Units. These letters provide valuable information about the Unit goals and key vocabulary that will be used, as well as information about how parents can be helpful to their children in learning mathematics. You can personalize the letters to include your name and contact information. You can send letters home with your students or send them electronically. Some teachers have found it helpful for their students to write personal letters to their parents or guardians at the end of each Unit to share specific examples of their learning.

Student Notebooks

Students can use a three-ring binder to hold their texts and their work. Some teachers ask students to organize their binders into sections such as the following:

- Student Edition of current Unit
- Journal: a record of the in-class Problems with Summarize notes
- Mathematical Reflections
- Vocabulary: student-created Mathematics Dictionary
- Homework: ACE questions and additional practice exercises
- Assessments: Individual Check Up Quizzes, Partner Quizzes, Unit Tests and Projects

Other teachers have found that a simpler organization of student notebooks is effective:

- Front pocket for the current work in an Investigation
- Student Edition and Mathematics Dictionary
- Back pocket for assessed student work to include in-class Problems, ACE, Mathematical Reflections, and Quizzes

Student Portfolios

At the end of each Unit, key artifacts from the Unit are shifted to an in-class mathematics student portfolio. The portfolio may include the following:

- Unit Record Sheet (reflecting all assessed items from the Unit)
- Two samples of best work selected by the student
- All Mathematical Reflections
- Quizzes and the Unit Test and Project
- Student Self-Assessment
- Pre- and Post-Assessment Reflections

Preparing to Implement CMP

This section will help you plan for your school year from Unit to Unit and Problem by Problem. Planning to facilitate lessons using the Launch–Explore–Summarize (LES) Instructional Model will be discussed in detail along with ACE questions, Mathematical Reflections, Mathematical Practices, Vocabulary, and Differentiated Instruction. Finally there will be some suggestions about how to handle student and teacher absenteeism.

Planning Your School Year

As you consider the scope of the school year, you may find it helpful to develop a timeline with beginning and ending dates for each Unit, including time for assessments, as well as for local and state standardized testing. The teacher support provides a suggested number of class periods for each Unit's completion. As the year progresses, you may need to refine the timeline. You may find it helpful to have discussions with your coworkers about the teaching and learning priorities based on the high-stakes tests for your particular school or district.

Planning a Unit

The first stage in planning to teach a Unit is becoming familiar with the key concepts and the way the Unit develops concepts, reasoning, and skills. In general, the Unit subtitle gives a broad view of the important ideas that will be developed. For example, *Moving Straight Ahead* has the subtitle *Linear Relationships*, which identifies linear relationships as the central idea. What the title does not reveal is what aspects of linear relationships are developed and how understanding is enhanced. The following suggestions can serve as a guide for getting to know a Unit at this more detailed level.

- Understand the mathematics and how it is being developed. Read the Goals of the Unit, Unit Description, and Content Connections to Other Units.

- Read the Summary of Investigations in the teacher support and the Mathematical Reflections in the student books. These outline the development of the mathematics in the Unit.

- Look over the Assessment Resources. They give you an idea of what students are expected to know at various points in the Unit and show the level and type of understanding students are expected to develop.

- Work all of the Problems and ACE for each Investigation.

- Make use of the help provided in the teacher support.

- As you work on the Problems, anticipate what Mathematical Practices might surface during the Problem and how they can foster students learning.

- Use the LES as a guide for teaching each Problem and consider using the Focus Question with your students for each Problem.

- Keep notes on important ideas or suggestions for the next time you teach the Unit.

- Use the Mathematical Reflections as benchmarks for your students' understanding and as a focus for the Mathematical Practices.

- Reevaluate where you and your students are each day. Teacher reflections are an important part in becoming a more effective teacher.

The following questions will help guide your planning of a Unit. Guidance in answering these questions can be found throughout the student book and teacher support in Goals and Standards, Mathematics Background, Unit Overview, Problem Overview, and answers.

- What are the big mathematical ideas of this Unit?

- What do I want students to know when this Unit is completed?

- What mathematical vocabulary does this Unit bring out?

- What might be conceptually difficult?

- What are important connections to other Units?

- How might one Unit give leverage for the next?

Planning an Investigation

The following questions will help you uncover the developmental and learning trajectories in each Investigation. It is also helpful to read the description of the Investigation, the essential understandings of the major goals that are being addressed in the Investigation, the Focus Question, and the Mathematical Reflections.

- What part of the main mathematical goal of the Unit is being developed in the Investigation?

- How does each Problem in the Investigation contribute to the development of the mathematics?

- What level of sophistication do I expect *all* my students to achieve in answering the questions in the Investigation?

- What opportunities exist in the Investigation to extend and connect the students' learning beyond the basic expectations?

- What type of student responses will show development in understanding the big ideas of the Unit?

- What mathematical ideas will need emphasis?

- What connections can be made among the Problems in this Investigation, to other Investigations in this Unit, and to other Units?

- How can I prepare for and structure the writing assignment for the Mathematical Reflections to maximize learning?

- What ACE questions are appropriate for my students to do and when will they best fit?

- How long should this Investigation take?

- What can I do to ensure the amount of time spent in class is appropriate for the Problems and the goals of the Investigation?

Planning a Lesson

Begin by actually doing the Problem yourself. The learning process that your students will experience will become evident. You will be able to anticipate where students may struggle. You will discover how the Problem connects to prior learning as well as how it leads into the next Problem. The teacher's role during a typical daily lesson is to facilitate student learning and to orchestrate the lesson. Within each phase of the lesson the teacher listens and poses questions to elicit student reasoning.

The students' role during a typical daily lesson is to explore a concept or skill with a problem-solving mindset. Within each phase of the lesson students listen to each other's ideas and pose clarifying questions to each other. This exchange deepens their understanding of a concept or skill. Students actively share their problem-solving strategies and conclusions. Recording their reasoning and conclusions is a key element of students being able to share the ownership of their learning with others. Creating a visual display of learning will occur regularly in each Investigation.

Launch

The Launch ensures that all students have access to the context and content to explore that lesson's Big Idea concept or skill. Connecting to prior knowledge and encouraging them to delve into the task without giving away too much of the Problem is the challenge. A new component of CMP3 is the Focus Question, which is designed for the teacher to use as a guide to monitor students' progress during class. Occasionally, some teachers have posed the question to the whole class during the Launch as a challenge or advance organizer, or during the Explore as a way of deciding if it is time to summarize. They should be able to respond to the question during the Summarize. The students' role is to garner enough information to answer the questions in the mathematical task. Some teachers post the Focus Question in place of the lesson objective.

Some Problems have a "boxed-Launch" question before the Problem, which offers a choice for opening up the Problem task for students. For more information on this feature, see page 32 of Components.

Questions to consider when planning the Launch:

- What prior knowledge do my students need to call upon?
- How will I launch this Problem to ensure that all students have access to begin the task?
- What do the students need to know to understand the story and the challenge of the Problem?
- What advantages or difficulties can I foresee?
- How can I keep from giving away too much of the Problem?
- How can I make it personal to them?

Explore

The purpose of the Explore phase of the lesson is for students to explore a rich Problem, which will enable them to analyze and generalize a concept or skill. Students may tackle the mathematical task individually, with a partner, or with a small group, depending on the challenge and format of the Problem. The students' role during the Explore phase is to delve into the Problem. When appropriate, students should collaborate with their peers to make sense of what the questions are asking and to make a visual display of their learning for others to consider during the Summarize.

The teacher's role during this phase is to provide for individual needs and to plan for the Summarize phase. To do this, the teacher must observe and listen to the students at work. The teacher will pose questions to support struggling students, taking care to follow the students' thinking rather than the teacher's pathway of reasoning. The teacher will pose questions to push the thinking of those students who quickly complete the task and demonstrate that they are ready to be challenged further. Consideration must be given to when to end the Explore. Also, the teacher needs to decide the opening question for the Summarize. A teacher must plan which students' reasoning and conclusions, and which sequence, will provide a stimulating discourse on the mathematics.

Questions to consider when planning the Explore:

- Will I organize the students to explore this Problem individually, as pairs, or as small groups? Or can they organize themselves to best engage the task?

- What materials should be made available for students?

- Will students display their learning in individual papers, on chart paper, on construction paper, or by oral presentation?

- What are different strategies I anticipate them using?

- What Mathematical Practices do I anticipate students using?

- What kinds of questions can I pose to prompt their thinking if the level of frustration is high?

- What kinds of questions can I pose to make them probe further into the Problem if the initial question is answered?

- What kinds of questions can I pose to encourage student-to-student conversation about their thinking, reasoning and learning?

- What kinds of strategies will I be looking for to facilitate the summary, and how will I sequence them to stimulate a productive summary?

- How will the Focus Question help to decide when it is time to end the Explore?

Summarize

The purpose of the Summarize phase of the lesson is to orchestrate whole-group student discourse about their discoveries during the Explore phase of the lesson. It is during the Summarize that the teacher guides the students to reach the mathematical goals of the Problem and to connect their new understanding to prior mathematical goals and Problems in the Unit. Student conjectures and conclusions are shared and considered by their peers. Conclusions are solidified and sometimes questions are posed for further exploration in future lessons. The teacher begins by posing an opening question that will get the conversation started. After that, the students should lead the Summarize by presenting their conjectures and conclusions with mathematically sound support.

The teacher and students ask clarifying questions. Students draw conclusions addressing the mathematical goals of the lesson. Answering the Focus Question can help guide the Summarize.

Questions to consider when planning the Summarize:

- How can I help the students make sense of and appreciate the variety of methods that may occur?

- How can I orchestrate the discussion so students lead the summary of their thinking in the Problem?

- What mathematics and processes need to be drawn out?

- How will these ideas be recorded?

- Which ideas need to be made visible and displayed for future reference?

- What needs to be emphasized?

- What ideas do not need closure at this time?

- What do we need to generalize?

- How can we go beyond? What new questions might arise?

- What will I do to follow up, practice, or apply the ideas after the Summarize?

Reflect

At the end of each lesson it is productive to take note of student understandings:

- What evidence do I have of what my students learned about the Focus Question?

- What revelations occurred? What struggles did students have?

- How does this affect my instructional decisions for the next lesson? For the next time I teach this Problem?

- Where will I have time to revisit these ideas in the next Problem, Investigation, or Unit?

Utilizing Components

The ACE exercises were written to provide additional learning opportunities for your students. Initially most teachers used them as homework assignments. Over the course of implementing this curriculum, some teachers have expanded their flexibility in utilizing ACE exercises in other ways, such as with "bell ringer" or "opener." A rule of thumb is to answer the exercises yourself with the level of detail that you expect from your students while timing yourself. Take that time and multiply it by three or four to estimate how long it will take your students to complete. There are suggestions in the teacher support for which ACE exercises align with each of the Investigation's Problems.

> Application exercises tend to be very similar to the in-class Problem using a similar context or a new context but the same mathematical concepts or skills.
>
> Connection exercises reflect prior learning or foreshadow future learning. The concepts or skills are reinforced from the daily lesson Problems.
>
> Extension exercises take the concepts and skills from the Investigation to the next level or expand on the Problem. Often these questions have a greater depth and openness to them. Many students can and will benefit from doing some of these Problems. Students who are ready will typically find these questions interesting and worthy of their thinking time.

Here are some suggestions for implementing ACE exercises.

- You can use the ACE exercises for homework. Some questions to consider:

  Why homework?
  What do I intend for my students to gain from the homework assignment?
  How will it further our collective learning?
  How will students get feedback about their work on the ACE questions?

Consider how much time you will devote to homework correction both during class and outside of class and the time you will need to spend planning and implementing the daily lessons. You may also consider offering different ACE assignments to different students that align with where they are in their learning.

- Often you can select an ACE exercise to use as an entry activity or exit slip. One procedure is to have students respond to the question on mini-whiteboards they hold up for a quick assessment. Another procedure is to have students respond on a sticky note and stick it on the door as they exit class. You can readily sort their responses to assess who is ready to build on the concept or skill and who may need some additional practice or support.

- You can select various ACE exercises as additional learning opportunities for students. These exercises may be chosen by you or selected by individual students. To help students choose, you may point out that the ACE exercises are designed to help students become more confident in their understandings. Students who believe that they would benefit from additional practice choose from the exercises that align with the day's lesson. You may also use the ACE exercises to differentiate instruction for various learners. You can assign different ACE to individual students who need additional practice to solidify their understandings or need an additional challenge to deepen their understanding beyond the class discussion.

Here are suggestions for additional components.

- At the close of each Investigation, you can lead a whole class conversation around the Mathematical Reflection questions. Students should have the opportunity to discuss their understandings and then record their individual responses to the questions in their notebooks or journals. You can also post each question on a sheet of chart paper or on a section of your whiteboard. Each student or small group of students can record their responses and respond to each other in "chalk talk" format. For a chalk talk, your writing does the talking instead of talking aloud. Students write an initial response and then their peers add their thinking in the form of new ideas and connections.

- You can plan for opportunities in which students can reflect on their experiences and name the Mathematical Practices that they used. At the close of each Investigation, various Mathematical Practices are highlighted for students to recognize how those practices were used during the Investigation. Take a few minutes during the Summarize of the Problem to ask students to reflect on which of the Mathematical Practices were used during the class period. You will enhance student understanding of their learning and processing mathematically.

- Essential vocabulary terms are developed during each Unit. You can plan for a time for students to record their definitions with specific examples for the terms as they occur in the Unit. Students create their own mathematical dictionaries to reference from year to year in middle school and beyond. Some teachers ask students to create a blank dictionary on lined paper with one to three pages for each letter of the alphabet. Students then add the essential vocabulary terms as the year progresses. Other teachers prepare terms in alphabetical order by Unit. Students add their definitions and a specific example for each vocabulary word. Displaying each essential vocabulary term with student displays of learning on the memory wall (described in Preparing Your Classroom Environment) will enable students to have a readily accessible reference when engaged in discourse around Problems.

The teacher support also contains a wealth of information to help you plan your lessons.

Suggestions for Working With Pairs and Small Groups

Working collaboratively allows students to tackle more complicated and more conceptually difficult Problems. Carefully managed, collaborative learning can be a powerful tool for teachers to use during classroom instruction. CMP suggests two types of collaborative-learning groupings: partner work and small-group work.

Many of the Problems in CMP are mathematically demanding, requiring students to gather data, consider ideas, look for patterns, make conjectures, and use problem-solving strategies to reach a solution. For this reason, the teacher support often suggests that students work on a Problem collaboratively. Group work supports the generation of a variety of ideas and strategies to be discussed and considered, and it enhances the perseverance of students in tackling more complicated multistep and multipart Problems.

It is appropriate to ask students to think about a Problem individually before moving them into groups, allowing them to formulate their own ideas and questions to bring to the group. These multiple perspectives often lead to interesting and diverse strategies for solving a Problem.

Group work is also suggested for some of the Unit Projects. These projects tend to be large, complicated tasks. Working in a group allows students to consider a variety of ideas and helps them complete the task in a reasonable amount of time. You will want to determine group configurations in an efficient manner so class time is not wasted.

You may find it easiest to decide before class how students will be grouped. There are various methods you can use to establish groups, such as assigning students to a group for a whole Unit or randomly drawing for group assignments on a more frequent basis. You may also want to arrange the seating in the room to minimize movement during the transitions from individual to group to whole-class settings.

Guidelines for Working in Pairs and Small Groups

It is important that you clearly communicate your expectations about group work to your students and then hold them to those expectations. You may want to hand out or post a set of guidelines so students understand their responsibilities. Below is a suggested set of guidelines.

Student guidelines for group work:

- Move into your groups quickly and get right to work.

- Read the instructions aloud or repeat what the teacher has challenged you to find out. Be sure every group member knows what the challenge is.

- Part of group work is learning to listen to each other. Don't interrupt your classmates. Make sure each person's ideas are heard and that the group answers each person's questions.

- If you are confused, ask your group to explain. If no one in the group can answer the question, and it is an important question, raise your hand for the teacher.

- If someone in your group uses a word or an idea you do not understand, ask for an explanation. You are responsible for learning all you can from your group. You are also responsible for contributing to the work of your group. Your explanations for others will help you to understand better.

- Give everyone in the group a chance to talk about his or her ideas. Talking out loud about your thinking will help you learn to express your arguments and clarify your ideas.

- If your group gets stuck, go over what the Problem is asking and what you know so far. If this does not give you a new idea, raise your hand for the teacher.

- Be prepared to share your group's ideas, solutions, and strategies and to explain why you think you are correct. Make sure you look back at the original Problem and check that your solutions make sense.

- You are responsible for recording your group's ideas and solutions in your notes.

Supporting Differentiated Instruction

Planning for differentiated instruction begins with trying each Problem for yourself while keeping in mind how your students may tackle the task, especially special education students, gifted students, or English Language learners. Based on your personal experience, you can anticipate where your students may excel or struggle with the Problem. While preparing for the Explore phase of the lesson, you should generate questions to pose to students who are having difficulty as well as to students who are ready for an additional challenge. Finally, the Summarize phase allows you to differentiate how students will share their discoveries. See Part 4: A Curriculum for All for a discussion of working with special groups.

Pacing

When using CMP, you should try to maintain a steady pace that will allow you to get through as much of the material as possible. Because ideas are developed over several Problems, it is important for you not to spend too much time on any one Problem. In some districts, district coordinators set timeline schedules to help teachers establish a sense of pacing. Each Unit contains pacing schedules for 50–60 minute periods and block scheduling that were based on field testing. It is difficult to dictate pacing. It depends on the number of years you have been implementing CMP, the needs of your students in any given year, the number of days allocated to teaching, and the length of your class period.

Over the course of a year, the 10-minute difference between a 50- and a 60-minute class period amounts to about one Unit. Also in this era of standardized testing, some schools are adding review days, test prep days, pretesting, and standardized testing of various kinds in addition to the Common Core tests. In some districts the number of days devoted to reviewing or taking tests is more than 30 days. This shortens the time for teaching by 1 to 2 months.

In the first year of implementation, you may feel the need to supplement the materials with drill and practice. This will take time away from CMP and slow the pace. Rest assured that you can trust the curriculum, because it incorporates practice into the lessons.

You may have other concerns about homework, grading, basic skills, and collaborative learning. These concerns may affect how you set the pacing of a Unit. You should address these issues during professional development or staff meetings.

Collaborating With Colleagues

Many teachers find it valuable to plan with a colleague before, during, and after teaching the Unit. Student work is often a focus for their discussions, as it provides a platform for discussing the mathematics in the Unit, Investigation, or Problem. Discussion can also cover effective teaching strategies and other issues related to teaching. Appendix G gives sets of summary questions that can be useful when planning a lesson either alone or with colleagues. The teacher support also contains a wealth of information to help you plan your lessons.

Student Absences

It is likely that most students will be absent at some time during the school year. Having procedures for bringing those students back into the conversation upon their return is helpful.

- Designate a specific location for extra lab sheets and a dated set of assignments. You will enable students who have been absent to find out what they missed.

- If students are seated in teams, each team can be responsible for helping an absent team member catch up upon his or her return to school. You can establish notetaking buddies so students have someone to provide the notes.

It is important to keep in mind that concepts and skills are built over time. Students will have multiple opportunities over the course of a Unit and over the course of the year to develop and demonstrate the understandings of skills and concepts. Therefore, missing one lesson should not significantly affect student understanding.

Teacher Absences

Planning lessons that can be implemented by a guest teacher is challenging. A few options:

- Select a set of ACE questions from a previous Investigation that will enhance students' understanding in the current Investigation

- Discuss the responses to the Mathematical Reflections with the guest teacher during the day prior to your planned absence and assign the writing of the responses to the students

- Proctor an individual Check Up Quiz or Partner Quiz

- Assign vocabulary entries

- Practice test-taking strategies for standardized tests and electronic assessments

- Proctor a preassessment for a new Unit of study

If you are fortunate to have professional development opportunities for your middle school mathematics guest teachers or your guest teacher is an experienced CMP teacher, you may be able to leave a lesson design for the Launch, Explore, and Summarize of a Problem.

It is important to foster an environment for collaborative learning from the opening day of school through the end of the school year. Evidence of the Mathematical Practices are seen and heard naturally in a CMP classroom when the curriculum is implemented with integrity.

You can foster collaborative learning by valuing students' reasoning, thinking, and physical displays of learning as they work during the Explore and Summarize phases of the lesson. If you view your role more as a guide to learning rather than an affirmer of skills and knowledge, students will take ownership of their learning and value sharing their ideas with one another.

Collaborative learning during the Explore phase is most effective when the Problem is deep enough to be tackled by a small group of three to four students. Collaborative partner work is also enhanced when students have a few minutes of individual time to think about the Problem. This individual investment in thinking enriches student collaboration during the Explore phase. When the Summarize phase is based on students' input from their exploration, students realize that they own their learning. There is a sense of community-built understanding. Encourage students to ask questions of each other.

Many of the ideas in this section need to be addressed during the planning stage.

In this section, you will find suggestions for the following:

- Choosing and establishing classroom norms
- Initiating and promoting substantive student discourse
- Making thinking visible
- Differentiating for learners
- Enacting the Mathematical Reflections and Mathematical Practices
- Relating to the middle-school learner

Choosing and Establishing Classroom Norms

The goal is to foster an environment where students view learning as their own and strive to work collaboratively to a deeper understanding. Establishing a classroom culture where student thinking is visible and valued will help achieve that goal.

Getting Started

The following suggestions invite students to participate in establishing classroom norms.

- During the initial days of school, have students imagine the "best class ever." Ask what words they would use to describe it. Brainstorm a list of adjectives and phrases.

- On the following day ask, "How can we make this ideal class happen?" Students will generate proposed class norms.

Sample Plan

Ask students, "Imagine the ideal class, the best class you ever hope to have. What words would you use to describe it?" Then follow the 3-2-1 Protocol within teams of three to four students as follows:

- Individually write down three descriptors.

- Choose two to share with the rest of your team.

- Select one descriptor that your team can support.

- Share with the rest of the class and record the results on chart paper.

Throughout the year, you can reference students' words and reflect together on how well the class is upholding those ideals.

Student and Teacher Awareness

Ask the following questions to facilitate student–teacher interaction. For each question, have teams of students create a written response on a half a sheet of paper. Then have teams present their responses aloud.

- What should middle school teachers know about middle school students?

- What should middle school students know about middle school teachers?

- What are some common beliefs shared by both middle school students and middle school teachers?

These questions will help you establish active listening skills while demonstrating how much you value student thinking. Having students share their responses will help students to demonstrate that same respect for one another. Once you establish your classroom as a collective learning community, students will view themselves as participating members in questioning and validating mathematical ideas.

Promoting Student Discourse

Initiating and promoting substantive student discourse is at the heart of the craft of teaching. Discourse begins with a mathematical challenge that is worthy of exploration and deepens students' mathematical understandings. Three examples of ways to promote student discourse are described below.

Five Practices for Orchestrating Productive Mathematical Discussions

An excellent resource is a book by Margaret S. Smith and May Kay Stein, *Five Practices for Orchestrating Productive Mathematics Discussions*[1]. This book also includes a Professional Development Guide. The five practices are as follows:

- **Anticipating** In the Anticipating phase, the teacher predicts during planning how students will respond to a particular mathematic task. He or she considers possible alternative strategies that students may use, as well as potential misconceptions that may surface.

- **Monitoring** Monitoring occurs as the teacher circulates during the Explore of the lesson in a CMP classroom. He or she listens to student discussions while asking clarifying questions and posing new challenges.

- **Selecting** This Selecting phase involves choosing the strategies for students that occur during the Explore that will best illustrate and promote the desired understanding of the Focus Question.

- **Sequencing** In Sequencing, before the Summarize, the teacher plans which students will share their thinking, and in what order, so as to maximize the quality of the discussion.

- **Connecting** Finally, the Connecting practice which occurs during the Summarize involves posing questions that enable students to understand and use each other's strategies, and to connect the Problem's Big Idea to previous learning. Connecting practice may also foreshadow future learning.

The Five-Representation Star

The five-representation star (Preston and Garner, 2003) can be used to stimulate discussion. For example, at an appropriate time during the Summarize of a Problem, ask students to talk about which representations were useful in solving and communicating their thinking.

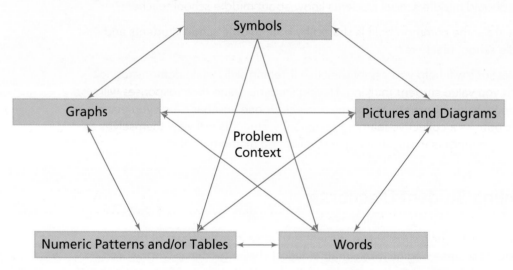

Algebraic relationships are common when considering these five representations. Below is an example of a problem relating the width of a rectangle to the area of a rectangle with five representations:

Words A rectangle has a perimeter of 12 meters with a width of *x* meters. What is the length? How does the area relate to the width, *x*?

Diagram

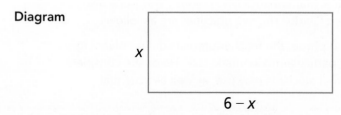

Table

x	0	1	2	3	4	5	6
A	0	5	8	9	8	5	0

Graph

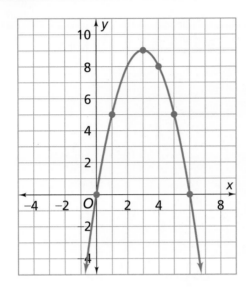

Symbol $A = x(6 - x)$

The perimeter of a rectangle is equal to twice the width plus twice the length. So, when the perimeter is 12 meters, the width plus the length must be 6 meters. This means that the maximum width is 6 meters, which would make the length 0 meters. The area would be equal to zero square meters.

These values correspond to the values in the table. Students may draw various rectangles and make a table of values for widths from 0 to 6 meters, noticing that this is the limit of the values for the width. They may also notice that the maximum area occurs when the width equals the length. In this case, the maximum area of 9 square meters occurs when each dimension, the width and the length, is 3 meters.

Students may also explore rational numbers. For example, they may consider a width of 5.9 meters and a length of 0.1 meters, which results in an area of 0.59 square meters.

Students typically need some guidance to understand the difference between the domain and range of the problem situation, and the domain and range of the function used to model that problem situation. For instance, in this case, the values of the width must be between zero and 6 meters. The area must be between zero and 9 square meters. The domain of the function $A = x(6 - x)$ is not limited, however, to positive values for x. Thus, x can be any real number. Similarly, the values for the range may be negative, with a maximum of 9.

Relationships between numeric equations may also be communicated using these five representations. Consider the case of multiplying two mixed numbers, $5\frac{1}{2} \times 4\frac{3}{4} = 26\frac{1}{8}$.

Words Jane is tiling her bathroom floor. The floor is $5\frac{1}{2}$ feet long by $4\frac{3}{4}$ feet wide. What is the area of the floor that Jane is tiling? If each tile is one square foot, how many tiles does Jane need to buy?

Diagram An area model fits this context nicely.

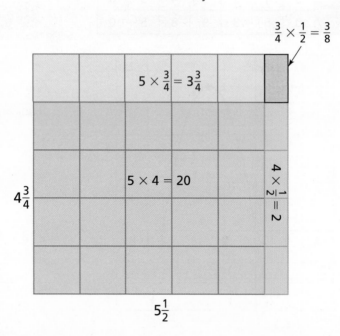

$$\frac{3}{4} \times \frac{1}{2} = \frac{3}{8}$$

$$5 \times \frac{3}{4} = 3\frac{3}{4}$$

$$5 \times 4 = 20$$

$$4 \times \frac{1}{2} = 2$$

$4\frac{3}{4}$

$5\frac{1}{2}$

Numeric Pattern Students who understand multiplication as repeated addition may add $5\frac{1}{2}$ four times and then add $\frac{3}{4}$ of $5\frac{1}{2}$, or $22 + 4\frac{1}{8} = 26\frac{1}{8}$.

Graph The problem can also be represented on a number line as repeated addition.

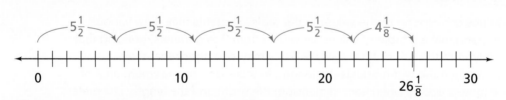

$5\frac{1}{2}$ $5\frac{1}{2}$ $5\frac{1}{2}$ $5\frac{1}{2}$ $4\frac{1}{8}$

0   10   20 $26\frac{1}{8}$ 30

Symbols The equation $5\frac{1}{2} \times 4\frac{3}{4} = 26\frac{1}{8}$ can be illustrated in ways that correspond to the solution methods student choose.

For instance, the area model corresponds with the distributive property:

$$5\frac{1}{2} \times 4\frac{3}{4} = \left(5 + \frac{1}{2}\right) \times \left(4 + \frac{3}{4}\right)$$
$$= 5 \times 4 + 5 \times \frac{3}{4} + \frac{1}{2} \times 4 + \frac{1}{2} \times \frac{3}{4}$$
$$= 20 + 3\frac{3}{4} + 2 + \frac{3}{8} = 26\frac{1}{8} \text{ square feet}$$

So, Jane will need to purchase 27 or more tiles to tile her bathroom floor. More specifically, if Jane is accurate in cutting and fitting the tiles, she would likely need a minimum of 22 tiles plus 6 more tiles for the last row for a total of 28 tiles.

Using Talk Moves

Use a third strategy, talk moves, to facilitate classroom discussions:

- **Prompt** Teachers prompt students to answer a question.
- **Wait Time** Teachers provide adequate time for students to respond to a question.
- **Revoice** Teachers repeat a student's answer to emphasize and clarify what the student said.
- **Restate** Teachers ask a student to restate what another student has said to ensure that students listen closely to each other.
- **Apply Reasoning** Teachers ask students to evaluate, critique, and use each other's responses and strategies. (Chapin, O'Connor, and Anderson, 2003)

A professional development resource for facilitating effective and mathematically productive classroom discussions is the *Mathematics Discourse in Secondary Classrooms* (MDISC) project (Herbel-Eisenman, Steele, and Cirillo, in press)

Making Thinking Visible[2]

When you are establishing student ownership of their learning, a first step is to have students prepare artifacts that will be displayed for peer observation followed by whole-class or small group dialogue about their artifacts. Those student-created artifacts may be on chart paper, on smaller construction paper, written on a smart board or whiteboard, or on regular paper to be captured with a document camera. In some CMP classes, students share their work through videos. When students know that their peers are going to be viewing their work while making specific comments, they put forth greater effort to communicate more effectively. Asking students to select various artifacts that will be displayed on the class memory wall will also encourage students to make their thinking visible to others.

Gallery Walks

Groups display their work on poster paper. You can then use some or all of these in the Summarize. Students can move around from poster to poster, leaving a comment or question. You can provide the groups with a question to ask as they view the posters.

Making Thinking Visible is a book by Ron Ritchhart, Mark Church, and Karin Morrison. The book provides rationale for having students' thinking made visible and also shares multiple thinking routines that foster visible thinking. In addition there are "Pictures of Practice" to provide specific examples to show student work from classrooms. Some of the specific Pictures of Practice are work from CMP teachers and their students.

The following routines from the book are useful for introducing and exploring Big Idea concepts at the beginning of a CMP Unit:

- **See, Think, Wonder: Unit Introduction** "As you preview the Unit, what do you see? What do you think you will be learning? What do you wonder about this Unit?"

- **Think, Puzzle Explore: Launching a Problem** "What do think may occur here? What are you puzzling about? How can you explore to confirm or counter what you're thinking?"

- **Chalk Talk: Vocabulary Sense-making** Post each essential vocabulary term in the middle of a sheet of chart paper. Each student has a marker and rotates from term to term adding his or her definition or comment about that term. Students may not talk. Your "chalk," in this case a "marker," does the talking. You could also use this format for Mathematical Reflections by posting each question on a different sheet of chart paper around the classroom. Students could add their understandings, specific examples, and clarifying questions.

The following list of routines is helpful for delving deeper in big idea concepts throughout a Unit:

- **What makes you say that?** This routine is effective in daily discourse during which students initially engage in the whole-class conversation. When students make a prediction, you can follow up by asking "What makes you say that?" to clarify what reasoning they used to make that prediction. When students make a claim about a situation, you can pose the question "What makes you say that?" to see what evidence they used to come up with that claim.

- **Claim, Support, Question** This routine is effective to use as students are conducting a gallery walk while quietly (no talking) observing each other's visual displays of learning around a key exploration. Students are asked to make a claim or conjecture while providing support or evidence for that claim. The teacher follows up the claims with questions such as, "What questions do you still have about these claims?" or "What additional questions did your classmates' visual displays of learning bring up for you?" Crafting the Summarize phase around students' challenging each other's conjectures will deepen student understanding of key mathematical ideas.

These routines are useful for synthesizing and organizing ideas at the close of an Investigation or a Unit:

- **Headlines** For this routine, students are asked to capture their new learning from a Unit or an Investigation by composing a headline—a catchy phrase or sentence similar to those seen in newspapers. Students write their headlines on strips of paper that can be posted on the memory wall. It is especially informative when you ask students to explain their headline on the back of their paper strips.

- **Connect, Extend, Challenge** This routine can be used effectively when comparing student strategies for drawing conclusions about a situation. For example, the Orange Juice Problem in the seventh-grade Unit Comparing and Scaling is likely to have multiple student-selected strategies for determining which orange juice mixture is the most flavorful or the least flavorful. As students display their problem-solving techniques and conclusions, you can begin the Summarize by posing questions such as: "What connections do you see among each other's strategies? How does a strategy that is different from yours extend your thinking or reasoning? How would a different strategy challenge your thinking? Do you have a challenge to pose about a strategy or conclusion that is displayed?" Students may write their responses to these questions prior to engaging in small-group or whole-group discussions. The teacher may circulate during this writing phase to get a sense of which ideas to bring out in the whole-class discussion.

- **I used to think . . . Now I think . . .** This routine provides teachers and students with an opportunity to formally recognize a change in their thinking from the beginning of an Investigation to the end or from the start of a Problem to its conclusion. Students confront their original thinking about a concept and reflect on what has changed about that thinking. Acknowledging a change in thinking is powerful for all learners. This is easily done with sticky notes.

Discourse on Mathematical Reflections and Mathematical Practices

The Mathematical Reflections questions provide an opportunity for the teacher and students to discuss the goals of the Investigation. After the class discussion, which can take place orally or in written form, students record their responses to the Mathematical Reflection questions to have a record of their current understandings. The teacher gains an understanding of student thinking during the discussion and then can assess individual understanding based on each student's written work.

Each CMP lesson allows students to engage in the Mathematical Practices. Using the Mathematical Practices Reflections at the close of each Investigation allows students to name what they have done. Students demonstrate to themselves the power of the Practices. Some teachers also include a discussion of the Mathematical Practices during the Summarize of a particular Problem where a specific practice was evident and widely used by students.

The Role of Student Work in Promoting Understanding and Reasoning

CMP3 features student work implicitly throughout the curriculum. However, if the Standards for Mathematical Practice are to be tested on national assessments, students need opportunities that develop the practices as well as make those practices explicit. To this end, CMP3 uses examples of student work throughout the student editions and teacher support to address the standard: *Construct viable arguments and critique the reasoning of others*. These examples enhance students' conceptual understanding, refine their competence with mathematical procedures, and broaden their capacity make sense of situations.

Student work occurs in three places with slightly different purposes. In each case, the examples occur after students have had time to work on the ideas themselves. Student work in CMP3 exemplifies the goals detailed below.

- **Connect mathematical ideas within a learning progression** Usually located between two Problems, their purpose is to review or summarize strategies just developed and transition into the next Problem.

- **Refine student understanding** Located within a Problem, some student work serves to refine student thinking, surface alternate strategies, and push students toward some resolution of the mathematical situation. Student work can provide a quicker way to engage students in examining aspects of mathematics that are not easily discovered or noticed. Such examples tend to occur in units that focus on developing algorithms, for example, solving equations.

- **Strengthen student understanding of and proficiency with a procedure or concept** Student work appears in the ACE exercises in various forms. The purpose is to strengthen students' mathematical reasoning and skill by situating content in new contexts. Student work in the ACE often involves presenting solutions that include common errors in which students are asked to examine the solution and correct any errors they may find.

Many instances of student work address all three goals. These most often occur within a Problem so that nuances may be explored during the discussions in the Summarize.

Providing for Individual Needs

The first opportunity for differentiation with students is during the Launch. Based on your experiences with your students, you may launch the day's Problem in a way that best meet the needs of your students. Launching the Unit and individual Investigation Problems so that all students have access to start the Problem is the key.

During the Explore the teacher's observations and follow-up questions posed will differentiate instruction for learners. Posing questions to redirect or clarify situations for struggling students is beneficial to learners. Keep in mind that students should be encouraged to continue their line of reasoning rather than be redirected to the teacher's line of reasoning. Posing questions to encourage students to think more deeply or to justify their responses is appropriate as well. Finally, posing questions to challenge students to take the Problem concept to the next level of difficulty is also effective.

The Summarize allows for differentiation as students share their thinking with their peers. With the focus question in mind, use the Summarize to build on student understanding from a basic level to a more sophisticated level. Not all students need to be at the same level of understanding for a given Problem. Their knowledge will continue to grow throughout the Unit and in the following Units. The Focus Question can be a guide to whatever level of understanding is appropriate for each individual.

The results of the collaboration that occur during the Explore continue into the Summarize, but now groups come together as a whole class to share and refine ideas and strategies. It is important that all students have an opportunity to participate in the Summarize. The classroom conversation that occurs during the Summarize provides an important opportunity to push students' mathematical thinking. By examining and testing ideas, students can learn mathematical skills and strategies and make connections and generalizations. You might use the following suggestions to increase interaction and participation:

- Encourage students to respond to another student's or group's presentation and conjectures

- Have students summarize the essence of a student's or group's presentation

- After a student or a group presents, have others in the class ask questions to challenge the student's or the group's thinking

- Ask a student to create and post an incorrect solution to stimulate the thinking of the class and generate a conversation

- If you have a student who struggles, find opportunities for him or her to present when you know he or she has a correct answer

- If there is repetition among strategies, have students discuss the similarities or contribute new thoughts, rather than just repeat ideas

- Encourage students to look for common ideas in their strategies and representations

Relating to the Middle School Learner

Another consideration is to take advantage of the natural attributes of middle school learners who have concerns about fairness, equality, justice, social interaction, and empathy. Posing questions around those ideas that live beyond the mathematics classroom will provide additional leverage for engaging students in mathematical tasks. For example, when introducing the seventh-grade Unit *What Do You Expect?*, you can ask students to write about what it means for something to be fair and how to be sure that something is fair. Fairness is an issue that matters to middle school students and to our society. While engaging in the Problems for *What Do You Expect?*, you can repeatedly come back to ask how the mathematics in a Problem helps us in determining fairness.

Reflecting on Student Learning

It is through reflection that teachers continue to grow and to develop the kind of classroom environment that encourages all students to become independent, confident, and reflective learners. The following questions are all part of teacher reflections on the effectiveness of the classroom environment:

- What do my students know? What are my students able to do? What is the evidence? How does this shape what I plan for tomorrow?

- How do I help students to engage in the mathematical tasks, and how are the tasks effective in helping them learn mathematics?

- How do I use the activities to stimulate the richness of discussion that helps students to develop mathematical power?

- How does the classroom discourse encourage learner independence? Curiosity? Mathematical thinking? Confidence? Disposition to do mathematics?

- What can I do to ensure that the classroom environment suits every student and supports his or her mathematical development?

Many teachers write brief notes or comments on important ideas or suggestions for what worked and what to do differently the next time they teach the Unit. They use the classroom discussions, exit slips, homework, or Mathematical Reflections as benchmarks for student understanding. They reevaluate where they and their students are each day. They reflect on each student's understanding, answering these questions:

- What do I know about each student?

- Is a particular student participating in class discussions?

- Is he or she attempting or completing homework?

- What evidence do I have of what my students learned?

- How should this affect my instructional decisions?

Assessments

In this climate of accountability and addressing individual student needs, some schools have found it particularly helpful to use some pre- and post-assessments. Their initial thinking about pre- and postassessments was of a set of test questions given at the beginning of a Unit and then given again at the end of the Unit, with the only change being the order of the questions or the numerical values in the questions. They felt that that kind of assessment was not very informative and a poor use of class time, which is at such a premium.

Therefore, schools developed other assessments that were intended to be more helpful to both students and teachers. Teachers have found it beneficial to have strategies that demonstrate student growth in understanding. Various formats inform teachers of students' current conceptions as well as misconceptions, allowing teachers to make more informed decisions about instruction during the Unit. Here are two examples:

- **Shapes and Designs** Display sets of photographs from nature, art and architecture in the real world. Ask students to describe the shapes and designs that they see. In addition ask students to predict what they will learn in the Unit. At the close of the Unit the open question can be posed again so students can add to their responses about what they know about shapes and designs.

- **Looking for Pythagoras** Pre-assessment single question: What do think you know about right triangles?

  Post-assessment single question: Now what do you know about right triangles?

For an end-of-year assessment, some teachers create a one-or-two page outline with each Unit title and ask students to write down answers to questions such as "What are the big ideas that you think are the most important to remember?" for each Unit.

Some teachers create a point system to assess student work on the daily Problems, ACE Exercises, Mathematical Reflections, and on the formal assessments in Check Up, Partner Quiz, Unit Test, and Unit Project. You can also use a standards-based grading system to assess student understanding. Lastly, you can look through students Problem work and ACE Exercises to find some that demonstrate their best evidence of understanding for each of the goals.

Examples of Grading from CMP Classroom Teachers

The multidimensional assessment in CMP provides opportunities to collect broad and rich information about students' knowledge. Teachers face the challenge of converting some of this information into a grade to communicate a level of achievement to both students and parents. The following assessment items offer teachers an opportunity to assign grades: ACE exercises, CheckUps, Quizzes, Mathematical Reflections, Looking Back, Unit Tests, Projects, Notebooks, and Self-Assessments. The use of these assessments for grading and the value assigned to them vary from teacher to teacher. While most teachers view the Problems as the time to learn and practice mathematical concepts and skills, some teachers will occasionally assign a grade to a Problem. Some teachers also choose to grade class participation.

Two teachers' grading schemes for their CMP mathematics classes follow. These are given as examples of possible grading schemes. Note that each of these teachers has made independent decisions about how best to use the assessment tools in CMP for grading purposes.

Example 1: Ms. Jones's Grading System

- **Participation** I try to take several things into account when grading students in mathematics class. I work to build a learning community where everyone feels free to voice his or her thoughts so that we can make sense of the mathematics together. I try very hard to assess and grade only those things that we value in the classroom.

  Because participating in discussions and activities is so important in helping the students make sense of the mathematics, this is one part of the students' grades. They rate themselves at the end of each week on how well they participated throughout the week. Below is a sample of the grading sheet they fill out. The participation grade counts as 15% of their total mathematics grade.

Participation Grading Sheet   Name _____

Week of _____

We have completed almost a full week of math class. Think about how well you participated in class this week.

1. Answer the following questions, as they will help you give yourself a fair participation grade for this week.

   ❑ Did you participate in the discussions?   ❑ Did you ask questions when you didn't understand?

   ❑ Did you come prepared to class, having done your homework, so that you could ask questions?   ❑ Did you LISTEN carefully to others?

2. Now count your "yes" responses.

   If you answered "yes" to ALL of them, HOORAY for you! You are doing a great job. Give yourself a **5**.

   If you answered "yes" to most of them, give yourself a **4**.

   If you answered "yes" to a couple of them, give yourself a **3**.

   If you answered "no" to several of these, give yourself a 2, and rethink your role in this class or talk to your teacher.

3. I grade myself a _____ for this week.   Signature _____

• **Journal** Ideas become clear when we talk about them and when we write about them. Because I feel it is very important to be able to communicate mathematically in writing, students' journals also figure into their grade. We use the journals for problem solving, communicating what they do and do not understand, and reflecting on each Investigation to summarize the ideas. I try to collect them at least once every two weeks so I remain in constant communication with each student. The journal grade counts as 15% of their total grade. I use the rubric shown at the bottom of the page to grade journals.

Journal Grading Sheet

You will earn a 5, if:

• You effectively communicate your thoughts.
• You use appropriate vocabulary.
• You use a variety of strategies to solve problems.
• You write as if you are talking about mathematics.
• Your journal is well organized, and entries are labeled and dated.

You will earn a 4, if:

• You are effective in communicating your thoughts most of the time.
• You use some appropriate vocabulary.
• You use some different strategies when solving problems.
• Your journal is fairly well organized, and most entries are labeled and dated.

You will earn a 3, if:

• You attempt to communicate your thoughts but your entries are hard to follow at times; be sure to write ALL that you know.
• You use some appropriate vocabulary but need to use more.
• You need to work on using a variety of strategies to solve problems.
• Your journal is not organized with the entries labeled and dated.

If you earn a 2:

• Please see me.

Date Graded	Grade Received
_____	_____
_____	_____
_____	_____

- **Homework** The curriculum is problem-centered. This means that the students will investigate mathematical ideas within the context of a realistic problem, as opposed to looking only at numbers. Students spend much of each class period working with a partner or in a small group trying to make sense of a problem. We then summarize the investigation with a whole class discussion. The ACE exercises assigned offer students an opportunity to practice those ideas alone and to think about them in more depth. Homework assignments are very important! They provide students the opportunity to assess their own understanding. They then can bring their insight and/or questions with them to class the next day. We usually start each class period going over the exercises that caused difficulty or that students just wanted to discuss. Keeping up with the homework (given about three or four times a week) helps students to stay on top of their learning. It also allows me to see what students are struggling with and making sense of Homework assignment grades count as 20% of their total grade.

- **Partner Quizzes** All of the quizzes from CMP are done with a partner. Because a lot of what we do in class is done with others, I want to assess students "putting their heads together," as well. Again, I try to grade what I value, which is working together. Quiz grades count as 20% of their total grade.

- **Final Assessment** At the end of each unit an individual assessment is given. Sometimes it is a written test, sometimes a project, and sometimes a writing assignment. These serve as an opportunity for students to show what they, as individuals, have learned from the whole unit. Test and project grades count as 30% of their total grade, as they are a culmination of the whole unit.

- **Grading Summary**
  - Participation 15%
  - Journals 15%
  - Homework 20%
  - Partner Quizzes 20%
  - Tests and Projects 30%

• Example 2: Mr. Smith's Grading Scheme

Journals (Part of the Notebook)
Collect student journals once a week.

Scoring Rubric for JOURNALS

5 Work for all Investigation problems (done in class, to date) and Reflections (well labeled and easy to find/follow)

4 Most class work and Reflections (well labeled and easy to find/follow)

3 Some missing class work or Reflections (not well labeled or easy to find/follow)

Below a 3 is not acceptable. Students have to come in at lunch or after school and meet with me and work on their journal until it is at least level 3.

Participation
Participation means questioning, listening, and offering ideas. Students are given a participation grading sheet every Monday, to be handed in on Friday. Students fill these out throughout the week, giving evidence of their participation in the class. On the sheets they are to note when and how they contribute to class discussion and when they use an idea from class discussion to revise their work or their thinking.

Scoring Rubric for PARTICIPATION

5 Student has made an extra effort to participate and help others in the class to understand the mathematics. Student gave evidence of participating all 5 days of the week.

4 Student made an effort to participate, giving evidence of at least 4 days of participation for the week.

3 Student made some effort to participate, giving evidence of at least 3 days of class participation for the week.

Below a 3 is not acceptable. I talk with student about his or her lack of effort. If no improvement is seen in the next week, a parent or guardian is called and informed of the problem.

Homework (selected ACE exercises)
In class, before homework is checked or collected, students are given the opportunity to ask questions about the assignment. I do not give answers or tell how to solve the exercise but, with the class's help, work with students to help them understand what the exercise is asking. Students have the right to revise any of their work while this conversation is

going on and not be marked down. Grading is strict on this work because students have the opportunity to take care of it themselves and get help.

Scoring Rubric for HOMEWORK

✔+ Close to perfect

✔ All problems attempted, most work done correctly

✔– Most problems attempted, some given answers wrong or incomplete

✔–– Not much work, most work wrong or incomplete

0 No work

Projects
A 6-point holistic rubric is used for all projects.

Scoring Rubric for PROJECTS

5 Project is complete, mathematics is correct, work is neat and easy to follow.

4 Project is mostly complete, most of the mathematics is correct, work is neat and easy enough to follow.

3 Project has some missing pieces, some of the mathematics is correct, work takes some effort by the teacher to follow.

2 Project is missing some major parts, there are several problems with the mathematics, it takes extra effort for the teacher to follow the work.

1 Project shows little to no significant work.

0 No project is submitted.

Check-Ups, Partner Quizzes, and Unit Tests
With partner quizzes, only the revised paper (the one turned in the second time) is scored for a grade.

Scoring Rubric for Check-Ups, Partner Quizzes, and Unit Tests
Each assessment has its own point-marking scheme devised by me. Points are determined by the amount of work asked for to solve each problem. Not all problems are awarded the same number of points.

Assigning grades to numbers and checks
5's and ✔+ = A
4's and ✔ = B
3's and ✔– = C
2's and ✔–– = D
1's and 0's = E

Comments on Partner Quizzes

The quizzes provided in the Connected Mathematics assessment package are a feature unique to the curriculum. The assumptions under which the quizzes were created present a unique management and grading situation for teachers.

- Students work in pairs.

- Students are permitted to use their notebooks, calculators, and any other appropriate materials.

- Pairs submit a draft of the quiz for teacher input, revise their work, and turn in the finished product for assessment.

Partner Quizzes are designed for students working in pairs. There are several ways to choose student pairs for a quiz. Most teachers use one or more of the following:

- Students choose their own partners

- Partners are chosen in some random way

- The teacher picks the pairs to work together

- Seating assignment determines partners

Many teachers keep track of who works with whom and have a rule that you cannot have the same partner twice until you have been paired with everyone in the class at least once.

It is assumed that each pair of students will have one opportunity to revise their work on the quiz based on teacher feedback before submitting it for a grade. When a pair has completed the quiz, they can submit separate papers or one paper with both names on it.

Giving feedback generally involves telling students which questions they have answered incorrectly or how many of the possible points they would receive for a question. It should be seen as an opportunity to let students know if they are on track or if they need to rethink a Problem. Giving feedback should not mean reteaching or leading students to the correct solution. Here are some methods CMP teachers have used for giving feedback to students.

- Check the quizzes and write the number of points achieved next to each question. Then allow the pair to revise all the questions.

- Check the quizzes and write the number of points achieved next to each question. Then allow the pair to revise one question of their choice. (If they write in a different color, you need to check only the new information.)

- While students take the quiz, allow each pair to confer with you once about one Problem.

Allowing students to revise their work is a new concept for many mathematics teachers. If you have never done this before, you might ask one of the language-arts teachers in your school how he or she orchestrates revision work for student writing, since this is a common practice in that discipline.

Quiz questions are richer and more challenging than Check Up questions. Many quiz questions are extensions of ideas students explored in class. These questions provide insight into how students apply the ideas from the Unit to new situations. The nature of the Partner Quizzes provides a grading situation in which rubrics can assist in the evaluation of the students' knowledge. You may want to refer to the teacher suggestions, grading rubrics, and samples of student work in the teacher support.

Here are some instructions for individual students during Partner Quizzes:

- Solve the exercise yourself

- Ask yourself, Does my answer make sense?

- Compare your work to your partner's work

- Discuss how your work is the same and how it is different

If you and your partner are not sure about your answers or you disagree, go to your notes and see if you have anything to help you think about this Problem.

- Make sure you agree on what the Problem is asking you to do and what you have to answer.

- Check your vocabulary to see if you have understood all the words.

- Think about how this Problem is like another one that you did in class or as homework. Check your notes for that Problem.

- If you still disagree, each of you should write a different answer to the Problem.

CMP provides a rich collection of assessment tools and strategies for promoting rich classroom discourse, monitoring and assessing students' understanding and reasoning during class, and paper and pencil assessments.

[1] Margaret S. Smith and May Kay Stein, *Five Practices for Orchestrating Productive Mathematics Discussions*. NCTM. 2011
[2] Chapin, S., O'Connor, C., & Anderson, N. (2009). Classroom Discussions: Using Math Talk to Help Students Learn, Grades K-6 (second edition). Sausalito, CA: Math Solutions Publications.

A Curriculum for All Students

The *Connected Mathematics Project* (CMP) holds high expectations for its students—all of its students. This belief is reflected in the ideology and the overarching goal of the curriculum:

> All students should be able to reason and communicate proficiently in mathematics. They should have knowledge of and skill in the use of vocabulary, forms of representation, materials, tools, techniques, and intellectual methods of the discipline of mathematics. This knowledge should include the ability to define and solve problems with reason, insight, inventiveness, and technical proficiency.

CMP teaches conceptual knowledge and skill. As in the above goal, skill means not only proficiency, but also the ability to use mathematics to make sense of situations. CMP helps students to understand the methods, algorithms, and strategies they use.

> In a problem-centered curriculum like CMP, the important mathematical concepts and processes are embedded in the context of the problem. The context of the problem helps students develop understanding and skills. It also helps them retrieve and apply their knowledge as needed for future learning. This pedagogical grounding is valuable for all students.

CMP can be and has been successfully implemented in classrooms that include special needs students, gifted students, and English Language Learners. We believe that CMP provides all students with opportunities to engage in cooperative learning, to assume leadership roles, and to enhance self-esteem and self-acceptance. This section shows how effective strategies for special groups of students are already built into the CMP curriculum. Note that many of the strategies described in the following sections also work for all students.

There is a rich database of research around CMP. Many of these studies involve student learning, including special groups. For more information, see www.connectedmath.msu.edu or www.connectedmathematics3.com.

Some may claim CMP poses a challenge for special-needs students due to its language-based curriculum; however, the CMP framework incorporates many recommendations by researchers in the field of special education. Embedded strategies and cooperative learning groups assist in making mathematics accessible to special-needs students.

Embedded Strategies

The conceptual framework upon which CMP is built involves sound teaching principles and practices for students, which is essentially the same foundation for working with special populations. To begin with, CMP was developed with the belief that calculators should be made available to students, which aligns with accommodations that many special-needs students are given. Furthermore, CMP incorporates manipulatives in its curriculum. While it is stressed within the CMP framework that manipulatives are to be used only when they can help students develop an understanding of mathematical ideas, it should be clear that special needs students may need to use manipulatives more often than their general education peers.

CMP uses real-life problems, a pedagogical technique repeatedly stressed in reaching special-needs students in mathematics classrooms. Guiding the development of CMP was an emphasis on making meaningful connections for students, among various mathematical topics and between mathematics and other disciplines. Maccini and Gagnon (2000) demonstrated that embedding problems within real-world contexts improves the motivation, participation, and generalization for special-needs students.

Other practices within the CMP framework that facilitate teaching mathematics to all students, including those with special needs, include: repetition and review, keeping expectations high, and teaching conceptual knowledge. The ACE section at the end of every Investigation allows students to tackle additional exercises from the Unit as well as to work on problems connected to earlier Units. Furthermore, the Looking Back section summarizes the learning students have completed in the particular Unit, while making connections to prior Units.

Cooperative Learning Groups

CMP provides opportunities for students to work in small groups and pairs, as well as a whole class or individually. Educational research suggests that cooperative groups can be beneficial to all students; however, some attention should be paid to the groupings to ensure that students with special needs are able to participate actively. Merely placing a student within a group does not result in that student becoming a part of the group. While studies have shown that cooperative learning has positive benefits on students' motivation, self-esteem, cognitive development, and academic achievement, the very dynamic of these learning methods may exclude special education students due to their disparities in skills, such skills as content area, communication, and social abilities (Brinton, Fujiki, & Montague, 2000). In discussing the structure of cooperative groups, researchers stress the importance of providing opportunities for all students, including students with special needs (or any diverse learners) to participate.

In order to provide a curriculum appropriate for gifted students, adjustments in both the material and learning environment may be necessary. Maker and Nielson (1995) describe such modifications in content and process.

Content Modifications

- Students need a variety of problems to work on.

- The content of the curriculum needs to be organized around key concepts or abstract ideas, rather than some other organization (as noted by Bruner, 1960).

- Problems should be complex and students should be pushed to abstraction. (Additional opportunities for abstraction are described in teacher support, particularly in the Going Further features described below.)

Process Modifications

- Promote higher levels of thinking by stressing *use* rather than *acquisition* of information. (Students continue to use information from previous Units in the current Unit they are studying.)

- Provide open-ended questions in order to stimulate divergent thinking and to "contribute to the development of an interaction pattern in which learning, not the teacher, is the focus."[1]

- Guide student discovery of content and encourage questions. (Problems often ask students to think about the questions of why and how.)

- Offer opportunities for students to express their reasoning. (Students are constantly asked to explain or justify their responses in CMP.)

- Make group interaction a regular part of the curriculum for gifted students to enable them to develop social and leadership skills.

CMP is designed so that many of the modifications described by Maker and Nielson are embedded in the curriculum. Other simple modifications are possible in order support gifted students and still maintain the integrity of the curriculum. For example, Renzoulli and Reis (2003) discuss the Schoolwide Enrichment Model (SEM), which can be used to promote challenging and high-end learning in schools. The SEM model accommodates the needs of the gifted student and offers suggestions on how to adjust the level, depth, and enrichment opportunities provided by a curriculum.

Other Features

CMP offers students rich experiences with a variety of mathematical content. Students are introduced to important areas of mathematics, such as probability, statistics, and transformational and Euclidean Geometry early in their career so that they can see the vast terrain of mathematics. The algebra strand in CMP is organized around functions, which are the cornerstone of calculus, and the structure of the real numbers, which brings coherence to the exploration of algebraic ideas.

Particular features of CMP support the mathematically gifted child. In teacher support, there are questions in the Launch–Explore–Summarize sequence labeled Going Further that teachers can pose to students who are ready to advance. In the ACE assignments, the Extensions often go beyond what was done in the classroom; they can be used as additional exercises to push students' thinking. Along with the deep real-world mathematical situations offered in this curriculum, these features provide all students, including gifted students, challenging problems to explore each day.

English Language Learners (ELL) come into the classroom from a variety of countries with a diverse set of experiences. They face the daunting tasks of adjusting to a new home and cultural environment, learning a new language, making new friends, and making sense of the rules, appropriate behaviors, and mechanics of a new school. Simultaneously, ELL students are experiencing many losses while simultaneously trying to "fit in" with their new surroundings.

For teachers, working successfully with ELL students requires more than just teaching the course content. In order for ELL students to achieve academic success, teachers must also support language goals and general learning strategies in the mathematics classroom (Richard-Amato & Snow, 2005). In addition, it is critical to create a friendly, supportive, and predictable classroom community. Some general suggestions for teachers include:

- Learning about students' home countries, languages, and previous educational experiences.

- Valuing students' differences as resources.

- Staying connected to families.

- Communicating school norms and expectations clearly, and checking assumptions at the door. Instructing ELL students is a "lifelong process of learning, discovering, accepting, and trying" (Carger, 1997, p.45).

Classroom Environment and Teacher Talk

English Language Learners are often anxious about being in a classroom when they cannot speak the language. Efforts to create a friendly environment that is respectful of students' diverse experiences and sets high expectations for learning will greatly support ELL students' opportunities for success. Part of establishing this kind of learning environment includes modifying the ways in which teachers talk with students. Many of the suggestions below work for all students, including ELL students.

- Create a classroom community that recognizes and values students' diversity. Every child is born into a culture that socializes them to think in specific ways about things that may be taken for granted as common sense. When left unexamined, some cultural beliefs and practices can interfere with students' success in the classroom. It is important to find out who students are, where they come from, and which languages they speak.

- Keep expectations high and consistent, and provide effective feedback. Too often ELL students receive "feedback that relates to personality variables or the neatness of their work rather than to academic quality" (Jackson, 1993, p. 55). Comments should be focus on the academic components of students' work. It is important to communicate clearly and specifically to students about how to improve the overall quality of the work they do (Jackson, 1993).

- Slow down and simplify the language used. Consider intonation; avoid using slang, idioms, extraneous words, and long, complex sentences. Repeat key points. Rephrase to promote clarity and understanding. Summarize frequently. Use clear transition markers such as first, next, and in conclusion. Ask clear, succinct, high-level questions (Carrasquillo & Rodriguez, 2002, Jameson, 1998).

- Model what students are expected to do. Students may not comprehend the words or phrases being said, yet actions will support their understanding. For example, use visual prompts such as hand movements, facial expressions, or other body movements to suggest meaning.

- Pair instructional talk with visual communication cues such as pictures, graphs, objects, and gestures (Peregoy & Boyle, 1997).

- Seat students toward the middle or front of the classroom, in a place where they can be monitored closely and where they can observe the classroom interactions of other students (Peregoy & Boyle, 1997).

- Even though content will vary, follow a predictable routine and a stable schedule. Predictability creates a sense of security for students who are experiencing a lot of change in their lives (Peregoy & Boyle, 1997).

- Have dictionaries and other learning tools available and easily accessible to students.

Teaching Students School Norms

Students come from diverse places and their constructs of school and purposes for education often greatly differ. Problems between teachers and ELL students often occur because of language differences and unidentified assumptions about the social aspects of schooling. Therefore, it is important for teachers to be explicit while helping students learn what is expected of them within the school building and inside the classroom.

- Create and consistently reinforce classroom norms to support students' understanding of what is expected socially and academically in the classroom.

- Post homework assignments in a public place in the classrooms so students can be responsible for checking their assignments and keeping track of whether or not they submitted them.

- Provide each student with a daily agenda. As a class, write the day's objectives, activities, and the homework assignment. Students should keep these agendas in their notebooks for personal reference. It is also helpful to provide space on the agenda for students to check off the homework assignment once it has been completed and turned in. (See page 111 for an example of a daily agenda link.)

Pedagogical Strategies in the Mathematics Classroom

English Language Learners benefit from a variety of instructional strategies that lower their anxiety and help make content more comprehensible. Mathematical objectives should be cognitively demanding and grade appropriate. Language-related adjustments should be made, including modifications to instructional delivery, but the cognitive demand of the mathematics should not be changed. The CMP framework inherently supports many, if not all, of the following strategies for ELL students. These strategies are also good teaching techniques for all students.

Effective Questioning

Teachers "frequently use few higher-order questions to all students, especially to those for whom they had low expectations" (Jackson, 1993, p. 55). Higher-order questions promote analytical and evaluative thinking, affirm students' self-perceptions as learners, and support students' view of themselves as knowledge producers rather than knowledge consumers (Jackson, 1993). (See pages 17–20 for a discussion of inquiry-based instruction.)

Cooperative Groups

Research evidence demonstrates that cooperative group work can have a "strong positive impact on language and literacy development and on achievement in content areas" (Richard-Amato & Snow, 2005, p. 190). (See page 7 for a discussion of cooperative group work.)

Active Participation

Actively engaging the students facilitates their learning of both mathematics and the English language. This can be accomplished through class brainstorms and predictions, and by encouraging students to ask questions of each other or to express and justify their ideas. It is also helpful to write students' ideas on the chalkboard so they can see them written correctly in English. (See pages 17–20 for a discussion of classroom interactions during the Launch–Explore–Summarize section of a lesson.)

Situational Context

If students are unfamiliar with names, places, or objects in a problem, it will be difficult for them to access the mathematics. Sometimes it is possible to change the context of a problem without affecting the mathematics or objectives of the lesson. Incorporate names and places from students' home countries or situate actions within their cultural practices. This is also a great opportunity for students to learn common English words used in daily life. Include words in math problems that students need to know by avoiding the use of slang, idioms, or extraneous language. (See page 13 for a discussion of context in a problem-centered curriculum.)

Written Expression

Use journals, quick writes, and outlines to provide students with opportunities to write in the mathematics classroom The following suggestions promote meaningful writing activities:

- Restate the problem in your own words.

- Explain how you solved the problem.

- How do you know your answer is right? (Richard-Amato & Snow, 2005)

- What do you know so far about …? (See page 88 for a discussion of student journals.)

Supporting Vocabulary Development

Students must understand mathematical terminology and key words to gain access to any math problem. You can support them by doing the following:

- Isolate important vocabulary terms and phrases by circling or underlining them in the text

- Create and maintain a Word Cluster or Vocabulary Chart in the classroom and in students' notebooks where new terms and their definitions are written in both English and the student's first language. Pictures are also useful additions. (See xx for a discussion of the development of vocabulary in CMP.)

- Practice speaking hard-to-pronounce words verbally as a class. It is beneficial for students to practice reading and pronouncing words correctly. (See page 111 for five guidelines for simplifying language.)

- Use graphic organizers to scaffold learning activities and provide ELL students access to the mathematical content. Graphic organizers include Venn diagrams, concept webs, timelines, lists, outlines, tree diagrams, and charts. You will find graphic organizer shells in the Teacher Resources.

Reading, Writing, and Waiting

Finally, the following strategies will enhance ELL students' abilities to participate in classroom discussions and to express their ideas in writing assignments.

- **Give Time to Prepare** Give students time to read silently before asking them to discuss their ideas with a small or large group. It is also recommended to provide time for students to write their ideas on paper before they share them publicly. This will give students time to sort through their ideas before they are asked to perform in front of teachers and peers.

- **Write and Speak Directions** Post task directions on the overhead or chalkboard while simultaneously reading the directions and having students follow along. This affords ELL students the opportunity to read the English text silently while they hear it spoken correctly.

- **Encourage Writing in English** Encourage ELL students to write in English even if the spelling and grammar is incorrect. It is also helpful for students to use a combination of English and their first language when they write in their notebooks.

- **Allow Extra Wait Time** Use extra wait time so ELL students will have an opportunity to hear the question, translate the work, understand its content, formulate a response, and then speak.

Assessment of English Language Learners

Students' lack of English proficiency will affect test performance when tests are given only in English. It is also necessary to consider how students' cultural backgrounds and previous experiences might affect their ability or willingness to participate in an assessment activity. "Because schooling practices tend to conform more or less to middle-class European-American experiences and values, students from other cultural backgrounds may be misassessed by virtue of cultural and other experiential differences." (Peregoy & Boyle, 1997, page 93) Therefore, assessment practices should allow students to show what they know in a variety of ways.

- When creating assessments, consider the diversity of students' cultural, linguistic and special needs (Peregoy & Boyle, 1997).

- Use a variety of assessments in a variety of formats including small-group work, individual activities, drawing pictures, creating posters, engaging in interviews, constructing portfolios, journal writing, projects, and self-assessment. (See pages 52–58 for a discussion of assessment in CMP.)

- Be clear and consistent with grading systems and standards. Rubrics are excellent tools for itemizing the criteria on which students will be assessed and helping students understand what is expected from them (Richard-Amato & Snow, 2005).

- Peer editing is an opportunity for students to read, edit, and comment on each other's work while gaining reading and writing experience.

- Often ELL students get so bogged down in the reading comprehension that they never get to the mathematics. It will be much more meaningful and productive for the students if they are assigned 5 or 6 well-designed exercises (and they'll be more motivated to try them), rather than a page or two of 10 to 20 exercises.

- Allow sufficient time for all students to complete the assessment.

Rebus Techniques

The following suggestions follow guidelines known as rebus techniques for English Language Learners. Rebus is a general term referring to the use of pictures or other visual images to represent words or symbols. Some of these techniques are similar to those in the preceding sections.

Original Rebus Technique

On a sheet of paper, students copy the text from all or part of a page before it is discussed. During discussion, students then generate their own rebuses for words they did not understand as the words are made comprehensible through pictures, objects, or demonstrations.

This strategy ensures that ELL students benefit from written communications in the same way as their English-proficient peers. While written text summarizes key concepts, includes background information, and provides directions for completing tasks, ELL students often do not benefit from such communication.

In the past, ELL students have been traditionally paired with English-proficient students who are asked to read aloud written text. However, this approach does not provide ELL students with access to written communication. For example, ELL students are asked to rely on memory when trying to recall the written information, something not required of their peers. Furthermore, simply reading information aloud does not ensure that the words are made comprehensible to the ELL student. Therefore, the Original Rebus Technique offers a strategy that makes written communication meaningful to ELL students, without depending on peer cooperation or memory.

1. Teachers identify text perceived to be difficult for ELL students to comprehend. Examples of such text may be questions appearing in Mathematical Reflections, Applications, and Connections sections of each CMP Unit.

2. ELL students receive a copy of the rewritten text when the corresponding page is introduced to the class. As the information from the student book is read aloud, teachers make key words understandable. For example, a teacher may demonstrate the word "snapshot" by showing a photo of a pet.

3. After students comprehend the word, the teacher writes it on the board so ELL students can connect the written word with a specific meaning. At this time, ELL students create an original rebus over that key word on their sheet of paper. This rebus will help them to recall the meaning of the word when referring back to the text during independent work.

Note: It is essential that ELL students draw their own rebuses. This ensures that whatever symbol they choose to draw has meaning to them. The problem with providing professional or teacher-drawn rebuses is that simple drawings, by themselves, do not often convey a universal understanding of the words. For example, many English-proficient students were not able to correctly identify a rebus when the word below was covered, yet could do so when they were able to view both the word and rebus. This suggests that the written word, not the rebus, conveyed the meaning in such situations. Moreover, if ELL students are required to create their own rebuses, they then choose which words need to be coded. Depending on the level of English proficiency, the number of coded words can vary greatly among students.

Diagram Code Technique

Students use a minimal number of words, drawings, diagrams, or symbols to respond to questions requiring writing. Learning to organize and express mathematical concepts in writing is a skill students develop over time. If ELL students are not given this same opportunity, they miss an important component of the math curriculum. This strategy provides alternate ways for students not yet proficient in writing English to express mathematical thinking on paper. While their responses will not be in the same format as those of their English-proficient peers, ELL students still have the same challenge: they must record and communicate mathematical ideas so that someone else can understand their thinking.

1. At the beginning of the program, teachers model and encourage ELL students to use this approach when writing answers to questions presented in the program.

2. To introduce this approach, the teacher writes several questions requiring written responses on the board. These questions should be simple with obvious answers.

3. The teacher then shows the ELL students how to answer each question without writing complete sentences and paragraphs. At the end of this session, the teacher should have modeled answering questions by using and/or combining minimal words, drawings, diagrams, or symbols.

Note: This approach can be used for any written response in the program, but it is especially useful for responding to questions found in Mathematical Reflections. Since this part of the CMP curriculum provides a vehicle for assessing how well students have understood key concepts of the Unit, this approach enables teachers to evaluate their ELL students' progress as well.

Chart Summary Technique

This technique involves presenting information by condensing it into a pictorial chart with minimal words. This extension of the Diagram Code technique offers ELL students another way to organize and express mathematical thinking with a minimal amount of writing.

1. At the beginning of the program, the teacher shows various charts on any subject. The charts need to be simple, include pictures, and have a minimal number of words.

2. The teacher then creates and writes a question on the board that relates to each chart. For example, the teacher might show a chart of the life cycle of a plant divided into four sections. For this chart, the teacher could ask this question: What are the growth stages of a plant?

3. The teacher continues by showing how the chart answers this question by pointing to the drawings in each section, showing the seeds, roots, stem, and flower. The teacher also points out how each section has been labeled.

4. At the end of this session, ELL students should be able to respond to a question by creating a chart with pictures and minimal words.

Note: This approach may be an alternative for ELL students when responding to some of the Unit Projects requiring detailed writing.

Rebus Scenario Technique

Teachers make use of rebuses on the chalkboard during discussions and when presenting information. While modifications for primary mathematical concepts may be perceived as necessary for ELL students, there may be a tendency to omit such techniques for "enrichment" information, such as text appearing under Did You Know? However, if programs offer English-proficient students such information, then ELL students should also have an opportunity to acquire the same knowledge. Therefore, the Rebus Scenario Technique offers teachers a simple way to ensure that all students have access to both the core and enrichment aspects of CMP.

Note: If there are English-proficient "artists" in the classroom, teachers may opt to implement this approach in a slightly different way. Prior to the lesson, a teacher can ask an artistic student to come to the chalkboard to draw rebuses for targeted words. When using this approach, the teacher can then just point to the appropriate drawings during the lesson. If there is no time prior to a lesson, the artistic student can be asked to draw the rebuses as key words are presented. With this latter approach, it is important that the artist knows which words to represent as rebuses and to draw quickly.

Enactment Technique

Students act out mini-scenes and use props to make information accessible. This technique ensures that all students comprehend hypothetical scenarios presented throughout CMP. With this technique, ELL students are not excluded from lessons involving situations reflective of real-life scenarios.

1. Teachers decide which simple props, if any, will enhance the enactment. These props are gathered prior to teaching the lesson.

2. At the time of the lesson, students are selected to assume the roles of characters mentioned in a CMP problem or scenario.

3. These students then pantomime and/or improvise speaking parts as they enact the written scenario presented in CMP.

Note: There may be a tendency to select only English-proficient students for mini-scene roles; however, many parts can also be given to ELL students. For example, roles such as pantomiming shooting baskets or pretending to ride a bicycle, can be easily enacted by ELL students, as these kinds of parts do not require spoken English.

Visual Enhancement Technique

The use of maps, photographs, pictures in books, and objects makes information understandable by providing nonverbal input. This technique is most helpful for conveying information that is unlikely to be understood through enactment or creating rebuses. When pictures or real objects are added to lessons, English Language Learners have the opportunity to receive the same information presented to their English-proficient peers, who are able to understand the written text without visual aids. This approach ensures that ELL students equally acquire and benefit from descriptive and/or background information sections of the program.

1. Teachers decide if information on a page is unlikely to be understood with a rebus or by having students create an enactment. For example, maps are often used with this technique to help students understand what part of the world an informative section or investigation is centered around. In contrast, a mere rebus "outline" of the same country would not be likely to be understood by anyone. Likewise, topics such as video games, different kinds of housing, and newspaper advertisements are more easily comprehended by merely showing examples than by trying to draw something representative of the topic.

2. When teachers decide visual aids are the best approach for making information accessible, examples are sought prior to teaching the lesson.

3. Teachers then show the visual aid at the appropriate time during the lesson.

Note: In the first year of implementation, English-proficient students can earn extra credit by finding appropriate visual aids for targeted lessons. Teachers can then keep the pictures, objects (if possible), and book names (with page number) on file for use in subsequent years.

Summary

The six rebus techniques ensure that ELL students will receive the same mathematics curriculum as their English-proficient peers. Although the techniques differ in implementation, they all offer ways for ELL students to acquire and express the mathematical ideas presented in CMP. Although these approaches have been created specifically for ELL students, they can be equally effective for many other students, including those with special needs.

Visuals

Graphic organizers can be used by the teacher to present information or by the students to organize information and to compare and contrast concepts and ideas. Graphic organizers such as word clusters, rebuses, and vocabulary charts can be used to support vocabulary development. Venn diagrams, concept maps, and other techniques can help students organize information.

Word Clusters

Write mathematical terms on sentence strips and group them together to show how they are connected. Hang the sentence strips from the ceiling or on a wall for quick reference.

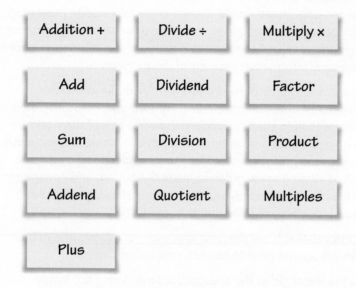

Rebuses

Create rebus pictures or symbols for words the students need help to understand.

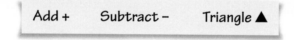

- Students can draw the symbols directly over the words.
- A sheet of these symbols can be kept in the vocabulary section of students' binders.

Vocabulary Charts

The use of word cognates (linguistically related words) help students connect words in English to words from their own language that are familiar. Not all words have cognates. However, all terms are put on this chart even if they don't have cognates.

Vocabulary Chart

Term	Description	Example	Cognate
Factor	One of two or more whole numbers that are multiplied to get a product.	$2 \times 3 = 6$	Factor
Prime Number	Numbers with only 2 factors, 1 and itself	$3 : 1 \times 3$ $7 : 1 \times 7$	Número Primo

Venn Diagrams

Use Venn diagrams as a way to compare and contrast information. The example below is from Data About Us.

Similarities

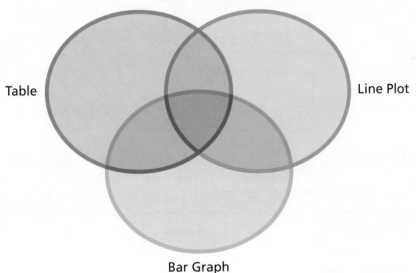

Table

Line Plot

Bar Graph

Concept Maps

Concept maps are used to organize topics or categories and to visually represent connections between concepts and ideas.

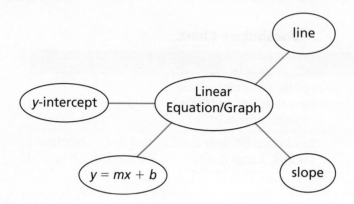

Tree Diagrams/Hierarchy

Use tree diagrams to organize ideas from the general to the specific and to support understanding of the relationships between concepts.

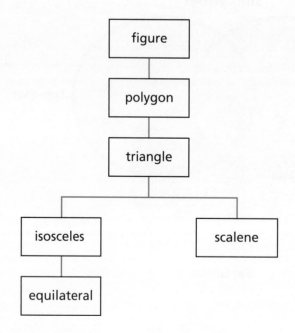

Charts, Lists, and Timelines

Other visuals that organize information include charts, lists, and timelines.

Five Guidelines for Simplifying Language

Guideline	Original Text	Simplified Version
1. Use short sentences and eliminate extraneous material.	Samuel is getting a snack for himself and his little brother, Adam. There are two candy bars in the refrigerator. Samuel takes half of one candy bar for himself and half of the other candy bar for Adam. Adam complains that Samuel got more. Samuel says this isn't true, since he got half and Adam got half. What might be the problem?	Sam and Adam have two candy bars. Sam eats half of one candy bar. Sam gives Adam half of the other candy bar. Adam is mad. He thinks Sam has more candy. What is the problem?
2. Change pronouns to nouns.	Jorge made two graphs but he forgot to label them.	Jorge made two graphs. Jorge forgot to label the graphs.
3. Underline key points or vocabulary.	**Problem 1.1** **A.** How are the graphs alike? How are the graphs different? **B.** How can you use the graph to find the total number of letters in all of the names? **C.** Collect the data for your class and use graphs to represent the data distribution.	**Problem 1.1** **A.** How are the graphs <u>alike</u>? How are the graphs <u>different</u>? **B.** How can you use the graph to find the <u>total number of letters</u> in all of the names? **C.** Collect the <u>data</u> for your class and use <u>graphs</u> to <u>represent</u> the data distribution.
4. Turn narratives into lists.	Look back at the graphs that you have made in this Unit. Find several graphs that show relationships in which y both increases and decreases as x increases. Describe each graph in words.	Look at the graphs you made. **A.** Find a graph where y increases and x increases. **B.** Find a graph where y decreases and x increases. **C.** Use words to describe each graph.
5. Use charts and diagrams.	Maria has $25.00 in the bank. She mows the lawn each week and earns $5.00 each time. Suzanna only has $15.00 in the bank. She baby-sits her little brother for $2.00 each weekday. Maria spends $3.00 each week to go to the basketball game with her friends. Suzanna spends $4.00 each week to go to the movies.	(see table below)

	Bank	Earns	Spends
Maria	$25.00	$5.00/wk	$3.00/wk
Suzanna	$15.00	$2.00/day	$4.00/wk

Daily Agenda • 6th Grade

Monday	Tuesday	Wednesday	Thursday	Friday
Objectives: Activities: Homework:	Objectives: Activities: Homework:	Objectives: Activities: Homework:	Objectives: Activities: Homework:	Objectives: Activities: Homework:

This section of the Guide provides suggestions for informing and engaging school administrators and the community and for preparing teachers to implement CMP with their students. In addition to preparing teachers to utilize Connected Mathematics (CMP), input and participation from the local community is essential.

CMP is a coherent set of materials designed to guide teachers and students in the development of mathematical knowledge that includes deep understanding, proficiency in skills, and the ability to make connections within mathematics and connections to other disciplines. In CMP this is accomplished by embedding the mathematics in problem situations.

Introducing a mathematical idea through a contextual problem that embodies the concept helps students develop meaning and use the knowledge they need to solve the problem. Students also draw upon the contexts of the problems to help them recall the mathematics associated with those contexts. In addition, these real-life situations provide a transition into the world of symbols, helping students to make sense of the symbols even in abstract situations. Solving such problems requires using many kinds of mathematical skills, so students are constantly practicing important skills as well as developing understanding and advancing their reasoning.

For the CMP curriculum materials to help students reach their full potential, teachers must develop the knowledge and skills to use the materials to engage students in appropriate ways. Hence, the focus of professional development for teachers enacting CMP is to enable them to learn mathematics content and the pedagogy they need to plan their instruction around an inquiry-based curriculum. A problem-centered curriculum is a radical departure from the traditional classroom in which most of us have learned or taught. Teachers need time and assistance to become familiar with the mathematical concepts and skills that are embedded in the problems. They also need to develop instructional strategies for helping students bring these ideas and skills to fruition.

CMP uses an inquiry-based instructional model, which promotes a different form of classroom interaction than has historically been used within mathematics instruction. Investigations encourage students to explore, to conjecture, to validate, and to communicate their ideas.

To guide classroom discussion, teachers need a deep and broad understanding of mathematics as well as knowledge of a variety of pedagogical strategies. Teachers also need a variety of assessment tools that can capture the richness and depth of students' understanding and reasoning and can inform instructional decisions.

Because CMP may be quite different from the mathematics curricula experienced by teachers, administrators, and parents and guardians in the community, a shift to CMP is likely to generate excitement as well as cause some discomfort and uncertainty. Some concerns are shared by all members of the community. For example, in the early stages of the adoption process, members of the community will want to know what data research already exists that describes the effectiveness of CMP. As the implementation proceeds, members of the community will be interested in the results of a well-planned, ongoing evaluation of student learning in their school district. Some issues are of greater concern to administrators and teachers than to parents and guardians. For example, administrators will need to plan for multi-faceted professional development to support teachers through different stages of the curriculum implementation, from novice first-year teachers to confident, successful teachers. Teacher concerns include the need for ongoing support, not just in the initial implementation stage, but also later in the development of a continuing, thriving culture of professionals working together to make decisions about how to improve the teaching and learning of mathematics in the building.

Parent and guardian concerns are likely to focus on two issues: how to help their students be successful in a curriculum that may look unfamiliar to them, and how CMP students will perform on high-stakes assessments. Below are some suggestions for informing, engaging, and preparing all members of the community as they tackle the necessary work—from early evidence gathering and planning to well-supported, successful implementation of CMP.

Curriculum by itself is not enough, but an engaging curriculum in the hands of a good teacher, with support of the administration, the local community, and long-term professional development can provide the kinds of mathematical experiences that support higher levels of performance for all students.

Gathering Evidence and Making Plans

CMP is standards-based and problem-centered. Adopting and implementing a standards-based mathematics curriculum can be a major step for school districts.

 Standards-based mathematics curricula focus attention on a core agenda of important and broadly useful mathematical ideas. Instead of traditional instruction that asks students to watch passively and imitate teacher demonstrations of routine computational techniques, these curricula engage students in challenging mathematical Investigations that help them construct a solid understanding of key ideas and a confident ability to solve tough mathematical problems.

(James Fey, *Montgomery Gazette, Montgomery County*, September 10, 1999.)

Parents and teachers may be more accustomed to textbooks that have examples followed by pages of skill exercises. Some teachers may be accustomed to instruction characterized by working a few examples for the whole class and then assigning a set of practice problems to be done independently by the students. Although many teachers supplement this pattern by occasionally having students solve non routine problems, such activity is not at the core of their curriculum or central to their teaching practices.

CMP asks teachers, students, and parents to play different roles. In the traditional curriculum, teachers demonstrate solutions, students observe, somewhat passively, parents and guardians support and supervise practice, and the textbook provides examples. In CMP classrooms, students actively investigate Problems and develop solutions, and teachers question, challenge, and orchestrate classroom discussions and summaries of the mathematics being learned. Parents and guardians will benefit from information about the rationale for the organization and sequencing of the Problems, the role of ACE exercises and Looking Back activities, and the way that student notebooks are designed to capture a student's evolving understanding of a topic. Problem-based curricula like CMP make different demands on all members of the community.

The mathematics in CMP is developed through a sequence of connected Problems in an inquiry-based classroom. This is a shift away from a focus on developing skills and procedures to a focus on developing a set of mathematical relationships, a specialized symbolic language, concepts, and ways of thinking, in addition to skills and procedures. School districts can make the implementation of CMP smoother by following guidelines for orchestrating this shift. Bay et al. (1999) list ten important factors related to successful selection and implementation of standards-based mathematics curricula. These include: administrative support; opportunities to study and pilot the curricula; time for daily planning and interaction with colleagues; knowledge of appropriate assessment techniques and tools; ongoing communication with parents; and articulation with colleagues at the elementary and secondary level.

Gathering Evidence

Before adopting CMP, school personnel should take time to gather evidence in the following ways:

- Seek reviews of research that might answer the question, *"Why do we want to change? What more do we want for our students that the current textbooks do not provide?"*

- Seek reviews of research that might guide evaluation of textbooks, rather than rely solely on the data provided by the publisher. *"What are we seeking in a new text, and how can we find helpful and reliable information?"*

- Know how middle school students in your district are performing on state or local assessments. Ask teachers to provide input into where they see strengths or weaknesses in the current curriculum materials. Involve a parent group in reviewing the evidence and establishing goals. *"Are there particular areas of strength or weakness?"*

- Seek, or request from the publisher, data describing the effectiveness of CMP or any other curricula under consideration. *"Was the curriculum used in a district like ours?"*

- Create an evaluation plan for measuring student achievement. Plan to collect baseline data the year before implementation. *"What is our goal for student achievement? What can we realistically expect? How will we evaluate student achievement over the long run?"*

- Seek information about the preparation and confidence level of teachers in the district. *"What support is there for teachers either in the textbook itself or from other sources?"*

Garnering Support

After gathering evidence, school personnel should garner administrative and community support.

- Superintendents, principals, and other administrators as well as school boards and parents must have access to clear information about the CMP materials. The administration and staff need a well-developed strategy for providing the mechanisms through which such information is made available to the school board and to parents and kept updated.

- Familiarize principals and other administrators with CMP. They should know the rationale for the change in curricular emphasis and how CMP will better meet the needs of students.

- Work with parents to gain support. Some districts have found that a parent/community advisory group is helpful. Involving parents during the conceptualization of the implementation can avoid misunderstandings later.

- Work with teachers to gain support. Request and respect input from all teachers.

Addressing Questions

CMP supporters should be prepared to address the following questions.

- *How does CMP "fit" with district and state frameworks?* CMP supporters should be ready with correlations of curriculum goals with local and state requirements and assessment instruments.

- *How does CMP handle basic skills?* The answer to this question, evidence of the impact of the curriculum on students' basic skills, is readily available. The results of independent research consistently show that CMP students do as well as, or better than, non-CMP students on tests of basic skills. And CMP students outperform non-CMP students on tests of problem-solving ability, conceptual understanding, and proportional reasoning. For more information on these studies, see www.connectedmath.msu.edu or www.connectedmathematics3.com.

- *Will CMP be used in all grades (6–8), with all levels of students? Will students with learning difficulties or reading difficulties find it too difficult?* See the section called A Curriculum for All Students in this Guide.)

- *If algebra is offered as a separate course in middle school, will CMP be used in this course? If so, how does CMP support the development of algebra concepts and skills?* Experiences of other schools that are successfully using CMP in 6–8, including for an eighth-grade algebra class, can be a powerful resource. For some of these experiences, see www.connectedmath.msu.edu.

- *How will students make the transition from CMP to high school? Who should be involved in making a transition plan?*

- *Are students coming out of our K–5 ready for CMP? Should we involve elementary teachers in making a transition plan from upper elementary to CMP?*

In order for the implementation of CMP to be successful, teachers need to be on board. The size, composition of, and past experiences of the school district and staff will determine how the following actions are handled.

- Consider piloting units before adopting the entire curriculum.

- Develop an implementation plan. *Will all students (and teachers) begin using the materials at the same time? Will they be phased in over the course of two to three years?*

- Establish plans for long-term professional development that coincide with the implementation schedule (more on this in the next section).

- Designate teacher or building leaders responsible for scheduling and planning professional development.

Districts need to take early action on the preceding items. The best professional development plans have gone astray because schools did not take the time to share the rationale for a new curriculum focus with the key players in their districts or to develop a wide base of support. If a district committee, representing all the key players, has collected evidence about CMP as suggested above, then any questions from parents or teachers can be honestly and rationally answered. If the adoption process has been transparent, then the community will have had an opportunity to ask questions and seek reassurance.

The Principal's Role

The successful principal of a school has many roles to play as he or she interacts with all members of the school's community. Broadly speaking, for district-level administrators, the interaction is about the business of managing a school; for teachers, the interaction is about the teaching and learning of a curriculum; and for parents the interaction is about the success of individual children. When CMP is adopted, the principal who takes the time to become knowledgeable about the curriculum will be better able to support teachers and answer parent questions. Becoming knowledgeable is the first step.

In the initial stages of selection and adoption, the district committee will have sought out evidence of reasons for adopting CMP, of current achievement levels of students, of the success of CMP in other districts, and of the preparation of teachers to implement CMP. The district committee will also have sought answers to questions about how students with disabilities or gifted and talented students succeed in CMP, about the place of Algebra in CMP, and about the issues to be considered in helping students make successful transitions from elementary school to middle school and from middle school to high school. This evidence and current thinking about these issues should be shared with principals so that they feel confident that a thoughtful decision has been made, and so that they can relate achievement goals and teacher preparation to their own buildings. The building principal needs to be knowledgeable so that he or she can speak confidently and supportively about the curriculum and related issues to teachers and to parents.

Since CMP is standards based and problem centered, the principal will need to find time to understand what these two terms mean, and what this kind of curriculum looks like in a classroom when it is being successfully implemented. In this role, the principal is acting like the principal teacher in the building, by asking questions such as, *"What research backs this kind of approach? What does this kind of curriculum mean for student groupings? What role does the teacher have? What help will the teacher need in organizing this kind of classroom? What can I do to help with classroom issues?"* If the principal is knowledgeable about the curriculum and teacher needs, then more teachers are apt to "buy-in" to the curriculum.

After becoming knowledgeable about the curriculum, the principal will also have to consider his or her role in professional development activities. When teachers attend professional development activities to help themselves successfully implement CMP, they learn firsthand about the mathematics in the Units, about the connections among Units, and about how Problems are sequenced to develop mathematical ideas. They also learn about pedagogical aspects of the curriculum: why the curriculum is organized the way it is, what the teacher's role is in the Launch phase of a lesson, in the student exploration of a Problem, and in the crucial Summarize phase. There is only so much a principal can do to learn about a curriculum by reading about it. The principal who actively participates in professional development will be much more knowledgeable and will be perceived as much more supportive by teachers. Just as teachers learn to ask questions about what their students have learned and how they can be more supportive of student learning, so too can the principal ask, *"Do some of my building's teachers seem to need more help with the mathematics than others? How can I get them this help? Who seems fearful or resistant? Why is that? What can I do to increase the confidence of the teachers in my building so that they can implement CMP? Do they need more information? More encouragement?"*

As the building leader, the principal is the point person when questions come from district administrators and from parents and guardians. Thus, the principal can be an advocate for teachers. When professional support for teachers needs district approval, the principal can make a case for what is needed; when concerned parents and guardians have questions about a teacher's unfamiliar classroom practices, the principal can knowledgeably reassure the parents and support the teacher.

It is important to be supportive of teachers in the evaluation process. When both teachers and principals understand the goals of CMP and how these goals are achieved, then the process of evaluating teachers has integrity and validity that would be lacking otherwise. Evaluation based on mutually valued goals and practices fosters professionalism. The opportunity for a principal to observe and evaluate how CMP is being enacted in a particular classroom can be an opportunity to reinforce these common goals and aspirations.

Communicating with Parents/Guardians

The building principal knows better than any other district administrator what his or her part of the district looks like, which parents he or she can expect to be involved in building activities and to have questions or concerns. The district can make general plans and suggestions to involve parents and guardians, but the principal is uniquely placed to know which plans best fit his or her school. From the list of suggestions below or from others, each principal must make a wise selection so that parents and guardians feel included and can be more supportive of their students' success in learning mathematics.

Involving Parents/Guardians

Some parents and guardians may have been involved in the initial stages described above, but most will become aware that a new curriculum has been adopted only after the fact. They may have questions about why CMP was adopted, why it looks different from traditional textbooks, and what evidence there is of student success. As mentioned above, the unfamiliarity of the problem-centered approach may be an obstacle that parents need help in overcoming. These are questions that a well-prepared district committee can answer or can arrange to have answered in a variety of ways.

Conscientious parents have always been concerned about their children's middle school education. Their concerns usually have two distinct foci:

- What is my role in helping my child be successful now?

- How well does this class prepare my child for high school mathematics and for post-secondary education?

Parents and guardians need to understand the goals of the program. Administrators and teachers can help them do this by keeping them informed, early and often, about both long-term and Unit goals. They should know that the primary goals of CMP are to have students make sense of mathematical concepts, become proficient with basic skills, and communicate their reasoning and understanding clearly. The concepts and topics that students study should be familiar to parents and guardians, but the problem-centered textbooks may not make the particular topic or skill as explicit as the associated student work and reflections will. Parents and guardians need advice and help in making good use of their students' classwork as a resource.

The emphasis in reasoning and communication may be less familiar. Curriculum leaders and teachers can help parent and guardians understand why reasoning and communication are valued and that the program provides many opportunities to demonstrate students' progress in these areas. There are many specific ways that a district can gain the support of parents and guardians, and keep them informed.

- **Form a Community Advisory Group** The group should be composed of knowledgeable and strong advocates for the program. The committee should consist of parents and guardians, teachers, university people (if there is a university in the area), business people (particularly those who appreciate the need for critical thinking) and administrators. This group will play a crucial role in the early stages of implementation and less of a role later as the success of CMP speaks for itself.

- **Present Information to the Community** As implementation matures, a district might create a pamphlet for parents and guardians, including the results of district evaluation studies that show how well CMP students did on state tests.

- **Conduct Parent Workshops** These can be helpful at the beginning of the school year, and at different stages of the implementation during the year. Topics to be discussed might include: overarching goals, evidence of effectiveness of CMP, specific mathematical information, the instructional model, mathematical expectations for students by the end of the year and the end of the program, the use of calculators, and transitioning to high school. An effective strategy for conducting these workshops is to engage parents and guardians in a Problem from one of the student Units, so they can experience firsthand how understanding and skill are developed in CMP. These workshops might be tailored to fit specific concerns such as use of calculators and other technology, and how these affect learning or the particular mathematical goals of a Unit that is about to start.

- **Send an Introductory Letter** An introductory letter complements the Parent Workshops outlined above. A sample letter is included in the *Parent Guide for CMP*.

- **Send a Parent/Guardian Letter** As students begin a new Unit, the teacher can send a letter to parents and guardians stating the goals of the Unit and suggesting questions that parents and guardians can ask their children. The *Parent Guide for CMP* contains a sample letter for each Unit.

- **Send Home Parent/Guardian Handbooks** A district can create and send home handbooks addressing the mathematics in Units and suggesting ways that parents and guardians can help their children.

- **Send Home Newsletters** A newsletter is an excellent way to highlight the mathematics students are studying. A newsletter might include student work, stories about student insights, summaries of rich class discussions, or other evidence of achievement. If your district already has a community newsletter, then it may be possible to include news from the mathematics classroom in the newsletter.

- **Inform Parents and Guardians of Resources** CMP provides a parent Web site offering both background information and specific mathematical help to parents seeking to assist their students with homework. See www.math.msu.edu/CMP/parents.

- **Tutoring Labs** Conduct a tutoring lab after school to reassure parents that additional help is available to students for homework. In one CMP district, a mathematics lab is held two days a week after school. Students sign up with their mathematics teacher to attend and must bring with them work to do, such as homework, redoing a past assignment, organizing their notebooks, working on vocabulary lists or projects, or studying for a test or quiz. Copies of Units, teacher support, and other materials and tools typically found in the classroom are available in the lab.

- **Printed Teacher's Guides** Make copies of the printed Teacher's Guides, with answers removed and make them available in the school library for students to check out.

- **Use a Supportive Parent/Guardian CMP Web site**

Helping Parents and Guardians Help Students

Parents and guardians are an invaluable resource to the district if their knowledge, good intentions, and caring can be channeled to be compatible with the problem-centered approach of CMP.

> "The first teachers are the parents, both by example and conversation."
>
> — *Lamar Alexander*

In helping children learn, a parent's or guardian's first goal should be to assist their children in figuring out as much as they can for themselves. They can help by asking questions that guide them, without telling them what to do. Good questions and good listening skills will help students make sense of mathematics, build self-confidence, and encourage mathematical thinking and communication. A good question opens up a problem and supports different ways of thinking about it. A list of such questions is available at www.math.msu.edu/CMP/parents, along with background information about the curriculum. This site can help parents and guardians to have meaningful mathematical conversations with their children. The Web site also offers specific mathematical information. A vocabulary list with examples to illuminate meaning and use of new vocabulary and example solutions of homework exercises are just two of the aids that parents and guardians will find at this site.

Parents and guardians are some of the most knowledgeable experts in their child's universe. Their expertise may be in the mathematical ideas, or in the learning process itself. For example, they can help with homework by learning how to scaffold a Problem for a child, without taking away all the gains to be made from the student's individual struggle.

Selecting and Implementing *Connected Mathematics*

The Units in CMP were identified, developed, and carefully sequenced to help students build deep understanding of and skill with important mathematical ideas. Once a Unit has been taught, the understandings and procedural skills developed are used in succeeding Units to build understandings of new concepts and skills. Therefore, the order in which the Units are listed in each grade is the recommended order (See the Contents in Brief by Unit table which presents the recommended unit sequence).

Two typical implementation plans are

- All three grades in the first year, and

- A three-year plan – one grade level at a time

If the school chooses to implement all three grades in the first year, it is important for teachers at each grade level to know what mathematics is taught in the previous year and in the succeeding year. Most of the material that is taught in sixth grade occurs in most sixth-grade textbooks; however, if something is taught in CMP that was not taught the previous year in your school, then the seventh-grade teachers may need to add an extra lesson or two to cover this topic. Sixth- and eighth-grade teachers should use the same procedures. After the first year, there should be very little, if any, adjustment needed to the curriculum that is prescribed for each grade.

How many Units a school teaches at each grade level is difficult to predict. Length of the class periods, number of days spent on instruction, district objectives, and the background of incoming sixth-grade students are just some of the variables. In addition, class periods vary from 40 to 90 minutes across the country. The difference of 10 minutes for each class period can mean as much as a difference of one Unit being taught per year.

Experience and research suggest that effective professional development models have some common characteristics. To be effective, professional development

- Begins prior to curriculum implementation and continues for at least the first three years of implementation.

- Is centered on the CMP curriculum.

- Develops teachers' knowledge of mathematics and pedagogy.

- Models and reflects good mathematical pedagogy.

- Addresses teacher concerns about change.

- Involves teachers in reflecting and planning for improvement.

- Creates strong leadership.

- Includes a plan for training new teachers as they join the district.

- Reflects strong support from administration and parents.

- Establishes a collaborative "community of learners" among teachers.

Change in itself can be problematic and for some teachers the changes associated with using CMP for the first time can be significant. The Concerns-Based Adoption Model (CBAM) (Hall & Hard, 1987; Hard et al. 1987; Loucks-Horsley, 1989; Freil and Gann, 1993) offers help in addressing these concerns. The stages of concern can be described as the following:

- **Self-Concerns** What is this new change, and how will it affect me?

- **Task-Oriented Concerns** How do I enact this change? What do I need to do to make this change happen with my students?

- **Impact-Oriented Concerns** How are my students learning? Are they learning more, and are they learning better? How do I work with others who are also enacting these new ideas?

Progressing through these stages of concern while implementing *Connected Mathematics* takes time—three years is a good target.

A variety of needs will surface throughout the three years of professional development and implementation. Early in the professional development component, time must be provided to address teachers' concerns about enacting a standards-based curriculum. In the beginning, these concerns may tend to focus on management, grading issues, special needs students, tracking, skills, transitions to high school, and so on. While these issues are important and should be addressed, they can divert attention away from content and instruction. We suggest that they be addressed gradually during the first phase of professional development. Give teachers time to voice their concerns early in the process and assure them that these concerns will be addressed. Many of these concerns become less urgent as the teachers engage in studying the mathematics and sharing their knowledge with colleagues. These experiences will help teachers integrate previous teaching practice with new expectations.

Good professional development to support CMP weaves mathematics, pedagogy, and assessment together. As teachers continue to engage in professional development activities, their concerns shift to student learning and the relationship between teaching and learning. These concerns merit continued attention; teachers need the opportunity to probe deeper into the mathematics, their practice, and student learning.

To make significant changes, professional development must address teachers' stages of concern while providing opportunities for teachers to

- Develop a deeper understanding and broader view of mathematics (mathematical knowledge)

- Strengthen their pedagogical knowledge (teaching and learning)

- Explore assessment aligned with inquiry-based instructional strategies (assessment)

- Foster and sustain collaboration for continued growth

Initially, these professional activities are most effective when facilitated by an outside teacher leader; however, the ultimate goal is to foster and sustain a collaborative teacher community in which these activities continue with local teacher leadership. In order for these activities to continue, teachers will need adequate time to collaborate with their colleagues.

Professional development must be based on sound criteria and principles that have evolved from research and been verified in practice. The research discussed above as well as other research described by Loucks-Horsley et al. (1996), our own extensive experiences, and the *Professional Standards for Teaching Mathematics* (NCTM, 1991) serve as important references for our professional development design. Three components—mathematics, teaching and learning, and assessment— are core areas of the professional development model and each comes to the foreground at critical times during the professional development.

Mathematical Knowledge

Mathematics education research has shown that teachers possess and continually refine a particular type of mathematical knowledge specific to teaching mathematics (Hill, Ball, & Schilling, 2008). Thus, professional development should begin with an emphasis on mathematical content. Teachers need to be comfortable with the mathematics embedded in the Problems of the curriculum. In addition, they need to form a more complete picture of how the mathematical ideas build on previous ideas and how those ideas in turn provide the foundation for the mathematics in subsequent Units and grades. Teachers also need to make connections between multiple solution strategies and between the five representations often used to communicate mathematics (Preston and Garner, 2003). See pages 78–80 of The CMP Classroom for a detailed description of using the five representations.

We place mathematical knowledge first because good instructional decisions and practice rely on deep understanding of the mathematics embedded in the Problems. Emphasizing pedagogy too soon may interfere with teachers' focus on the mathematics. However, effective instructional practices should be modeled as mathematics content is being learned.

Teaching and Learning

Once teachers have developed a strong understanding of the mathematics within the CMP curriculum, the focus of the professional development can shift to teaching and learning. When the focus shifts to pedagogy, teachers continue to develop their own understanding of the mathematics through conversations about student work and student understanding of the mathematics.

Teachers need to experience inquiry-based pedagogy in their professional development so that it will serve as a model for their own teaching. They also need to be involved in conversations about how to teach problem-centered materials. Because CMP requires a major shift from demonstrating mathematical procedures to facilitating classroom discussions around important mathematical ideas, professional development on pedagogy might begin with strategies for facilitating such discussions, such as Prompt, Wait Time, Revoice, Restate, and Apply Reasoning, which were discussed on page 81 of The CMP Classroom. One professional development resource for facilitating effective and mathematically productive classroom discussions is the *Mathematics Discourse in Secondary Classrooms* (MDISC) project (Herbel-Eisenman, Steele, and Cirillo, in press).

After teachers have taught several Units, they will need more in-depth work on instruction. The student books and teacher support can help teachers implement the curriculum within their own classrooms, but teachers also need time away from their classrooms to talk with peers and to fully investigate the potential of the curriculum. A resource for this ongoing professional development is the Five Practices for Orchestrating Productive Classroom Discussions (Smith and Stein, 2011). These Five Practices are

- Anticipating students' solution strategies

- Monitoring students' work

- Selecting students' solution strategies to share

- Sequencing students' solution strategies to highlight important mathematics

- Connecting and summarizing students' solution strategies

The CMP Classroom, explains how to use the Five Practices to enhance instruction.

Assessment

Once teachers have begun using inquiry-based instruction in CMP, it becomes clear that traditional forms of assessment are insufficient to gauge student learning. CMP offers a variety of assessment to support teachers, including embedded assessment, which may be unfamiliar to teachers and require them to develop new skills.

Concerns about how to assess student learning and how to grade assessments tend to arise later in the implementation process. Therefore, professional development involving assessment should occur after the teachers have experienced some of the curriculum and after the focus on teaching and learning. Professional development should also address the role of assessments in teachers' reflections and decisions. For example, with support and experience, teachers begin to see both formative and summative assessment as data they can use to drive instructional decisions. Furthermore, formative assessment is the very essence of teaching. Throughout a lesson, teachers are questioning, observing, and listening to students and adjusting their strategies as needed to accommodate and enhance learning. Homework, Check-ups, Quizzes and Unit tests provide additional assessment that also informs teachers' subsequent planning and teaching.

Contexts for Professional Growth

A strong professional development program for teachers implementing CMP should emphasize the five areas summarized in the chart. A more detailed description of each of these five areas will follow.

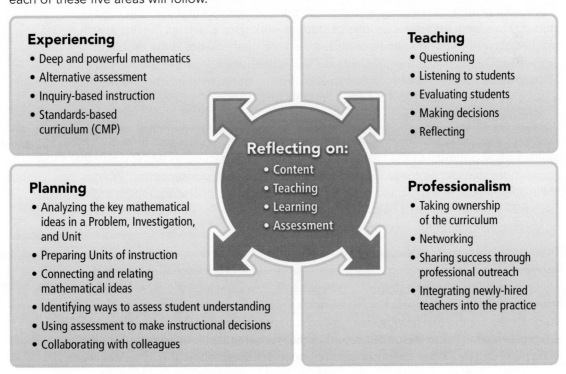

Experiencing
- Deep and powerful mathematics
- Alternative assessment
- Inquiry-based instruction
- Standards-based curriculum (CMP)

Teaching
- Questioning
- Listening to students
- Evaluating students
- Making decisions
- Reflecting

Reflecting on:
- Content
- Teaching
- Learning
- Assessment

Planning
- Analyzing the key mathematical ideas in a Problem, Investigation, and Unit
- Preparing Units of instruction
- Connecting and relating mathematical ideas
- Identifying ways to assess student understanding
- Using assessment to make instructional decisions
- Collaborating with colleagues

Professionalism
- Taking ownership of the curriculum
- Networking
- Sharing success through professional outreach
- Integrating newly-hired teachers into the practice

Experiencing

First and foremost, teachers need a deep understanding of the key mathematical ideas and reasoning that are embedded in the Problems. In addition, they need to see how student understanding of these ideas develops over time and connects to content in other Units. Thus, teachers should experience the curriculum in a way that is similar to what their students will experience. This does not mean they need as much time for each Problem, nor does it mean that they must do every Problem. Problems for the workshops should be chosen to highlight the development of key mathematical ideas. The supporting Problems can be more quickly examined so that the flow of development is clear, but the main focus is on the key idea.

Professional development leaders should model good teaching; they should set a context for teacher learning, encourage teachers to investigate, and help teachers make their conclusions explicit. This allows teachers to focus on making sense of the mathematics needed to solve the Problems posed. By setting the context as, *"How do you think your students might solve this problem?"*, the workshop leader can shift the focus to students' understanding. Teachers should be encouraged not to use their own knowledge to solve each Problem. The goal is not so much to find a solution to the Problem as it is to ask, *"What would my students bring to this problem? What solution strategies might they try? Which seem productive and rich in mathematical ideas? What are some of the misunderstandings that students might evince, and how can I best use discussions around these misunderstandings to help everyone learn more?"*

Some teachers may think that the Problems, or the mathematical ideas, are too hard. A powerful strategy for helping teachers with the mathematics and showing what students can learn is to use examples of student work. This alleviates the anxiety of teachers who have never learned or understood the mathematics in the Problem or have no confidence in their ability to do the mathematics. It allows teachers to ask questions they might be reluctant to ask. Looking at the mathematics from a student's point of view provides a comfortable environment for discussions of teaching and learning of the mathematics.

Follow-up discussions of the Problems help teachers better understand the mathematical potential of the Problems, the reasoning that students employ, and the connections that can be made. Teachers begin to value such questions as, *"What is the mathematics? At what stage are we in the development of understanding of the key idea? What do students need to bring to the problem? To what do these ideas connect in a student's future study of mathematics?"*

During the portion of professional development that focuses on mathematical knowledge, effective teaching strategies are modeled and occasionally discussed. However, explicit attention to teaching needs to follow. Teachers will need help with the teaching model. Knowing how to launch a Problem, how to assist and guide all students during the exploration, and how to summarize student understandings and strategies are crucial to the development of the mathematics. A good stimulus for a discussion on teaching is the observation of good teaching, either live in a classroom or on video. Analyzing students' strategies can lead to conversations on how the classroom environment and discussion may have affected learning. This is also a time for teachers to collaborate and make sense of evidence of good teaching.

Developing the habit of asking, *"What aspects of the launch were effective? What aspects of the summary were effective? How would I address that student question?"* prepares teachers to make the same demands of themselves.

Planning

Planning is key to success with any problem-centered curriculum such as CMP. During professional development, teachers plan together to teach a Problem, asking, *"What are the mathematical ideas? What difficulties will students encounter? What mathematical discoveries might they make? How will I launch this Problem?"* It is crucial that administrators recognize that, while the planning load reduces somewhat after the initial implementation stage, there will always be a need for teachers to plan lessons and reflect on what students learned from the lessons. Administrators need to help teachers find time for planning and reflecting. This will help teachers optimize their professional development time.

For each class session, it is important that teachers identify the mathematical concepts or strategies, their stages of development, and the time needed to develop these understandings. The power of CMP does not lie in any one activity or in any one Unit. Important ideas are studied in depth within a Unit and further developed and used in subsequent Units. It is both the depth of understanding within Units and the careful building and connecting of the Units that allow students to develop to their fullest mathematical potential.

Initial planning can occur over the summer, prior to the implementation of the CMP. However, teachers also need time during the year to plan, particularly with their colleagues. Planning sessions allow teachers to share problems they have experienced, learn new ideas from their colleagues, probe the mathematics more deeply, look for connections, and plan upcoming class sessions.

Once teachers are comfortable with the mathematics and the inquiry-based instructional model, they can look more closely at assessment and determine how to use assessments to evaluate students' knowledge and to inform their teaching. More thorough discussions on assessment are appropriate during the second year of teaching CMP and continued professional development. However, examining student work with a colleague is valuable. Asking questions about what the students' work shows not only deepens teachers' knowledge, but it can also serve as a guide to planning effective teaching strategies. During planning time, teachers can also discuss management and grading strategies as well as ways to address the needs of diverse student populations.

Teaching

> We have taken the stand that curriculum and instruction are not distinct—"what to teach" and "how to teach" are inextricably linked. The circumstances in which students learn affects what is learned.
>
> (Lappan & Phillips 1998. p. 84)

Teachers need to create a classroom environment that fosters collaboration between students as they reason through and solve problems, justify their ideas and solutions, and look for connections between mathematical ideas. Teachers must pose a Problem that provides a challenge for students, allow them to explore the Problem, and guide a class discussion on solutions to the Problem, all of which require the teacher to play many roles at the same time.

Teachers need to learn how to ask questions that can effectively probe students' understanding. They also need to learn to listen carefully to their students. These may be new skills for many teachers, even those with many years of experience. District administrators who take the time to become knowledgeable about inquiry-based learning are better able to support teachers directly. They can help set the expectation that teachers will collaborate with each other as the curriculum is enacted.

The CMP curriculum requires a paradigm shift for both teachers and students. The old paradigm, in which the teacher demonstrates procedures while students listen, take notes, and imitate the teacher, is based on the idea that the teacher knows all and that students come in as blank slates. Under the new paradigm, the teacher poses a problem and facilitates student learning by listening, questioning, and orchestrating class discussions. It is based on the idea that the teacher knows the necessary mathematics and teaching strategies and continues to learn more while students build on their prior experience and knowledge of mathematics to solve problems. This paradigm shift requires that teachers continually expand their knowledge of teaching and learning mathematics. This is best achieved through collaboratively planning, enacting, assessing, and reflecting on student learning.

Teachers must set and achieve high expectations for understanding, problem solving, representing, and communicating for all students on a daily basis. In order to make progress, they also need to reflect on their practice, focusing on student understanding. By establishing a school environment in which administrators support collaboration and expect teachers to work together, teachers throughout the whole school can begin to focus on questions such as, *"What evidence do I have that my students learned something? What did they learn?"*

Reflecting

Professional development activities should model reflective practices. It is through reflection on their teaching and their students' understanding that teachers continue to grow in their capacity to build powerful mathematical experiences for all students. Planning with a colleague and peer coaching are some ways to encourage reflection.

Videos of lessons can serve as catalysts for reflections. However, caution must be exercised when analyzing videos: the focus should be on student learning rather than a critique of the teacher. Centering conversations on student learning can help teachers think about their practice. *"What do I like about my students' ways of approaching the problem?" Why do I think this is effective? What should I do to encourage more of this? What aspects of my students' actions are not productive?*

Why is this? What can I do to redirect my students?" Finding the fine line between trying to help the students be successful in solving a Problem and allowing the students freedom to explore a more open Problem will take reflection and growth over time.

Similarly, using rich collections of student work in professional development activities can help teachers reflect on the role and importance of the summary phase of the lesson. When teachers study a collection of student work, some say that all of the solutions are acceptable. Others correct those that are not acceptable and go on to the next lesson. But it is the analysis and comparison of the collection of student work that can bring the important mathematics to the forefront.

To be effective, discussions on student learning should go hand in hand with discussions on teaching. A focus on student learning leads naturally to a discussion of the development of ideas over time. Talking and planning with colleagues in different grade levels provides the opportunity for teachers to build and share a coherent curriculum vision. Collaboration and reflection are key elements in creating a community of teachers and administrators within the school that can support improvement in teaching and learning over time.

Professionalism

Encouraging teachers to share their successes is one way for schools and districts to promote teacher ownership of the curriculum. Sharing can be done within the school by mentoring new teachers or through shared planning times, through district newsletters, through online discussion groups, or by volunteering to speak at local or state meetings. Networking, attending professional meetings, and joining mathematics teachers' associations are all ways to continue to grow in mathematical knowledge and in pedagogical strategies.

Often overlooked is the problem of teacher turnover, which occurs in many middle schools. It is critical to develop a plan to provide professional development for new hires. It is equally important to develop collaborative relationships with experienced mathematics teachers. Such relationships are mutually beneficial to the new and experienced teachers and, in many instances, result in lowering the rate of attrition of new teachers.

As teachers become comfortable with CMP, it becomes a natural part of the fabric of the school. A sense of complacency, a *"We've done it!"* feeling, sets in. This is the time to take a more exacting look at the potential of the curriculum and ask, *"Can we do better?"* This is the time when teachers should look more deeply at the mathematics embedded in the Problems and find ways to better promote student understanding. These more advanced professional development experiences can re-energize teachers and result in improved student learning. Moving to this level of implementation is a crucial step and is very often overlooked. Professional development should not be a one-time or a brief experience; rather, it should help teachers stay fresh, enthusiastic, and highly effective over time.

The Strength of Collaboration

It is through the collaborative process of sharing ideas; planning, examining student work; looking for gaps; and finding ways to make even bigger gains in student understanding, reasoning, and communication that teachers continue to move forward. In the early stages of implementation, the community may include the entire staff of mathematics teachers, but as implementation continues, it is likely that teachers will rely heavily on their grade-level colleagues for support, ideas, and guidance. Professional development opportunities are needed to ensure that these collaborations are able to continue throughout the implementation, even after the curriculum appears to be institutionalized at the school.

Collaboration might focus on student understanding, perceived weaknesses as evidenced on local and state testing; teacher strategies; reports from teachers who have attended state or national conferences; preparing presentations for administrators, parents, meetings at the state or national level; and effective use of technology.

CMP Teacher Support as a Professional Development Resource

The teacher support that accompanies each Unit of CMP offers help with the same components that are included in a good professional development program. Part of the professional development should be to model how this content might be used. But the content should not be considered a replacement for the professional development necessary to get teachers started or for the district's support of continued collaboration and professional development after the initial implementation phase. For an in-depth look at the content in the teacher support, see Teacher Materials in the Components section.

In order to achieve the goal of creating a classroom environment that enables students to learn together, it is essential that teachers be given time and opportunities to work with each other. No matter how informative the teacher support materials are, teachers will get more from them if they can plan or reflect with a colleague.

What to Look for in a CMP Classroom

Evaluation of teachers has become an important political issue, but determining what constitutes good teaching is a complex task. We believe that good teaching comes in many different forms and that what is most important is what the students are doing. When CMP has been successfully implemented, students are engaged, and they explore important mathematics through challenging tasks. Students work together to tackle problems. They make conjectures, provide arguments, consider alternate strategies, challenge ideas, and communicate their understandings through various media. In earlier work with the Show-Me Center, we developed a guide that can be used to observe CMP classrooms. You will find this classroom observation guide in Appendix D. We have also developed a coaching guide that can be used by coaches, administrators, and peers. You can find that guide in Appendix G.

Summary

During their careers, teachers play different roles, often simultaneously. It is important that professional development activities reflect the following four roles:

- Teachers as learners of mathematics
- Teachers as teachers of mathematics
- Teachers as collaborators with other teachers
- Teachers as agents of change working with administrators, parents, and other teachers

In a long-term professional development model, teachers will play each of these roles. The order in which these roles are listed is intended to reflect the priority that should be given these roles over time.

Professional development should help teachers identify the mathematics embedded within the Problems and the depth of understanding that *Connected Mathematics* helps students develop. It is important for teachers to understand the careful development of the concepts and skills throughout a Unit and see how these ideas build on prior understanding from previous Units. Thus, focusing on the development of mathematics is a priority for the first year of professional development. At the same time, exemplary teaching will be modeled and discussed.

Teaching plays a more prominent role during the second year of professional development. Collaboration is an effective way to support teachers' growth at this time. Analyzing student work can help teachers begin discussing mathematics, learning, pedagogy, and assessment. Planning a Unit of instruction together is another way in which teachers can collaborate. Mentoring and coaching are other activities that can help build strong learning communities. Finally, communicating the philosophy of CMP to administrators, other teachers, and parents is necessary if progress is to continue. The stages and activities within the professional development model should address each of these crucial roles.

As schools adopt CMP, they need to make a specific plan for professional development of teachers. A summary of the major ideas and issues related to professional development and enactment of CMP discussed in this section appears below.

CMP has been carefully developed, field tested, revised and, evaluated. The vision of Connected Mathematics is articulated in NCTM's Principals and Standards for School Mathematics (NCTM 2000).

> Principles and Standards for School Mathematics describes a future in which all students have access to rigorous, high-quality mathematics instruction, including four years of high school mathematics. Knowledgeable teachers have adequate support and ongoing access to professional development. The mathematics curriculum is mathematically rich, providing students with opportunities to learn important mathematical concepts and procedures with understanding.
>
> *(NCTM, 2000, p. 1).*

Working as a community ahead of time to carefully select materials; becoming knowledgeable about the strengths of the materials and the reasons for selecting them; examining students' transition into CMP as well as their transition into high school; preparing parents, guardians, administrators, and school board members; and planning the implementation and professional development for teachers will make a smooth and powerful implementation of CMP.

Key Issues Related to Implementation of Connected Mathematics

The following is a summary of the major ideas and issues related to professional development and implementation discussed in this part of the Guide.

Planning

- Gather evidence to support the change in curriculum

- Establish a plan for implementing or phasing in the curriculum over three years

- Gain the support of administration, parents, and teachers

- Plan long-term professional development for teachers

- Establish a long-term evaluation plan

Long-Term Professional Development for Teachers

- Focus on mathematics content

  o Identify and understand the big mathematical ideas in a Unit

  o Understand the development of mathematical concepts and reasoning from Problem to Problem, Investigation to Investigation, and from Unit to Unit

  o Understand the development of algorithms

  o Identify the skills embedded in the curriculum

  o Recognize connections between mathematical ideas within a Unit, across Units, across grades, and to applications.

  o Make connections between multiple solution strategies and between mathematical representations.

- Focus on inquiry-based instruction
    - Examine the recommended instructional model
    - Explore teacher facilitation of classroom discourse
    - View and discuss the CMP learning environment.
    - Discuss appropriate pacing of the curricula
- Focus on assessing student learning
    - Examine various dimensions of assessment (content knowledge, mathematical practices, mathematical disposition, work habits)
    - Examine various assessment components offered within CMP

- Address specific teacher concerns
    - Discuss and review various classroom management strategies
    - Monitoring grading, dealing with absences, teaching second language students, helping special needs students, and so forth.
- Support ongoing curriculum enactment
    - Establish time and protocols for teacher collaboration
    - Maintain community support through ongoing communication
    - Monitor student progress through systematic collection and review of data

Part VI
Unifying Themes and Mathematical Strands

Connected Mathematics (CMP) develops mathematical concepts and skills in four important mathematical strands: Number and Operation, Geometry and Measurement, Data Analysis and Probability, and Algebra and Functions. It is challenging to separate Units by topic, as proportional and algebraic reasoning cut across many of the Units. Furthermore, number also plays a role in every Unit. This is one of the strengths of CMP. Understandings are built on and connected to prior understandings from the content areas. Therefore, while the focus of a Unit is usually within one strand, the other strands play important roles in developing the understanding of the major ideas in the Unit.

Units Organized by Strand

Strand	Unit
Number and Operations	Prime Time
	Comparing Bits and Pieces
	Let's Be Rational
	Decimal Ops
	Accentuate the Negative
	Comparing and Scaling
	Stretching and Shrinking
	Looking for Pythagoras
	Function Junction
Geometry and Measurement	Covering and Surrounding
	Shapes and Designs
	Stretching and Shrinking
	Filling and Wrapping
	Looking for Pythagoras
	Butterflies, Pinwheels and Wallpaper
Data Analysis and Probability	Data About Us
	What Do You Expect?
	Samples and Populations
	Thinking With Mathematical Models (Investigation 4)
Algebra and Functions	Variables and Patterns
	Moving Straight Ahead
	Thinking With Mathematical Models
	Growing, Growing, Growing
	Frogs, Fleas, and Painted Cubes
	Say It With Symbols
	It's In the System
	Function Junction
	Looking for Pythagoras

■ Grade 6 Unit   ■ Grade7 Unit   ■ Grade 8 Unit

As you study the goals and development of the mathematics in the Units in each strand and in the collection of Units that comprise each grade-level course, it will be helpful to ask:

- *What are the big ideas of the strand and key objectives of each Unit in the strand?*

- *How are the key concepts of the strand developed in depth and complexity over time?*

- *What prior knowledge will students have that I can draw on in developing the goals of each Unit in the strand?*

- *What connections are made between the Units of this strand and those of other strands which are interspersed in the sequence of Units?*

Unifying Themes

The "Connected" in Connected Mathematics has several meanings. First, there are contexts that connect to the world in which students live. Second, there are mathematical ideas that serve as unifying themes to connect Units and strands together. Lastly, goals are developed in symbiotic tandem with each other, and over Units and grade levels. The result is a coherent whole.

Within each *Connected Mathematics* (CMP) Unit, the Problems are carefully sequenced to address important goals. This might imply that the goals are a discrete, linear sequence, but goals are often developed in parallel, as well as in sequence. For example, while exploring relationships among variables in *Variables and Patterns*, students are simultaneously beginning to develop strategies for solving equations, two prominent goals for CMP's Algebra and Functions strand.

Likewise, organizing Units by mathematical strands does not imply that all the goals for each Unit are related to the same strand. A Unit might be listed in the one strand but also carry key mathematical goals for another strand. For example, *Looking For Pythagoras*, while primarily about the Pythagorean Theorem, also carries forward the development of the Number and Operations strand by introducing students to irrational numbers and the set of real numbers. The Pythagorean Theorem also leads naturally to the equation of a circle and other important ideas.

Not only does goal development transcend the boundaries of a strand, but some mathematical ideas are so powerful that they permeate several strands and serve as unifying themes. Two of these overarching themes are proportional reasoning and mathematical modeling.

Proportional Reasoning

Ratios make their first appearance in *Comparing Bits and Pieces*. Here students use ratios to compare quantities, learn about unit rates and rate tables, and develop strategies for working with percentages. These Number and Operations goals are developed further in *Let's Be Rational* and *Decimal Operations*. *Stretching and Shrinking*, in the Geometry strand, amplifies the development of proportional reasoning with the big ideas of similarity and scale factors. This is followed by

Comparing and Scaling, which is again in the Number and Operations strand, but students also develop strategies for solving proportions, an Algebra and Functions strand goal. Proportional reasoning plays a key role in *Moving Straight Ahead*, a Unit about linear functions, in which students relate a constant rate of change in a table to a constant slope on a graph and to the constant of proportionality in equations of the form $y = mx$. Finally, to complete the permeation of all the strands, proportional reasoning plays a supporting role in *Samples and Populations*, a Unit from the Data Analysis and Probability strand, in which students make predictions about population characteristics by scaling up information from random samples.

Mathematical Modeling

The CCSSM say "Modeling is best interpreted not as a collection of isolated topics but rather in relation to other standards." In some sense, mathematical modeling is what every Unit in CMP is about. When students write number sentences in the Grade 6 Number and Operations Units, or write symbolic expressions for contextual situations in Algebra Units, they are creating a model of a situation. Not only does this kind of model capture something important about quantities in the situation, but it can be manipulated into equivalent forms, to expose new understandings or solve problems. Graphs and tables can also be descriptive or analytic models. In Data and Probability Units, students choose variables, represent data with an appropriate graphical model, and analyze the distribution using statistical models. Modeling gets explicit focus in *Thinking With Mathematical Models*. Students (1) identify the variables in the situation, (2) formulate graphical and algebraic models for the relationships between variables, (3) analyze the models and make predictions, (4) improve on the models by using a line of best fit, and (5) measure how well their statistical model fits the data.

One particular aspect of modeling is quantitative reasoning. CMP integrates quantitative reasoning throughout the curriculum. When students model problem situations, they may first define their variables, choose their units of measurement for the variables, and abstract the situation, creating a seemingly decontextualized, coherent representation. Then, as they manipulate the symbolic representation, they consider the units again to attend to the meaning of quantities and make sense of processes and results. This is the sense–making habit that supports students as they construct or interpret expressions, equations and formulas, and solve multi-step problems. When students collect data and model a situation with a descriptive graph they must define quantities carefully and choose units and scales for the axes. When they calculate a statistic they must consider units again, as well as the level of accuracy appropriate for the context.

Number and Operations Strand

Every branch of mathematics and nearly every application of mathematics uses numbers and operations in essential ways for reasoning and problem-solving tasks. The applications in CMP involve whole numbers, integers, fractions, decimals, percents, ratios, and irrational numbers. The overarching goal in the CMP3 Number and Operations strand is to extend student understanding and skill in the use of numbers and operations to represent and reason about quantitative information.

There are nine primary Units in the CMP3 Number and Operations strand. These Units aim to:

- Extend knowledge of whole numbers, fractions, and decimals, develop the ability to know which representation and which operation to choose, and develop fluency in operations with those numbers;

- Develop concepts of ratio, rate, and proportion, particularly equivalence of ratios, and apply to real-world problems;

- Develop understanding of the meaning of percents and facility with applications;

- Introduce negative, irrational, and complex numbers and the structural properties of each number system.

The learning progressions that work toward each of those broad goals are described in the following sections.

Extending Whole Numbers, Fractions, and Decimals

Proficiency in the use of common fractions depends on understanding the multiplicative structure of whole numbers. This includes understanding the concepts of factor, multiple, prime number, greatest common factor, and least common multiple. *Prime Time* begins the CMP3 curriculum by developing ideas of elementary number theory while engaging students in games and problem-solving tasks that set the tone for a classroom that operates as a community of learners in which all participants are active participants. *Prime Time* also begins the Algebra and Functions strand of the curriculum by developing student understanding of arithmetic expressions, the Distributive Property, and the Order of Operations.

The review and extension of fraction and decimal number understanding and skill is focused in the two Grade 6 Units, *Let's Be Rational* and *Decimal Ops*. In both Units, students develop number sense and problem solving habits of mind by addressing four key questions:

- What kind of numbers will accurately represent the quantities involved?

- What operations on those numbers will provide answers to the core questions posed?

- What is a good estimate for the result of those operations?

- What exact result is produced by applying a standard computational algorithm for the operations?

The name change from *Bits and Pieces II* (CMP2) to *Let's be Rational* signals an extension of students' understandings about fractions and decimals. Negative numbers are introduced and students order these numbers on the number line, observing that, for example, $-\frac{3}{4}$ and $\frac{3}{4}$ are the same distance from zero but on opposite sides of zero. A consequence of the addition of by-hand computations with multidigit numbers in *Decimal Operations* is that students can see that any fraction $\frac{a}{b}$ can be written as a decimal, which will either repeat or terminate, by computing $a \div b$.

The Units focused on fraction and decimal operations also begin the work on basic ideas of algebra by exploring *fact families* that connect pairs of related operations, equivalent equations, and equivalent expressions. For example, the multiplication/division fact family relating 4, 6, and 24 includes the following equations:

$$4 \times 6 = 24$$
$$6 \times 4 = 24$$
$$4 = 24 \div 6$$
$$6 = 24 \div 4.$$

Students work on computational skills and simultaneously develop skill in solving simple equations. Use of fact-family reasoning enables solution of one-step equations. For example, to solve $4x = 24$, students reason that $x = 24 \div 4$, or to solve 6% of $x = \$4.80$, students reason that $x = \$4.80 \div 0.06$.

The Distributive Property of Multiplication Over Addition and Subtraction, introduced in *Prime Time* allows writing of arithmetic calculations in a variety of equivalent forms. For example,

$$4(5 + 1) = 4(5) + 4(1).$$

The Distributive Property is used in the Algebra and Functions strand in support of the overarching goal of writing and interpreting equivalent expressions. As the integer, rational, real, and complex number systems are developed in succeeding Units, students are repeatedly asked whether such very useful structural properties of operations do or should continue to apply in the new contexts.

Ratios, Rates, Scale Factors, and Proportions

Problem 1.1 in *Comparing Bits and Pieces* presents some fundraising goals and then asks students whether some claims about each fundraising goal are true. The aim of Problem 1.1 is to focus student attention on the common mathematical challenge of comparing quantities accurately and fairly. It also highlights the difference between comparison by subtraction (or addition) and comparison by division (or multiplication).

Problem 1.1 introduces the proportional reasoning concepts of ratio, rate, and percent that are then developed in subsequent Problems of the Unit. The Problem serves a second important function of helping teachers to determine the breadth and depth of students' prior knowledge of ratio, rate, and percent. Problem 1.1 also illustrates our guiding principle that students will grasp new concepts most readily if they encounter them in familiar contexts to which they can first apply their informal sense-making and then abstract underlying common mathematical structures.

Subsequent problems in *Comparing Bits and Pieces* develop the concept of ratio and rate more explicitly, based on the idea that a ratio of *a* to *b* means every *a* of one quantity is related to *b* of a second quantity. Equivalence of ratios is developed by reasoning about what makes sense in meaningful contexts and then equivalence of ratios is connected to equivalence of fractions. The ways that working with ratios is different from working with fractions are also highlighted. For example,

> Suppose there are 10 boys and 15 girls in one class and 12 boys and 9 girls in another class. The ratio of boys to girls in the two classes combined is 22 to 24 (not $\frac{10}{15} + \frac{12}{9}$ or even $\frac{10}{25} + \frac{12}{21}$).

From this informal, sense-making, intuitive beginning, the concepts of ratio and rate develop in breadth and depth across the Grade 6 and Grade 7 CMP3 courses. Unit rates and rate tables are introduced in the second Investigation of *Comparing Bits and Pieces*, and after refining and applying these ideas in other Number strand Units, are revisited in an algebraic context in *Variables and Patterns* near the end of Grade 6.

In Grade 7, *Stretching and Shrinking* develops thinking about ratios in terms of geometric similarity and scale factors, and *Comparing and Scaling* brings ratios, rates, scale factors, and rate tables together to develop strategies for solving proportions. Building on the concepts of equivalence and scaling, *Comparing and Scaling* enables students to develop reasonable algorithms for solving proportions, underpinned by sound conceptual understanding.

These fundamental proportional reasoning ideas are then extended and applied to work on linear functions, rates of change, and slope of graphs in the algebra Units *Moving Straight Ahead* in Grade 7 and *Thinking with Mathematical Models* at the start of Grade 8. The Number strand and the Algebra and Functions strand both make use of the concepts of rate and proportionality.

Throughout this development of proportional reasoning concepts and skills, students are continually asked two key questions:

> *When does it make sense to compare quantities by ratio or rate?*
>
> *How can ratios or rates be expressed in equivalent forms to answer questions that involve proportions?*

Percents

In almost every practical quantitative reasoning task, percents are the most common tool for framing and resolving questions that call for comparison of quantities. They offer standardized language and procedures for describing the relationship between two quantities from both additive and multiplicative perspectives.

Additive Perspective Examples

> If an item originally priced at $15 is on sale for $9, the price reduction is $6. Also, $6 is 40% of the original price, or the sale price is 60% of the original price.
>
> If a city's population increases from 25,000 to 30,000, the increase is 5,000 which is 20% of the original population. The new population is 120% of the original population.

While each of these examples represent additive reasoning, the increase or decrease can be expressed as a percent.

Multiplicative Perspective Examples

What is 30% of 90	$0.30 \times 90 = n$
36 is what percent of 90?	$p \times 90 = 36$
45 is 25% of what number?	$45 = 0.25 \times n$

The prior work with fact families relating multiplication and division pays rich dividends in learning how to deal with percent problems. Of course, percents appear throughout the geometry, data, probability, and algebra Units of each grade.

Negative Numbers

Traditional introductions to negative numbers focus on integers—positive and negative whole numbers and 0. The development in CMP3 takes a somewhat different path. In compliance with CCSSM requirements, we begin in the sixth-grade Unit *Comparing Bits and Pieces* by extending the rational number line to include negative numbers. The development there is limited to location of positive numbers and their opposites and the concept of absolute value. Later in Grade 6, a problem in *Variables and Patterns* extends the coordinate plane to all four graphing quadrants, using negative numbers informally with the assumption that sixth-grade students will almost certainly have had some encounters with them.

The heart of the development of negative numbers is the Grade 7 Unit *Accentuate the Negative*. We promote sense-making through games with wins and losses and other story contexts, number line models, and chip models to build on student intuitions and derive standard rules for operating with negative numbers. In the spirit of *connected* mathematics, we mix tasks about negative rational numbers among those limited to integer values.

In addition to using informal reasoning and models for numbers and operations, we again connect with the fact-family idea in the derivations of algorithms. For example, after establishing rules for multiplication (product of two negative numbers is the subtle case), rules for division follow:

$$(-30) \div 5 = -6 \text{ because } -30 = 5(-6)$$

$$(-30) \div (-5) = 6 \text{ because } -30 = (-5)(6)$$

The final Investigation of *Accentuate the Negative* takes a retrospective view of the family of number systems—whole numbers, integers, and rationals—and highlights the basic structural properties that are common to all, especially the distributive property. Since *Accentuate the Negative* occurs relatively early in Grade 7, negative numbers are available for applications in other Units, most notably in *Moving Straight Ahead* about linear functions.

Irrational and Complex Numbers

The development of standard number systems and operations in CMP3 is completed in two Units of the Grade 8 curriculum—*Looking for Pythagoras* and *Function Junction*. *Looking for Pythagoras* makes the standard connection between square roots and diagonals of squares or hypotenuses of right triangles. It deals with decimal representation of rational (repeating) and irrational (non repeating) numbers, and, per CCSSM specifications, introduces cube roots as well. The number π pops up earlier, in Grade 7, when circumference and area of circles is tackled in *Filling and Wrapping*.

Complex numbers have traditionally been a topic of high school Algebra II courses, but the CCSSM syllabus for Algebra I calls for introduction of complex numbers. Thus, in our effort to offer CMP3 materials that support a full introductory algebra course, we have included complex numbers in *Function Junction*. The development there is mathematically fairly standard, continuing the pattern of extending the number system to include meaningful numbers that provide solutions for equations not solvable in preceding simpler number systems. For example,

$3x = 2$ is not solvable in whole numbers, but it is solvable in rational numbers;

$3 + x = 2$ is not solvable in positive numbers, but it is solvable in integers;

$x^2 = 2$ is not solvable in rational numbers, but it is solvable in real numbers;

$x^2 = -1$ is not solvable in real numbers, but it is solvable in complex numbers.

Conclusion: Conceptual Knowledge and Procedural Skills

The specific Number and Operations Units of CMP3 develop all the concepts and procedural skills specified in the CCSSM with a consistent focus on meaningful derivations of ideas, techniques, and applications. When students complete all Units in the strand and the important connections in other content strands, they should be well prepared conceptually and technically to represent quantities with appropriate numerical forms, to identify operations that will answer questions of interest, to estimate results of planned operations, to perform algorithms to produce exact computational results, and to interpret those results in the contexts from which questions arose. Furthermore, they should have sound understanding of the key structural properties of number systems that allow and guide the more general reasoning about quantity using algebra.

Geometry and Measurement Strand

Natural and designed objects in the world around us are outlined, supported, and decorated by an endless variety of geometric shapes. The overarching goal of the Units in the *Connected Mathematics 3* (CMP3) Geometry and Measurement strand is to develop student understanding of the connections between form and function of common shapes. For example, triangles provide structural stability to bridge trusses because they are rigid figures. Hexagons are common shapes of decorative tiles, because of their many symmetries and the fact that they can be used to cover flat surfaces without overlap or gaps. Builders use 3-4-5 triangles to check perpendicularity of framing, because every such triangle must be a right triangle.

There are six Units in the Geometry and Measurement strand and connections to Geometry and Measurement topics in many Units of the other content strands. The central objectives of the strand are:

- Extend understanding and skill with geometric measurement to perimeter and area of polygons and circles and surface area and volume of right prisms, cylinders, cones, and spheres;

- Develop understanding of similarity and congruence for geometric figures, using both concepts of transformations and conditions relating side and angle measurements to establish those relationships;

- Develop proportionality connections between linear, area, and volume measurements for similar figures;

- Extend understanding of coordinate graphing to four quadrants; and

- Develop the Pythagorean Theorem for right triangles and the related distance formula for points on a coordinate grid.

The learning progressions that work toward each of those broad goals are described in the following sections.

Extending Understanding and Skill with Geometric Measurement

Students entering the sixth grade are likely to know how to find the area of a rectangle and the volume of a rectangular prism. The sixth-grade Unit *Covering and Surrounding* reviews basic perimeter, area, and volume ideas, but it extends the core idea of covering (and filling) a figure with copies of a unit length (segment), area (square), or volume (cube) in several ways. First, it highlights and helps students see the difference between perimeter and area by asking "What are the dimensions of a rectangle with fixed perimeter and maximum area?" and "What are the dimensions of a rectangle with fixed area and minimum perimeter?" For example, the following visual shows two rectangles with an area of 16 square units but with different perimeters.

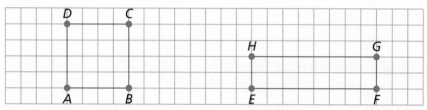

Area *ABCD* = 16 square units
Perimeter *ABCD* = 16 units

Area *EFGH* = 16 square units
Perimeter *EFGH* = 20 units

Second, *Covering and Surrounding* utilizes the principle that figures can be cut into pieces and assembled in new shapes without changing the area to develop logically the formulas for area of triangles and parallelograms. This principle is illustrated below.

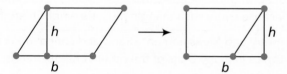

The area of the parallelogram on the left is the sum of two areas, a trapezoid and a triangle. The area of the rectangle on the right is also the sum of the same two areas. In both cases $A = bh$ square units. Students are connecting a geometric idea, area, to an algebraic idea, relationships.

Finally, *Covering and Surrounding* lays the foundation for volume calculation in any prism by highlighting the facts that such a prism can be viewed as a stack of several layers of unit cubes and that the number of such cubes in each stack is equal to the area of the base of the prism.

These same general measurement principles are applied in the Grade 7 Unit *Filling and Wrapping*. *Filling and Wrapping* extends area and volume calculation to circles, polygonal prisms, and cylinders. In each case, students extend the basic ideas that apply very neatly to rectangular figures to approximation of other more complex figures. The area of a circle is approximated by covering a circle with radius squares as shown here.

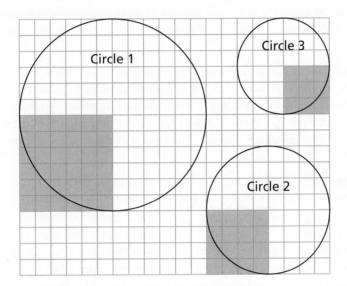

Area and circumference of a circle are connected by dissection. The circle below is dissected into eight sectors and then these sectors are rearranged to form an approximate parallelogram. As we dissect the circle into more and more sectors the base of the parallelogram approaches half the circumference C of the circle, and the height of the parallelogram approaches the radius r of the circle. The area of the parallelogram is approximately $0.5Cr$ or $0.5(2\pi r)r$ or πr^2.

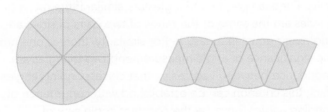

And volume of a cylinder is calculated by applying the 'area of base times height' principle introduced with rectangular prisms. Area and volume is completed in *Say It With Symbols* in Grade 8 with surface area and volume of cones and spheres.

In Grade 7, *Shapes and Designs* reviews and extends angle measurement. Several Problems lead to fundamental results about angle measures in polygons: the derivation of the formula for exterior and interior angle measures of any polygon, and the development of the relationships among measures of angles formed by intersecting lines and parallel lines cut by transversals. Taken together, these extensions of measurement concepts and skills lay a solid foundation for development of similarity and congruence concepts in grades 7 and 8.

Develop Understanding of Congruence and Similarity

From an informal perspective, two geometric figures are said to be congruent if they are exactly the same shape and size. Two figures are said to be similar if they are the same shape, but possibly different in size. There are at least two standard ways to make those informal understandings mathematically precise, one static and one dynamic.

The standard way of establishing **congruence** for figures like two triangles is to say that there is a correspondence between vertices of the figures under which corresponding pairs of sides and angles are equal in measure. The more dynamic approach to congruence is to say that there is a distance-preserving transformation (reflection, rotation, translation, or glide reflection) that maps one figure exactly on top of the other.

The static criterion for **similarity** says that two triangles are similar if there is a correspondence between vertices such that corresponding angles are equal in measure and the *ratios of lengths* for corresponding sides are equal. The more dynamic, but mathematically equivalent approach to similarity starts with the concept of dilation transformations and scale factors. For example, a dilation with scale factor $\frac{3}{2}$ and center point P maps each point X to an image point X' so that $PX' = \frac{3}{2} PX$. Then two geometric figures are similar, with scale factor k if there is some composite of dilation and rigid motion transformations that maps one figure exactly on top of the other.

From both the static and dynamic perspectives one wants to eventually arrive at answers to the question, "What minimal information about the sides and angles of two figures (especially triangles) will guarantee that they are congruent or similar?" For congruence of triangles, there are several familiar criteria—Side-Angle-Side, Side-Side-Side, and Angle-Side-Angle being most common. For similarity of triangles there are comparable results. For example, two triangles are similar if the ratios of lengths of corresponding sides are the same or the ratios of two pairs of sides are equal and the included angles are equal in measure. For similarity, there is one more criterion that highlights the significance of angle measurement: two triangles are similar if there is a correspondence between vertices so that corresponding angles are equal in measure. In fact, this criterion can be established with congruence of only two pairs of corresponding angles (because the constant angle sum of 180° in every triangle then forces the third pair of angles to be congruent).

The development of congruence and similarity in CMP3 emphasizes the more dynamic approach through transformations and it begins with the conceptually richer concept of similarity. The Grade 7 Unit *Stretching and Shrinking* engages students in a variety of hands-on dilation activities that stretch and shrink the size of simple figures (and connect with enlargement and reduction functions of copiers). This experience shows how size, but not shape, of dilated figures changes and how angle measures are preserved by similarity transformations.

The story of congruence and similarity, begun somewhat informally and visually in *Shapes and Designs* and *Stretching and Shrinking*, is completed in the Grade 8 unit *Butterflies, Pinwheels, and Wallpaper* in which the dynamic and static approaches come together and are applied to a variety of standard problems.

Develop Proportionality Connections of Similar Figures

In *Stretching and Shrinking*, students are asked to compare ratios of side lengths in similar figures to give a visual foundation for proportional reasoning. Then comparison of perimeters and areas of similar figures introduces the fundamentally important, "How are scale factors of dilations related to changes in perimeter and area of figures?" The general principle that linear dimensions are changed by the dilation scale factor k and areas are changed by k^2 is revisited and extended in subsequent measurement tasks. In *Filling and Wrapping* in Grade 7, students discover that if a solid figure is dilated by scale factor k, the volume is changed by factor k^3.

Extend Understanding of Coordinate Methods and the Pythagorean Theorem

The pervasive use of computer tools for graphic tasks as diverse as architectural drawing, robotic manufacturing, and movie production has made coordinate methods in geometry fundamental skills for many workers today. This trend is reflected in the CCSSM objectives for middle grades mathematics, and in the CMP3 geometry Units that meet those expectations.

The first Unit of Grade 6, *Prime Time*, asks students to plot factor pairs to find the visual pattern in those numbers. A related task in *Covering and Surrounding* asks students to display the patterns of lengths and widths that give constant area but different perimeter and constant perimeter but different area. These connections to algebraic relationships of variables are explored again in *Variables and Patterns*, which begins the focus on expressions and functions in the Algebra and Functions strand. *Variables and Patterns* and *Accentuate the Negative* in early Grade 7 extend graphing to all four quadrants.

Students are able to find distances on coordinate grids using informal methods in *Covering and Surrounding* and formal methods in *Looking for Pythagoras*. The latter Unit develops the Pythagorean Theorem and the standard distance formula. In addition, in *Looking for Pythagoras*, students develop the equation of a circle, a geometry idea expressed algebraically. Coordinates and the distance formula come together again in *Butterflies, Pinwheels and Wallpaper*, to develop coordinate rules for congruence and similarity transformations.

Conclusion: Connections

The preceding description of developments in the Geometry and Measurement strand of CMP3 indicates the flow of key geometric concepts over the three-year course of study. In the spirit of *Connected Mathematics*, those geometric ideas and methods are applied and enhanced by work on Problems in many other Units. The most prominent and powerful connection of Geometry and Measurement to other strands of the CMP3 curriculum is the interplay of rational number and proportionality concepts in the Number and Operations strand with similarity. However, since the CMP3 approach to algebra emphasizes functional relationships between quantitative variables, the geometric methods of coordinate graphing are also prominent in every algebra Unit. That visualization of relationships between variables is also central to our development of the mathematical modeling theme in data analysis. Area models provide strong support for work with fractions, decimals, and probability. Lastly, concepts of geometry and measurement throughout CMP3 provide invaluable visual resources for problem solving and abstract reasoning about all facets of the mathematics.

Data Analysis and Probability Strand

Statistics

Statistics is the science of collecting, analyzing, and interpreting data to answer questions and make decisions in the face of uncertainty. Since statistical reasoning is now involved throughout the work of science, engineering, business, government, and everyday life, it has become an important strand in the school and college curriculum.

Understanding variability, the way data vary, is at the heart of statistical reasoning. Variation is understood in terms of the context of a problem because data are numbers with a context. There are several aspects of variability to consider, including noticing and acknowledging, describing and representing, and identifying ways to reduce, eliminate or explain patterns of variation.

Three Units of CMP3 address the Common Core State Standards for Mathematics (CCSSM) for statistics: *Data About Us* (Grade 6), *Samples and Populations* (Grade 7), and *Thinking with Mathematical Models* (Grade 8). The over arching goal of these Units is to develop student understanding and skill in conducting statistical investigations. A typical statistical investigation involves four phases:

- Posing a statistical question
- Collecting relevant data
- Analyzing the distribution(s)
- Interpreting the results in light of the question asked

A statistical investigation is a dynamic process that often involves moving back and forth among the four interconnected phases. For example, initial data collection and analysis might suggest refining the question and gathering additional data. Work at any stage might suggest change in representations or analyses of the data before presentation of results. Below is a visual of this dynamic process.

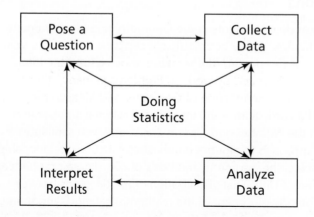

Posing Questions

The question asked impacts the rest of the process of statistical investigation. A statistical question anticipates an answer based on data that vary versus a deterministic answer. Questions may be classified as summary, comparison, or relationship questions.

Summary questions focus on descriptions of data and are usually about a single data set. Examples: What is your favorite kind of pet? How many pets do you have?

Comparison questions involve comparing two or more sets of data across a common attribute.
Examples: How much taller is a sixth-grade student than a second-grade student?

Relationship questions are posed for looking at the interrelationship between two paired numerical attributes or between two categorical attributes.
Examples: Are students with after-school jobs more likely to have late or missing homework than students with no such jobs?

Collecting Data

In *Data About Us* and *Samples and Populations* students collect one-variable (univariate) data. In *Mathematical Models* students collect two-variable (bivariate) data. The data collected, and the purpose for their use, influence subsequent phases of the statistical investigation.

The concepts of numerical and categorical data are introduced in the Grade 6 Unit, *Data About Us*. Different questions elicit different types of data; we might ask questions that elicit numerical answers, or questions that elicit non numerical answers.

Examples of **numerical data:**
We can collect data about household size and organize them by frequencies in a line plot showing how many households have one person, two people, and so on. We can collect data about student heights and organize them by intervals of 4 inches in a histogram by using frequencies of heights from 40 to 44 inches tall, and so on.

Examples of **categorical data:**
We can collect data about birth years and organize them by using frequencies of how many people were born in 1980, 1981, 1982, and so on.
We can collect data about favorite types of books and report frequencies or relative frequencies in a bar graph of people liking mysteries, adventure stories, science fiction, and so on.

Once a statistical question has been posed and relevant data types identified, the next step of an investigation is collecting data cases to study. The topic of sampling is addressed in the Grade 7 Unit *Samples and Populations*. The essential idea behind sampling is to gain information about a whole population by analyzing only a part of the population. A census collects data from the entire population whose attributes are being studied. Generally, conducting a census is not possible or reasonable because of such factors as cost and the size of the population. Hence, there is a need to collect samples of data and use the data from the samples to make predictions about populations.

A central issue in sampling is the need for representative samples. To ensure representative samples, we try to select random samples. A number of strategies for making random choices, such as drawing names from a hat, spinning spinners, tossing number cubes, and generating lists of values using a calculator or computer, are developed earlier in *What Do You Expect?* These strategies are used later in *Samples and Populations.* Students realize that there is an equally likely chance for any number to be generated by any spin, toss, or key press. In *Samples and Populations,* students realize that these numbers may be used to select members of a population to be part of a sample. In other words, there is an equally likely chance for any member of a population to be included in the sample when samples are chosen randomly.

In *Samples and Populations,* students develop a sound, general sense about what makes a good sample size. Even with a random sampling strategy, descriptive statistics such as means and medians of the samples will vary from one sample to another. The potential accuracy of a sample statistic (i.e., as a predictor of the population statistic) improves with the size of the sample. As a rule of thumb, sample sizes of 25 to 30 are appropriate for most of the problems that students encounter at this level.

Sample data might be numerical or categorical, univariate or bivariate. Knowing the type of data helps us to determine the most appropriate measures of center and variability, and make choices of representations.

Analyzing Distributions

The primary purpose of statistical analysis is to provide an accounting of the variability in collected data. In order to do this, it is generally very helpful to display and examine patterns in the distribution of data values. The distribution of data refers to the way data occur in a data set, necessitating a focus on aggregate features of data sets. When students work with data, they are often interested in the individual cases. However, statisticians like to look at the overall distribution of a data set. Distributions, unlike individual cases, have properties such as measures of central tendency (i.e., mean, median, mode) or spread (e.g., outliers, range, interquartile range, mean absolute deviation) or shape (e.g., clumps, gaps, symmetric, skewed).

Designing Representations

The graphs addressed in CMP3 serve three different purposes. First, there are graphs that summarize frequencies of occurrence of individual cases of data values, such as line plots, dot plots, and frequency bar graphs. Second, graphs can also be used to group cases in intervals. This is useful when there is greater variability in spread and/or few data values are identical so tallying frequencies is not helpful. The two graphs used that group cases in intervals are histograms and box-and-whisker plots (also called box plots). These graphs are discussed in *Data About Us* and *Samples and Populations.* Finally, in *Thinking With Mathematical Models,* coordinate graphs, like scatter plots, are used to show association between paired numerical variables.

Statistical graphs model real-world situations and facilitate analysis. Students have to select an appropriate type of graph model, label with appropriate units for the quantities under examination, and summarize with useful levels of accuracy. These ideas are part of a broad modeling strand, which gets explicit mention in the CCSSM for High School.

An important attribute of a graph is its shape. The shape of the graph may help answer such questions as:

- Which data values or intervals of values occur most frequently?

- Are there gaps in the data?

- Are there unusual data values or outliers?

- What data values or intervals of data appear to be typical?

- How can we describe the variability among the data values?

- Are there more data values at one end of the graph than at the other end?

- Do the variables appear to be related or not (bivariate data)?

Some of these questions can be answered with numerical measures, as well as with general observations based on looking at the graph of a distribution.

Measures of Center and Variability

There are several numerical measures of center or spread that are used to summarize distributions. These are essential tools in statistics. In CMP, students learn about three measures of central tendency: *mode*, *median*, and *mean*. Consider these data:

Name	Number of People in Household
Ollie	2
Yarnell	3
Gary	3
Ruth	4
Paul	6
Brenda	6

- In these data, there are two such values (3 and 6), so we say the distribution is bimodal. A distribution may be unimodal, bimodal, or multimodal.

- The median marks the location that divides a distribution into two equal parts. In these data, the median is 3½ people.

- The mean is 4 people.

There are three interpretations of mean (or average) used in CMP.

1. The fair share or evening out interpretation is looking at the data value that would occur if everyone received the same amount. This is the model emphasized in grades 6–8.

2. The balance model is when differences from the mean "balance out" so that the sum of differences below and above the mean equal 0. This model is hinted at when students work with the MAD (mean absolute deviation) in *Data About Us* and *Samples and Populations*.

3. The typical value is a general interpretation used more casually when students are being asked to think about the three measures of center and which to use.

It is important that students learn to make choices about which measure of center to choose to summarize for a distribution. Sometimes the choice is clear: the mean and median cannot be used with categorical data. Mode may be used with both categorical and numerical data. Sometimes the choice is less clear and students have to use their best judgment as to which measure provides a good description of what is typical of a distribution. The median is not influenced by values at the extremes of a distribution and so might be chosen if we do not want extremes to influence what is considered typical. The mean incorporates all values in a distribution and so is influenced by values at the extremes of a distribution. If we want these to influence what is considered typical we choose the mean.

In *Thinking With Mathematical Models*, students are introduced to a new idea related to judging what is typical of a distribution: a line of best fit. Since each data point in a scatter plot has two variables, and the question is whether these variables relate to each other or not, the distribution may be summarized by a line, not a single numerical value. When it is appropriate to draw a line of best fit, the line passes among the points making an overall trend visible. Technically the line of best fit is influenced by all the points, including those that are very atypical of the trend. In *Thinking With Mathematical Models*, students choose whether a line of best fit is an appropriate model. If it is, they can use their understanding of linearity to draw the line and use its equation to predict data values within or beyond the collected data.

Variability is a quantitative measure of how close together—or spread out—a distribution of measures or counts from some group of "things" are. In *Data About Us* and *Samples and Populations* students are introduced to several *measures of variability*. Several questions may be used to highlight interesting aspects of variation.

- What does a distribution look like?

- How much do the data points vary from one another or from the mean or median?

- What are possible reasons why there is variation in these data?

As with measures of center, it is just as important for students to develop the judgment skills to choose among measures of variability as it is for them to be able to compute the measures. Again, there are constraints on the choices.

In the Grade 6 Unit *Data About Us*, students use *range*, the difference between the maximum and the minimum data values, as one measure of spread. In addition, students are encouraged to talk about where data cluster and where there are "holes" in the data as further ways to comment about spread and variability. The range is obviously influenced by extreme values or outliers; it may suggest a higher variability than warranted in describing a distribution.

Statisticians often want to compare how data vary in relation to a measure of central tendency, either the median or the mean. Two measures of variation, *interquartile range* and *mean absolute deviation*, are introduced in *Data About Us*. The interquartile range (IQR) is only used with the median. It is the range of the middle 50% of the data values. The IQR does not reflect the presence of any unusual values or outliers. It provides a numerical measure of the spread of the data values between the first and third quartiles of a distribution. The size of the IQR provides information about how concentrated or spread out the middle 50% of the data are. The mean absolute deviation (MAD) connects the mean with a measure of spread. In some data sets, the data values are concentrated close to the mean. In other data sets, the data values are more widely spread out around the mean. The MAD is a number that is computed using the differences of data values from their mean. The MAD is the average distance between each data value and the mean, and is therefore only used in conjunction with the mean.

In *Samples and Populations* students learn to use the means and MADs, or medians and IQRs, of two samples to compare how similar or dissimilar the samples are. Similarity might indicate that the samples were chosen from a similar population; dissimilarity might indicate that they were chosen from different underlying populations.

In *Thinking With Mathematical Models*, a fourth measure of variability, the standard deviation, is introduced. This measure is another way to connect the mean with a measure of spread. It is similar in interpretation and use to the MAD but its computation is slightly different.

With bivariate data, students cannot use the same measures of center and spread as for univariate data. We have seen above that, analogous to a measure of center being used to describe a distribution with a single number, a line of best fit can summarize bivariate data in a scatter plot with a single trend line. When statisticians suspect that the values of two different attributes are related in meaningful ways, they often measure the strength of the relationship using a statistic called the *correlation coefficient*. The correlation coefficient is a number between 1 and -1 that tells how close the pattern of data points is to a straight line. The correlation coefficient is a *measure of linear association*. A value of r, the correlation coefficient, close to -1 or 1 indicates the data points are clustered closely around a line of best fit, and there is a strong association between variables. This is analogous to a low measure of spread for one-variable data. A value of r close to zero indicates the data points are not clustered closely around a line of best fit, and there is no association between variables. The value of r is calculated by finding the distance between each point in the scatter plot from the line of best fit. These distances are called residuals. Visually, residuals recall the calculation of MAD, measuring distances of univariate data from the mean.

In *Thinking With Mathematical Models*, students are asked to explore associations between different categorical variables by arranging categorical frequency data in two-way tables. For example, to see whether employment outside of school hours affects student performance on homework tasks, data about four kinds of students are arranged in the following table:

	After School Job	No After School Job	Totals
On-Time Homework	8	25	33
Missing Homework	12	15	27
Totals	20	40	60

Interpreting Results

The final critical stage of any statistical investigation is interpreting the results of data collection and analysis to answer the question that prompted work in the first place. In all the Data Units students are asked to report their findings. These reports may be descriptive or predictive. Interpretations are made, allowing for the variability in the data. This generally means describing and/or comparing data distributions by referring to the following things:

- Measures of center

- Measures of variation

- Salient features of the shape of distributions like symmetry and skewness

- Unusual features like gaps, clusters, and outliers

- Patterns of association between pairs of attributes measured by correlation, residuals for linear models, and proportions of entries in two-way tables

Each of these ideas is developed in a primary statistics Unit. But there are also many significant connections in other Units that deal with fractions, decimals, percents, and ratios, and with the algebra of linear functions and equations.

Conclusion

By the completion of all primary and supporting Units for the statistics strand of CMP3, students will have mastered all of the content standards of the CCSSM in statistics and data analysis and will be well prepared for more sophisticated study in high school mathematics. Students will also develop a strong disposition to look for data supporting claims in other disciplines and in public life and students can apply insightful analysis to those data.

Probability

Propositions in the logical form *"If A then B"* are at the heart of mathematics. In algebra, we solve equations to show things like, "If $7x + 5 = 47$, then $x = 6$." In geometry, we prove things like, "If the sides of a triangle are in the ratio 3:4:5, then it is a right triangle." However, in many important quantitative reasoning tasks there is uncertainty in the *If, then* inferences that can be made. For example, outcomes in a game of chance can at best be assigned probabilities of occurrence. Outcomes of medical tests and predicted effects of treatments can be given only with caveats involving probabilities.

The theory of probability has developed to give the best possible mathematical reasoning about questions involving chance and uncertainty. Since outcomes of so many events in science, engineering, and daily life are predictable only by probabilistic claims, the study of probability has become an important strand in school and collegiate mathematics.

The CCSSM content standards for grades 6–8 specify probability goals only in Grade 7. Thus, there is one primary Unit at Grade 7, *What Do You Expect?*, that deals with all of these standards. However, there are significant connections to those topics in many other Units. Because of the heavy emphasis on number and operations before Grade 7, CMP students should be well prepared for the work with fractions, decimals, percents, and ratios that is essential in probability.

What Do You Expect? aims to develop student ability to do the following:

- Identify problem situations involving random variation and correctly interpret probability statements about uncertain outcomes in such cases

- Use experimental and simulation methods to estimate probabilities for activities with uncertain outcomes

- Use theoretical probability reasoning to calculate probabilities of simple and compound events

- Calculate and interpret expected values of simple random variables

These objectives and their connections to other content in the number, geometry, data analysis, and algebra strands are elaborated upon in the following sections.

Randomness

The word *random* is often used to mean "haphazard" and "completely unpredictable." In probability, use of the word *random* to describe outcomes of an activity means that the result of any single trial is unpredictable, but the pattern of outcomes from many repeated trials is fairly predictable. For example, tossing a coin is an activity with random outcomes, because the result of any particular toss cannot be predicted with any confidence. But, in the long run, you will have close to 50% heads and 50% tails. Similarly, the number of boys (or girls) in a three-child family is a random variable. Any specific three-child family might have zero boys, one boy, two boys, or three boys. But the proportion of many such families that have no boys will be close to $\frac{1}{8}$, the proportion that will have 1 boy will be close to $\frac{3}{8}$, and so on.

To draw correct inferences from information about probabilities, one has to appreciate the meaning of probability statements as predictions of the long-term patterns in outcomes from activities that exhibit randomness. Probabilities are numbers from 0 to 1, with a probability of 0 indicating impossible outcomes, a probability of 1 indicating certain outcomes, and probabilities between 0 and 1 indicating varying degrees of outcome likelihood. The probability fractions are statements about the proportion of outcomes from an activity that can be expected to occur in many trials of that activity. For example, the probability of getting 2 heads in 2 tosses of a fair coin is 0.25 because one would expect in many tosses of two coins that about one-quarter of the results would show heads on both.

Randomness also plays a role in *Samples and Populations*. Students realize that if sample outcomes are to be used to predict statistics about an underlying population, then it would be optimal if the sample were unbiased and representative of the population. One way to choose a sample that is free from bias is to use a tool that will select members randomly. Samples chosen this way will vary in their makeup, and each individual sample distribution may or may not resemble the population distribution. However, if many random samples are drawn, the distribution of sample means will cluster closely around the mean of the population. Thus, for any individual random sample of a particular size, we can calculate the probability that predictions about the population will be accurate. This calculation is beyond the scope of the Data strand in CMP but lies at the heart of using samples to make predictions about populations.

What Do You Expect? includes many problems that engage students in developing and interpreting probability statements about activities with random outcomes. The activities include games, hands-on experiments, and thought experiments.

Experimental Probability

Any probability statement is a prediction, in the face of uncertainty, about the likelihood of different outcomes from an activity involving randomness. One natural way to develop probability estimates for specific outcomes of experiments, games, and other activities is to simply perform the activity repeatedly, keep track of the results, and use the fraction $\frac{number\ of\ favorable\ outcomes}{number\ of\ trials}$ as an *experimental probability* estimate. Experimental data gathered over many trials should produce probabilities that are close to the theoretical probabilities. This idea is sometimes called the *Law of Large Numbers*. The Law of Large Numbers does not say that you should expect exactly 50% heads in any given large number of trials. Instead, it says that as the number of trials gets larger, you expect the percent of heads to be around 50%. For 1 million tosses, exactly 50% (500,000) heads is improbable. But for 1 million tosses, it would be extremely unlikely for the percent of heads to be less than 49% or more than 51%.

Coin tossing is one of the most common activities for illustrating an experimental approach to probability. However, most students will have intuitive sense about the outcomes that can be expected from coin tossing. Experimental methods are particularly useful and convincing when the challenge is to estimate probabilities for which there is no natural or intuitive number to guess. For example, if one tosses a common thumbtack on a hard flat surface, it can land in one of two conceivable positions—point down or point up (on its head). But the probability of each outcome is not immediately obvious (in fact, it depends on the size of the tack head and the length of the spike). *What Do You Expect?* includes several such nonintuitive activities to highlight the ideas and virtues of experimental approaches to probability.

A common and productive variation on experimental derivation of probability estimates is through *simulation*. A simulation is an experiment that has the same mathematical structure as an activity or experiment of interest, but is easier to actually perform. For example, if you don't have the patience to actually toss a coin hundreds of times, you could use a calculator random number generator to produce a sequence of single-digit numbers where you count each odd number outcome as a "head" and each even number outcome as a "tail."

Coin tossing itself can be used to simulate other activities that are difficult to repeat many times. Assuming equal probabilities for girl and boy births, you could simulate the births in three-child families by tossing three fair coins and observing the outcomes—tails for boys and heads for girls. You could repeat the coin toss often and record the numbers of boys and girls in each family. Then, you could use the frequencies of each number (0, 1, 2, or 3) divided by the number of families simulated to estimate probabilities of different numbers of boys or girls.

Experimental and simulation methods for estimating probabilities are very powerful tools, especially with access to calculating and computing technology. In addition to learning very useful probability reasoning tools, this experimental side of the subject provides continual reinforcement of the fundamental idea that probabilities are statements about the long-term results of repeated activities in which outcomes of individual trials are very hard to predict.

Theoretical Probability

In quite a few probability situations, there is a natural or logical way to assign probabilities to simple outcomes of activities, but the question of interest asks about probabilities of compound outcomes (often referred to as events). For example, returning to the questions about likelihood of different numbers of boys and girls in three-child families, it is reasonable to assume that the boy and girl births are equally likely. The *sample space* or *outcome set* for the experiment of having a three-child family can be represented by a collection of eight different chains of *B* and *G* symbols like this: {*BBB, BBG, BGB, GBB, GGB, GBG, BGG, GGG*}. Each individual family pattern is as likely as the others, so one can reason that each possibility has probability $\frac{1}{8}$. This result of reasoning alone is called a *theoretical probability*.

Theoretical probabilities, such as the probability of birth order boy-boy-girl, can be used to derive probabilities of further *compound events*, such as the likelihood of having exactly 2 boys in a three-child family ($\frac{3}{8}$) or the likelihood of having at most 1 boy in a three-child family ($\frac{4}{8}$). This kind of reasoning about probabilities by thought experiments illustrates the natural principle that the probability of any event is the sum of the probabilities of its disjoint outcomes. (The sum of the probabilities of BBG, BGB, GBB is $\frac{3}{8}$. The sum of the probabilities of GGG, GGB, GBG, BGG is $\frac{4}{8}$.) This principle and the assignment of probabilities by theoretical reasoning in general are illustrated in many Problems of *What Do You Expect?*

The power of theoretical probability reasoning can often be applied to save the toil of deriving probabilities by experimental or simulation methods. For example, suppose that a game spinner has the sectors shown in the following diagram.

In this case, it makes sense to use areas or central angles of the four sectors to derive theoretical probabilities of the outcomes Red $\left(\frac{1}{2}\right)$, Blue $\left(\frac{1}{4}\right)$, and Yellow $\left(\frac{1}{4}\right)$. Then, further reasoning implies that the P(Red or Blue) = $\left(\frac{3}{4}\right)$, P(not Red) = $\frac{1}{2}$, and so on.

Theoretical probabilities can utilize area models in another very powerful way. Suppose that on average a basketball player makes 60% of her free throws. You can show 60% as shown on the diagram below. If you then want to know the probability of making the first two free throws, you can shade 60% vertically on top of the first diagram to end up with the second diagram. There are four disjoint outcomes of this compound event, represented by four areas. The probabilities of making 0 (16%), 1 (48%), or 2 (36%) free throws are shown on the second diagram. (Of course, if the second part of the event is dependent on the first, and no second free throw is taken if the first is missed, then the probability of making 0 free throws is 40%, the probability of making 1 free throw, the first only, is 24%, and the probability of making 2 free throws is 36%.)

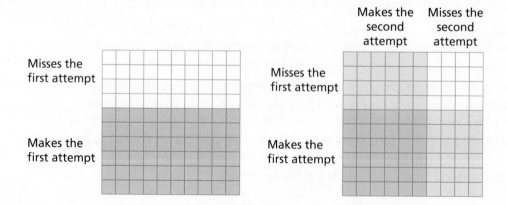

Several problems in *What Do You Expect?* develop student understanding and skill use of this sort of visual and theoretical probability reasoning. Modeling multiplicative situations with areas is used in several strands in CMP, from multiplication of fractions in *Let's Be Rational*, to the Distributive Property in *Prime Time* or *Frogs, Fleas and Painted Cubes*, to computation of probabilities of compound events in *What Do You Expect?*, to illustrating completing the square in *Function Junction*. CMP makes careful, strategic use of models throughout the curriculum.

While theoretical calculation of probabilities is often more efficient than experimental and simulation approaches, it depends on making correct assumptions about the random activity that is being analyzed by thought experiments. Furthermore, reliance on theoretical probability reasoning alone runs the risk of giving students the impression that probabilities are in fact exact predictions of individual trials, not statements about approximate long-term relative frequencies of various possible simple and compound events. Thus, the combination of experimental and theoretical probability problems in this Unit is essential.

Expected Value

In financial investments and games of chance, probability is related to resulting returns. When probabilities of individual outcomes are combined with numerical payoffs for each, the result is the *expected value* of the game or experiment or activity. For example, suppose that data is collected about some students competing in a basketball game that gives each of them throws at three different points on the court. Points are assigned to reflect the difficulty of making the throw. The probabilities have been found by performing an experiment and collecting data.

Throw Distance	Point Payoff	Kyla's Probability of Making the Throw
5	1	0.8
10	3	0.6
20	5	0.2

What score should Kyla expect in each play of the game? The calculation of expected value multiplies each payoff by the probability of that outcome and sums the products. In this case, the expected value is $1(0.8) + 3(0.6) + 5(0.2) = 3.6$.

Conclusion

What Do You Expect? develops all of the probability concepts and procedural skills specified in the content standards of the CCSSM with a consistent focus on meaningful derivations of ideas, techniques, and applications. When students complete the Unit and make the important connections in other content strands, they should be well on their way to developing understanding skills required for reasoning under conditions of uncertainty.

Algebra and Functions Strand

CMP is a problem-centered curriculum in which quantities or variables naturally arise in the context of a problem. In this curriculum, it makes sense to think about how variables are related, how relationships can be represented, and the information we can get from the way they are represented. CMP's approach intertwines the CCSSM algebra and functions strands into one coherent algebra and functions, strand across three years.

The CMP algebra and functions Units challenge students, from the very first Investigation in sixth grade to the very last Investigation in eighth grade, to represent algebraic relationships in words, tables, graphs, and symbols. Writing and reasoning with *symbolic expressions*, an important goal of the CCSSM, is incorporated throughout the program. *Equations* are first understood as symbolic rules that relate independent and dependent variables. One-variable equations are, therefore, specific instances, or snapshots, of function relationships, in which one of the variables is a known quantity. A natural outcome of combining functions and algebra through problem situations is that solving one-variable equations is first done using graphs, tables, or numeric reasoning and then by symbolic methods. Manipulating symbols to write *equivalent expressions*, another important CCSSM goal, reveals new insights into the relationship that represents a problem situation, and opens up other solution strategies.

As students continue to develop their understanding of linear and non linear, they also develop deeper understandings of expressions and equations that are required to represent more complicated situations and vice versa more complicated situations push the understanding of linear relationships. Because of CMP's emphasis on reasoning about and with relationships during grades 6–8, students are well prepared for the Common Core Functions standards.

Expanding Prior Understanding of Variables

Students enter sixth grade with some understanding of operations, such as when to apply them and how they are related, skill in writing number sentences to represent problem situations, and the ability to find an unknown in a number sentence. They have had opportunities to analyze patterns. CMP builds on these early understandings of the meaning of operations and the uses of variables.

From the perspective of developing an algebra and functions strand, variables are not simply letters that stand for unknown quantities, and operations are not simply instructions to compute a numerical result, although these are important parts of the picture. Rather, variables are quantitative attributes of objects, patterns, or situations, which change in response to changes in other quantities; and operations are the building blocks of functional relationships.

There are eight Units in the Algebra and Functions strand, over which these goals are developed as students refine their understanding of algebraic concepts. The first Algebra Unit is *Variables and Patterns*, in the sixth grade. This is not students' first encounter with variables, however. They have seen variable expressions, equations, patterns, and relationships in earlier, non algebra-strand Units. In *Covering and Surrounding*, students develop formulas and procedures, stated in words and symbols, for finding areas of figures. In *Let's Be Rational* and *Decimal Ops*, students write number sentences to solve problems and use fact-family knowledge to rewrite and solve equations.

The overarching goals of the Algebra and Functions strand are:

- Developing understanding of variables and relationships among variables
- Recognizing, interpreting, and representing relationships, including linear, quadratic, exponential, inverse variation, and polynomial functions
- Writing, interpreting, and using equivalent expressions and equations
- Solving equations and inequalities, including systems of equations

Developing Understanding of Variables and Relationships Among Variables

In *Variables and Patterns*, students look for patterns in graphs, tables, and equations representing relationships between variables, for various situations. For example, in Problem 3.2, part of which is shown below, students observe that all the graphs are straight lines, all the equations are in the form $y = mx$, and the point $(1, m)$ is on every graph. They also make the connection that the unit rate is m miles per 1 hour.

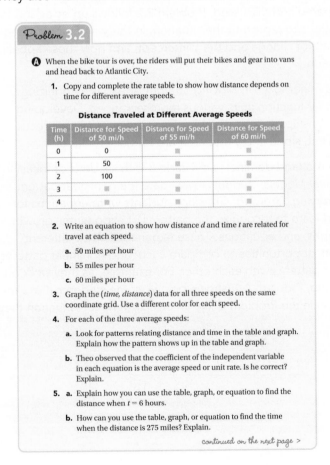

Problem 3.2

A When the bike tour is over, the riders will put their bikes and gear into vans and head back to Atlantic City.

1. Copy and complete the rate table to show how distance depends on time for different average speeds.

Distance Traveled at Different Average Speeds

Time (h)	Distance for Speed of 50 mi/h	Distance for Speed of 55 mi/h	Distance for Speed of 60 mi/h
0	0	▪	▪
1	50	▪	▪
2	100	▪	▪
3	▪	▪	▪
4	▪	▪	▪

2. Write an equation to show how distance d and time t are related for travel at each speed.

   a. 50 miles per hour

   b. 55 miles per hour

   c. 60 miles per hour

3. Graph the (*time, distance*) data for all three speeds on the same coordinate grid. Use a different color for each speed.

4. For each of the three average speeds:

   a. Look for patterns relating distance and time in the table and graph. Explain how the pattern shows up in the table and graph.

   b. Theo observed that the coefficient of the independent variable in each equation is the average speed or unit rate. Is he correct? Explain.

5. a. Explain how you can use the table, graph, or equation to find the distance when $t = 6$ hours.

   b. How can you use the table, graph, or equation to find the time when the distance is 275 miles? Explain.

continued on the next page >

As seen in Problem 3.2, the primary focus of *Variables and Patterns* is relationships among variables. Students are also working with three representations and solving equations. This is the beginning of the development of other goals in the algebra and functions strand: recognizing linear relationships, writing equations, and solving equations. In the seventh-grade Unit *Moving Straight Ahead*, students learn to use properties of equality to solve one-variable linear equations. In *Thinking With Mathematical Models, Growing, Growing, Growing, Frogs, Fleas, and Painted Cubes*, and *Function Junction*, students investigate other, nonlinear, relationships between variables.

Recognizing, Interpreting, and Representing Functional Relationships

In *Moving Straight Ahead*, the Algebra and Functions strand Unit in Grade 7, students identify the characteristics of a linear relationship represented in a table, graph, or equation. The main goal is to have students recognize the constant rate of change in the dependent variable as the independent variable changes by constant increments. Students also learn to solve one-variable linear equations.

In Problem 2.1 of *Moving Straight Ahead*, students decide how long a walking race should be between two brothers who walk at different rates and start at different points, if they want the little brother to win. To be sure that multiple representations for Problem 2.1 are compared and discussed, Problem 2.2 follows up by asking for a table, a graph, and equations to represent the situation. In this way, students begin to understand constant rate of change and the *y*-intercept, and how these appear in a table, graph, and equation.

As seen in Problem 2.2, a major focus in *Moving Straight Ahead* is recognizing the characteristics of a linear function in its various representations. Developing an understanding of relationships among variables also continues to be a focus throughout. Later in the Unit, slope and *y*-intercept are formally defined.

The Algebra and Functions strand dominates in Grade 8 with six Units of focus. In *Thinking With Mathematical Models*, students investigate the nonlinear pattern of inverse variation. In *Growing, Growing, Growing*, students write equations for exponential functions and learn to recognize the patterns of exponential growth or decay from tables, graphs, and equations. These experiences with different relationships give students opportunities to compare linear and nonlinear patterns and to compare nonlinear patterns with each other. For example, as they work on *Growing, Growing, Growing*, Problem 4.1 (shown below), some students make the conjecture that the relation in the Problem is like an inverse variation situation they have seen earlier.

Problem 4.1

A The paper Chen starts with has an area of 64 square inches. Copy and complete the table to show the area of a ballot after each of the first 10 cuts.

Areas of Ballots

Number of Cuts	Area (in.^{2})
0	64
1	32
2	16
3	▓
4	▓
5	▓
6	▓
7	▓
8	▓
9	▓
10	▓

B How does the area of a ballot change with each cut?

C Write an equation for the area *A* of a ballot after any cut *n*.

D Make a graph of the data.

E 1. How is the pattern of change in the area different from the exponential growth patterns you studied? How is it similar?

  2. How is the pattern of change in the area different from linear patterns you studied? How is it similar?

In both *Thinking With Mathematical Models* and *Growing, Growing, Growing*, as seen above, one major goal is to represent, compare, and contrast linear relationships with inverse variation and exponential relationships. In *Frogs, Fleas, and Painted Cubes* and in *Function Junction*, students continue to represent and interpret nonlinear relationships, including quadratic and polynomial relationships. In *Function Junction*, functional notation is formally introduced and used to represent functions symbolically and to study new functions such as piece wise linear, absolute value, and polynomial functions.

Writing, Interpreting, and Using Equivalent Expressions

Students' first experiences with equivalence are with fractions and ratios, in *Comparing Bits and Pieces* (Grade 6). Their first experience with equivalence of symbolic expressions and equations comes in *Variables and Patterns* (Grade 6), as they write an expression for the number of beams needed to make a tower in Problem 4.1 and find many possible expressions, such as

$$B = 4 + 3(n - 1) \text{ and } B = 1 + 3n.$$

To justify the equivalence of these expressions for *B*, students should be able to point out that substituting a value for *n* in either equation gives the same value for *B* and that using the Distributive Property on the first equation transforms it into the second equation.

Students also validate the reasoning behind each expression and come up with these different expressions and explanations:

- $B = 4 + 3(n - 1)$
  The first frame needs 4 beams, but each frame after that needs only 3.

- $B = 1 + 3n$
  You put down 1 beam and then keep adding 3 beams to make every step.

The primary focus in *Variables and Patterns* is on understanding relationships among variables. As students explain their reasoning, they naturally begin to interpret and use equivalent expressions.

In *Frogs, Fleas, and Painted Cubes* (Grade 8), students encounter situations that can be modeled with quadratic functions. They recognize that different, equivalent expressions may give useful information about the related graphs. For example, in Problem 2.3, students write two expressions for the area of the rectangle in red.

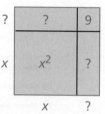

As seen in Problem 2.3, the primary focus *of Frogs, Fleas, and Painted Cubes* is on understanding the pattern of change in quadratic relationships and recognizing this pattern in various representations. Finding specific points on a graph, such as the *x*-intercepts which students do in Problem 2.4, connects this goal to using equivalent expressions and solving equations.

Writing and interpreting equivalent expressions continues to be a major focus in *Say It With Symbols*. For example, in Problem 1.3, students examine the structure of a given expression and write equivalent expressions around the topic of the area of parts of a pool.

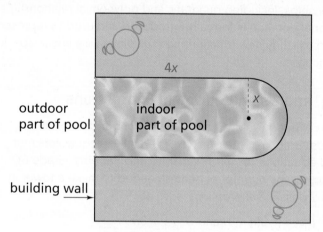

For example, students might write the following equivalent expressions for the area of the outdoor part of the pool.

$$x^2 + \frac{\pi x^2}{8} + \frac{\pi x^2}{8} \qquad \left(\frac{1}{2}x\right)(2x) + \frac{\pi x^2}{4}$$

The symbols are attached to context and thus relay different aspects of information about the situation. Many other equivalent expressions are possible.

Solving Equations and Inequalities, Including Systems of Equations

Students come to middle school with some knowledge about number sentences and finding unknown quantities. They use informal methods, such as fact families, to solve problems in Grade 6, particularly in *Let's Be Rational* and *Decimal Ops*. In *Variables and Patterns*, the first algebra Unit, students continue to use these informal methods, but, since they see two-variable relationships, they can also use graphs and tables to find solutions. In *Moving Straight Ahead* (Grade 7), properties of equality are introduced. From that point on, students are familiar with graphical, tabular, and symbolic ways to solve linear equations.

Moving Straight Ahead introduces symbolic methods of solving equations using coins and pouches. Each pouch holds the same but variable numbers of coins. For example, $3x + 4$ represents three pouches and four coins. In *It's In the System* (Grade 8), students recall that method of representation and use it to represent systems of linear equations.

It's In the System pulls together various methods for solving systems of equations and connects these to students' prior experiences, particularly in *Moving Straight Ahead*. CMP students often attach conceptual ideas to the problem context in which they were first introduced.

Students solve quadratic equations in *Function Junction*. Of course, not every quadratic expression can be factored, so another equivalent form for a quadratic expression is investigated. Students learn how to write the equation of any quadratic function in the equivalent vertex form. Once students have established this strategy, they can use it to solve any quadratic equation, thus completing the story about solving quadratic equations. They can also appreciate the derivation of the quadratic formula and see rich connections between graphical solutions and symbolic solutions.

Lastly, in *Moving Straight Ahead*, Problem 2.3, students are given the equations for two different plans for buying T-shirts: $C_n = 4.5n$ and $C_m = 49 + n$. They use graphs and tables to find when the costs of the two different plans are equal. Later, they use symbolic methods for finding the number of T-shirts for which the two plans are equal. This leads to the question, "For what number(s) of T-shirts is plan C_m less than plan C_n?" That is, when is $C_m < C_n$? Students use their knowledge of when the two plans are equal to answer the questions about inequalities. Solving inequalities continues in *Say It With Symbols* and again in *It's In the System*.

Conclusion

In the first CMP Algebra and Functions Unit, *Variables and Patterns*, students represent relationships with graphs, tables, and equations. They are thus introduced to patterns of change, a major organizing principle for the Algebra and Functions strand. As students work their way through subsequent algebra Units, they see and solve increasingly complex problems. They use multiple representations of and investigate different types of relationships, including linear, inverse, quadratic, exponential, polynomial, piece wise, and absolute-value relationships. As students develop understanding of these relationships and use them to model new situations, they also grow in their sophistication to interpret and write equivalent expressions and equations, and to solve equations and systems of equations.

Equivalence is an important organizing principle of the Algebra and Functions strand. It plays a major role from the first Unit, *Variables and Patterns*, in which students use properties and operations of real numbers to write and interpret equivalent expressions, to the last Unit, *Function Junction*, in which students add, subtract, and multiply polynomials and rewrite the results in equivalent forms. Additionally, in *Function Junction*, students analyze the quadratic formula by comparing it to the steps needed to rewrite the equation of a quadratic function in an equivalent, vertex form.

Developing strategies for solving various types of equations is a major theme of the Algebra and Functions strand. In *Variables and Patterns*, students may solve equations by using a table or graph, or by using fact families. In *Moving Straight Ahead*, they use properties of equality to solve equations. Solving an equation with more than one variable for one of the variables extends this work and is used in *It's In the System* and also in *Function Junction*. The CMP materials encourage students to make connections among symbolic and graphical representations and strategies for solving linear, quadratic, and polynomial equations. Simultaneously, they develop and refine their skills at symbol manipulation.

References

Bay, J. M., Reys, B. J., & Reys, R. E. (1999). The top 10 elements that must be in place to implement standards-based mathematics curricula. *The Phi Delta Kappan, 80*(7), 503–506. doi: 10.2307/20439492

Friel, S. N., & Gann, J. H. (1993). Making change in schools. *The Arithmetic Teacher, 40*(5), 286–289.

Hall, G. E., & Hord, S. M. (1987). *Change in schools: Facilitating the process.* Albany, NY: SUNY Press.

Herbel-Eisenmann, B., Steele, M., & Cirillo, M. (In Press). *Mathematics Discourse in Secondary Classrooms (MDISC): A case-based professional development curriculum.*

Hill, H. C., Ball, D. L., & Schilling, S. G. (2008). Unpacking pedagogical content knowledge: Conceptualizing and measuring teachers' topic-specific knowledge of students. *Journal for Research in Mathematics Education, 39*(4), 372–400.

Hord, S. M., Rutherford, W. L., Huling-Austin, L., & Hall, G. E. (1987). *Taking charge of change.* Alexandria, VA: Association for Supervision and Curriculum Development.

Lappan, G., & Phillips, E. (1998). Teaching and learning in the connected mathematics project. In L. Leutzinger (Ed.), *Mathematics in the middle* (pp. 83–92). Reston, VA: National Council of Teachers of Mathematics.

Loucks-Horsley, S., & Stiegelbauer, S. (1989). Using knowledge of change to guide staff development. In A. Lieberman & L. Miller (Eds.), *Staff development for education in the '90s* (pp. 13–36). New York: Teachers College Press.

National Council of Teachers of Mathematics. (1989). *Curriculum and evaluation standards for school mathematics.* Reston, VA: National Council of Teachers of Mathematics.

National Council of Teachers of Mathematics. (1991). *Professional standards for teaching mathematics.* Reston, VA: National Council of Teachers of Mathematics.

National Council of Teachers of Mathematics. (1995). *Assessment standards for school mathematics.* Reston, VA: National Council of Teachers of Mathematics.

National Council of Teachers of Mathematics. (2000). *Principles and standards for school mathematics.* Weston, VA: National Council of Teachers of Mathematics.

O'Conner, C., Anderson, N. C., & Chapin, S. H. (2003). *Classroom discussions: Using math talk to help students learn, grades 1–6.* Sausalito, CA: Math Solutions Publications.

Preston, R. V., & Garner, A. S. (2003). Representation as a vehicle for solving and communicating. *Mathematics Teaching in the Middle School, 9*(1), 38–43.

Smith, M. S., & Stein, M. K. (2011). *Five practices for orchestrating productive mathematics discussions.* Reston, VA: NCTM.

Stein, M. K., Engle, R. A., Smith, M. S., & Hughes, E. K. (2008). Orchestrating productive mathematical discussions: Five practices for helping teachers move beyond show and tell. *Mathematical Thinking and Learning, 10*(4), 313–340.

Appendix A
Mathematics Content by Unit

The following table lists the important clusters of related concepts, skills, procedures, and ways of thinking of each Unit in CMP3*.

Grade 6

Prime Time: Factors and Multiples Number theory, including factors, multiples, primes, composites, prime factorization; order of operations, distributive property	**Covering and Surrounding: Two-Dimensional Measurement** Area and perimeter relationships, area and perimeter of polygons, surface area and volume of rectangular prisms	**Variables and Patterns: Focus on Algebra** Variables, variable expressions, equations, inequalities; representations of relationships in tables, graphs, equations
Comparing Bits and Pieces: Ratios, Rational Numbers and Equivalence Ratio, unit rate, rate tables, rational numbers, decimals, percents, equivalence, absolute value, number line	**Decimal Ops: Computing With Decimals and Percents** Addition, subtraction, multiplication and division of decimals, estimation; solutions for $a\%$ of $b = c$	**Data About Us: Statistics and Data Analysis** Analysis of data distributions, including shape, measures of center (mean, median, mode) and variability (range, interquartile range, mean absolute deviation)
Let's Be Rational: Understanding Fraction Operations Addition, subtraction, multiplication, division of fractions, fact families		

Grade 7

Shapes and Designs: Two-Dimensional Geometry Polygons, measurement of angles, angle sum of polygons, conditions for unique triangle, parallel lines and transversals	**Comparing and Scaling: Ratios, Rates, Percents, and Proportions** Ratios, unit rate, rate tables, constant of proportionality, solving proportions, inc. markups, discounts, commission, measurement conversion	**Filling and Wrapping: Three-Dimensional Measurement** Area, circumference of circle; volume and surface area of rectangular and polygonal prisms, cylinders; volume of pyramids, cones, spheres; plane sections of prisms, pyramids; effect of scaling on surface area and volume
Accentuate the Negative: Integers and Rational Numbers Addition, subtraction, multiplication and division of rational numbers, absolute value, opposites, order of operations, distributive property	**Moving Straight Ahead: Linear Relationships** Representing linear relationships in graphs, tables, equations; solving linear equations; slope, intercept; writing equation for linear relationship given points	**Samples and Populations: Making Comparisons and Predictions** Sampling plans, effect of sample size, predicting population statistics, simulations, comparing sample statistics to draw inferences about two populations
Stretching and Shrinking: Understanding Similarity Enlarging a figure, effect of scale factors on perimeter and area, coordinate rules, ratios between and within similar figures; using similarity to find measures	**What Do You Expect?: Probability and Expected Value** Probability models, experimental and theoretical probability, analysis of compound events	

Grade 8

Thinking With Mathematical Models: Linear and Inverse Variation Linear models and equations, inverse variation models and equations, variability of numerical and categorical data	**Growing, Growing, Growing: Exponential Functions** Representing exponential growth with tables, graphs, equations; rules for exponents, scientific notation	**Say It With Symbols: Making Sense of Symbols** Equivalent expressions, solving linear and quadratic equations; identify and represent linear, exponential and quadratic functions
Looking for Pythagoras: The Pythagorean Theorem Use and proof of Pythagorean theorem and converse, square roots, cube roots, irrational and real numbers, equation of circle	**Butterflies, Pinwheels, and Wallpaper: Symmetry and Transformations** Symmetry, transformations, congruence, similarity, coordinate proofs	**It's In the System: Systems of Linear Equations and Inequalities** Solving linear systems graphically and algebraically

Algebra 1

Thinking With Mathematical Models: Linear and Inverse Variation Linear models and equations, inverse variation models and equations, variability of numerical and categorical data	**Frogs, Fleas, and Painted Cubes: Quadratic Functions** Representing quadratic functions, factoring quadratic expressions, patterns of change, effect of parameters	**It's In the System: Systems of Linear Equations and Inequalities** Solving linear systems graphically and algebraically, systems of functions and inequalities, solving systems of linear inequalities
Looking for Pythagoras: The Pythagorean Theorem Use and proof of Pythagorean theorem and converse, square roots, cube roots, irrational and real numbers, equation of circle	**Butterflies, Pinwheels, and Wallpaper: Symmetry and Transformations** Symmetry, transformations, congruence, similarity, coordinate proofs	**Function Junction: The Families of Functions** Function notation, inverses, arithmetic/geometric sequences, transformations on functions; completing the square, quadratic formula, polynomial expressions/functions/equations
Growing, Growing, Growing: Exponential Functions Representing exponential growth with tables, graphs, equations; rules for exponents, scientific notation; Exponential Decay; growth/decay factors and rates	**Say It With Symbols: Making Sense of Symbols** Equivalent expressions, solving linear and quadratic equations; identify and represent linear, exponential and quadratic functions.	

*Four additional Units continue to be available from CMP1 and CMP2 to meet specific state or local needs: *Ruins of Montarek*, *Clever Counting*, *Data Around Us*, and *How Likely Is it?*. These are stand-alone Units, which could enrich any grade.

GRADE 6

Prime Time

Factors and Multiples: Understand relationships among factors, multiples, divisors, and products

- Classify numbers as prime, composite, even, odd, or square
- Recognize that factors of a number occur in pairs
- Recognize situations that call for common factors and situations that call for common multiples
- Recognize situations that call for the greatest common factor and situations that call for the least common multiple
- Develop strategies for finding factors and multiples
- Develop strategies for finding the least common multiple and the greatest common factor
- Recognize and use the fact that every whole number can be written in exactly one way as a product of prime numbers
- Use exponential notation to write repeated factors
- Relate the prime factorization of two numbers to the least common multiple and greatest common factor of two numbers
- Solve problems involving factors and multiples

Equivalent Expressions: Understand why two expressions are equivalent

- Relate the area of a rectangle to the Distributive Property
- Recognize that the Distributive Property relates the multiplicative and additive structures of whole numbers
- Use the properties of operations of numbers, including the Distributive Property, and the Order of Operations convention to write equivalent numerical expressions
- Solve problems involving the Order of Operations and Distributive Property

Comparing Bits and Pieces

Fractions as Numbers: Understand fractions and decimals as numbers that can be located on the number line, compared, counted, partitioned, and decomposed

- Expand interpretations of a fraction to include expressing a fraction as a part–whole relationship, as a number, and as an indicated division
- Reason about the roles of the numerator and denominator in each of the interpretations of a fraction
- Use multiple interpretations of proper fractions, improper fractions, and mixed numbers
- Use decimals to represent fractional quantities with attention to place value
- Recognize that fractions are called *rational numbers* and that rational numbers are points on the number line
- Use the number line to reason about rational number relationships
- Use benchmarks to estimate the values of fractions and decimals and to compare and order fractions and decimals
- Recognize that fractions can represent both locations and distances on the number line
- Recognize that a number and its opposite are at equal distances from zero on the number line; the opposite of *a* is –*a* and the opposite of –*a* is *a*
- Recognize that the absolute value of a number is its distance from 0 on the number line and use it to describe real-world quantities
- Introduce percent as a part–whole relationship in which the whole is not necessarily out of 100, but is scaled or partitioned to be "out of 100" or "per 100"
- Apply a variety of partitioning strategies to solve problems

Ratios as Comparisons: Understand ratios as comparisons of two numbers

- Use ratios and associated rates to compare quantities
- Distinguish between a difference, which is an additive comparison, and a ratio, which is a multiplicative comparison
- Distinguish between fractions as numbers and ratios as comparisons

- Apply a variety of scaling strategies to solve problems involving ratios and unit rates
- Recognize that a unit rate is a ratio in which one of the quantities being compared has a value of 1; use rate language in the context of a ratio relationship
- Scale percents to predict new outcomes

Equivalence: Understand equivalence of fractions and ratios, and use equivalence to solve problems

- Recognize that equivalent fractions represent the same amount, distance, or location; develop strategies for finding and using equivalent fractions
- Recognize that comparing situations with different-sized wholes is difficult without some common basis of comparison
- Use partitioning and scaling strategies to generate equivalent fractions and ratios and to solve problems
- Develop meaningful strategies for representing fraction amounts greater than 1 or less than −1 as both mixed numbers and improper fractions
- Recognize that equivalent ratios represent the same relationship between two quantities; develop strategies for finding and using equivalent ratios
- Build and use rate tables of equivalent ratios to solve problems

Let's Be Rational

Numeric Estimation: Understand that estimation is a tool used in a variety of situations including checking answers and making decisions, and develop strategies for estimating results of arithmetic operations

- Use benchmarks and other strategies to estimate results of operations with fractions
- Use estimates to check the reasonableness of exact computations
- Give various reasons to estimate and identify when a situation calls for an overestimate or an underestimate
- Use estimates and exact solutions to make decisions

Fraction Operations: Revisit and continue to develop meanings for the four arithmetic operations and skill at using algorithms for each

- Determine when addition, subtraction, multiplication, or division is the appropriate operation to solve a problem
- Develop ways to model sums, differences, products, and quotients with areas, fraction strips, and number lines
- Use knowledge of fractions and equivalence of fractions to develop algorithms for adding, subtracting, multiplying, and dividing fractions
- Write fact families with fractions to show the inverse relationship between addition and subtraction, and between multiplication and division
- Compare and contrast dividing a whole number by a fraction to dividing a fraction by a whole number
- Recognize that when you multiply or divide a fraction, your answer might be less than or more than the numbers you started with
- Solve real-world problems using arithmetic operations on fractions

Variables and Equations: Use variables to represent unknown values and equations to represent relationships

- Represent unknown real-world and abstract values with variables
- Write equations (or number sentences) to represent relationships among real-world and abstract values
- Use fact families to solve for unknown values

Covering and Surrounding

Area and Perimeter: Understand that perimeter is a measure of linear units needed to surround a two-dimensional shape and that area is a measure of square units needed to cover a two-dimensional shape

- Deepen the understanding of area and perimeter of rectangular and nonrectangular shapes
- Relate area to covering a figure
- Relate perimeter to surrounding a figure
- Analyze what it means to measure area and perimeter
- Develop and use formulas for calculating area and perimeter

GRADE 6 *continued*

- Develop techniques for estimating the area and perimeter of an irregular figure
- Explore relationships between perimeter and area, including that one can vary considerably while the other stays fixed
- Visually represent relationships between perimeter and area on a graph
- Solve problems involving area and perimeter of rectangles

Area and Perimeter of Parallelograms and Triangles: Understand that the linear measurements of the base, height, and slanted height of parallelograms and triangles are essential to finding the area and perimeter of these shapes

- Analyze how the area of a triangle and the area of a parallelogram are related to each other and to the area of a rectangle
- Recognize that a triangle can be thought of as half of a rectangle whose sides are equal to the base and height of the triangle
- Recognize that a parallelogram can be decomposed into two triangles. Thus the area of a parallelogram is twice the area of a triangle with the same base and height as the parallelogram
- Know that the choice of base of a triangle (or parallelogram) is arbitrary but that the choice of the base determines the height
- Recognize that there are many triangles (or parallelograms) that can be drawn with the same base and height
- Develop formulas and strategies, stated in words or symbols, for finding the area and perimeter of triangles and parallelograms
- Find the side lengths and area of polygons on a coordinate grid
- Solve problems involving area and perimeter of parallelograms and triangles
- Solve problems involving area and perimeter of polygons by composing into rectangles or decomposing into triangles

Surface Area of Prisms and Pyramids and Volume of Rectangular Prisms: Understand that the surface area of a three-dimensional shape is the sum of the areas of each two-dimensional surface of the shape and that the volume of a rectangular prism is a measure in cubic units of the capacity of the prism

- Extend the understanding of the volume of rectangular prisms
- Relate volume to filling a three-dimensional figure
- Extend understanding of the strategies for finding the volume of rectangular prisms to accommodate fractional side lengths
- Relate finding area of two-dimensional shapes to finding the surface area of three-dimensional objects
- Develop strategies for finding the surface area of three-dimensional objects made from rectangles and triangles
- Solve problems involving surface area of prisms and pyramids and volume of rectangular prisms

Decimal Ops

Numeric Estimation: Understand that estimation can be used as a tool in a variety of situations, including as a way to check answers and make decisions

- Use estimates to solve problems and check answers

Decimal Operations: Revisit and continue to develop meanings for the four arithmetic operations on rational numbers, and practice using algorithms to operate on decimals

- Recognize when addition, subtraction, multiplication, or division is the appropriate operation to solve a problem
- Use place value to develop understanding of algorithms and to relate operations with decimals to the same operations with fractions
- Extend understanding of multiplication and division of multidigit whole numbers
- Develop standard algorithms for multiplying and dividing decimals with the aid of, at most, paper and pencil
- Find a repeating or terminating decimal equivalent to a given fraction
- Solve problems using arithmetic operations on decimals, including finding unit rates

Variables and Number Sentences: Use variables to represent unknown values and number sentences to represent relationships between values
- Write number sentences to represent relationships between both real-world and abstract values
- Use fact families to write and solve equivalent number sentences
- Use multiplication sentences to check division sentences

Percents: Develop understanding of percents through various contexts, such as sales tax, tips, discounts, and percent increases
- Develop models for percent problems
- Write and solve number sentences involving percents

Variables and Patterns

Variables and Patterns (Relationships): Develop understanding of variables and how they are related
- Explore problem situations that involve variables and relationships
- Identify the dependent and independent variables and describe how they are related in a situation
- Interpret the "stories" told by patterns in tables and coordinate graphs of numeric (x, y) data
- Represent the pattern of change that relates two variables in words, data tables, graphs, and equations
- Investigate situations that change over time
- Examine increasing and decreasing patterns of change
- Compare linear and nonlinear patterns of change by using tables or graphs
- Use tables, graphs, and equations to find the value of a variable given the value of the associated variable
- Explore relationships that require graphing in all in four quadrants
- Describe advantages and disadvantages of using words, tables, graphs, and equations to represent patterns of change relating two variables and make connections across those representations
- Write an equation to express the relationship between two variables in one and two operations: $y = mx$, $y = b + x$, and $y = b + mx$
- Calculate average speed and show how it is reflected in a table or graph and vice versa
- Recognize and express direct proportionality relationships with a unit rate $(y = mx)$ and represent these relationships in rate tables and graphs
- Solve problems that involve variables

Expressions and Equations: Develop understanding of expressions and equations
- Use properties of operations, including the Distributive Property and the Order of Operations, to write equivalent expressions for the dependent variable in terms of the independent variable
- Use tables, graphs, or properties of numbers such as the Distributive Property to show that two expressions are equivalent
- Identify parts of an expression using mathematical terms (sum, term, product, factor, quotient, coefficient); view one or more parts of an expression as a single entity
- Interpret and evaluate expressions in which letters stand for numbers and apply the Order of Operations as needed
- Recognize that equations are statements of equivalence between two expressions
- Solve linear equations of the forms $y = ax$, $y = b + x$, and $y = b + ax$ using numeric guess and check, tables of (x, y) values, and graphs or fact families
- Write an inequality and associate it with an equation to find solutions and graph the solutions on a number line

Data About Us

Statistical Process: Understand and use the process of statistical investigation
- Ask questions, collect and analyze data, and interpret data to answer questions
- Describe data with respect to its shape, center, and variability or spread
- Construct and use simple surveys as a method of collecting data

GRADE 6 *continued*

Attributes of Data: Distinguish data and data types
- Recognize that data consist of counts or measurements of a variable, or an attribute; these observations comprise a distribution of data values
- Distinguish between categorical data and numerical data, and identify which graphs and statistics can be used to represent each kind of data

Multiple Representations for Displaying Data: Display data with multiple representations
- Organize and represent data using tables, dot plots, line plots, ordered-value bar graphs, frequency bar graphs, histograms, and box-and-whisker plots
- Make informed decisions about which graphs or tables can be used to display a particular set of data
- Recognize that a graph shows the overall shape of a distribution, whether the data values are symmetrical around a central value, and whether the graph contains any unusual characteristics such as gaps, clusters, or outliers

Measures of Central Tendency and Variability: Recognize that a single number may be used to characterize the center of a distribution of data and the degree of variability (or spread)
- Distinguish between and compute measures of central tendency (mean, median, and mode) and measures of spread (range, interquartile range (IQR), and mean absolute deviation (MAD))
- Identify how the median and mean respond to changes in the data values of a distribution
- Relate the choice of measures of central tendency and variability to the shape of the distribution and the context
- Describe the amount of variability in a distribution by noting whether the data values cluster in one or more areas or are fairly spread out
- Use measures of center and spread to compare data distributions

GRADE 7

Shapes and Designs

Properties of Polygons: Understand the properties of polygons that affect their shape
- Explore the ways that polygons are sorted into families according to the number and length of their sides and the size of their angles
- Explore the patterns among interior and exterior angles of a polygon
- Explore the patterns among side lengths in a polygon
- Investigate the symmetries of a shape–rotation or reflection
- Determine which polygons fit together to cover a flat surface and why
- Reason about and solve problems involving various polygons

Relationships Among Angles: Understand special relationships among angles
- Investigate techniques for estimating and measuring angles
- Use tools to sketch angles
- Reason about the properties of angles formed by parallel lines and transversals
- Use information about supplementary, complementary, vertical, and adjacent angles in a shape to solve for an unknown angle in a multi-step problem

Constructing Polygons: Understand the properties needed to construct polygons
- Draw or sketch polygons with given conditions by using various tools and techniques such as freehand, use of a ruler and protractor, and use of technology
- Determine what conditions will produce a unique polygon, more than one polygon, or no polygon, particularly triangles and quadrilaterals
- Recognize the special properties of polygons, such as angle sum, side-length relationships, and symmetry, that make them useful in building, design, and nature
- Solve problems that involve properties of shapes

Accentuate the Negative

Rational Numbers: Develop an understanding that rational numbers consist of positive numbers, negative numbers, and zero
- Explore relationships between positive and negative numbers by modeling them on a number line
- Use appropriate notation to indicate positive and negative numbers
- Compare and order positive and negative rational numbers (integers, fractions, decimals, and zero) and locate them on a number line
- Recognize and use the relationship between a number and its opposite (additive inverse) to solve problems
- Relate direction and distance to the number line
- Use models and rational numbers to represent and solve problems

Operations With Rational Numbers: Develop understanding of operations with rational numbers and their properties
- Develop and use different models (number line, chip model) for representing addition, subtraction, multiplication, and division
- Develop algorithms for adding, subtracting, multiplying, and dividing integers
- Recognize situations in which one or more operations of rational numbers are needed
- Interpret and write mathematical sentences to show relationships and solve problems
- Write and use related fact families for addition/subtraction and multiplication/division to solve simple equations
- Use parentheses and the Order of Operations in computations
- Understand and use the Commutative Property for addition and multiplication
- Apply the Distributive Property to simplify expressions and solve problems

Stretching and Shrinking

Similar Figures: Understand what it means for figures to be similar
- Identify similar figures by comparing corresponding sides and angles
- Use scale factors and ratios to describe relationships among the side lengths, perimeters, and areas of similar figures
- Generalize properties of similar figures
- Recognize the role multiplication plays in similarity relationships
- Recognize the relationship between scale factor and ratio in similar figures
- Use informal methods, scale factors, and geometric tools to construct similar figures (scale drawings)
- Compare similar figures with nonsimilar figures
- Distinguish algebraic rules that produce similar figures from those that produce nonsimilar figures
- Use algebraic rules to produce similar figures
- Recognize when a rule shrinks or enlarges a figure
- Explore the effect on the image of a figure if a number is added to the *x*- or *y*-coordinates of the figure's vertices

Reasoning With Similar Figures: Develop strategies for using similar figures to solve problems
- Use the properties of similarity to find distances and heights that cannot be measured directly
- Predict the ways that stretching or shrinking a figure will affect side lengths, angle measures, perimeters, and areas
- Use scale factors or ratios to find missing side lengths in a pair of similar figures
- Use similarity to solve real-world problems

Comparing and Scaling

Ratios, Rates, and Percents: Understand ratios, rates, and percents
- Use ratios, rates, fractions, differences, and percents to write statements comparing two quantities in a given situation
- Distinguish between and use both part-to-part and part-to-whole ratios in comparisons
- Use percents to express ratios and proportions
- Recognize that a rate is a special ratio that compares two measurements with different units
- Analyze comparison statements made about quantitative data for correctness and quality
- Make judgments about which kind of comparison statements are most informative or best reflect a particular point of view in a specific situation

Proportionality: Understand proportionality in tables, graphs, and equations
- Recognize that constant growth in a table, graph, or equation is related to proportional situations
- Write an equation to represent the pattern in a table or graph of proportionally related variables
- Relate the unit rate and constant of proportionality to an equation, graph, or table describing a proportional situation

Reasoning Proportionally: Develop and use strategies for solving problems that require proportional reasoning
- Recognize situations in which proportional reasoning is appropriate to solve the problem
- Scale a ratio, rate, percent, or fraction to make a comparison or find an equivalent representation
- Use various strategies to solve for an unknown in a proportion, including scaling, rate tables, percent bars, unit rates, and equivalent ratios
- Set up and solve proportions that arise from real-world applications, such as finding discounts and markups and converting measurement units

Moving Straight Ahead

Linear Relationships: Recognize problem situations in which two variables have a linear relationship

- Identify and describe the patterns of change between the independent and dependent variables for linear relationships represented by tables, graphs, equations, or contextual settings
- Construct tables, graphs, and symbolic equations that represent linear relationships
- Identify the rate of change between two variables and the x- and y-intercepts from graphs, tables, and equations that represent linear relationships
- Translate information about linear relationships given in a contextual setting, a table, a graph, or an equation to one of the other forms
- Write equations that represent linear relationships given specific pieces of information, and describe what information the variables and numbers represent
- Make a connection between slope as a ratio of vertical distance to horizontal distance between two points on a line and the rate of change between two variables that have a linear relationship
- Recognize that $y = mx$ represents a proportional relationship
- Solve problems and make decisions about linear relationships using information given in tables, graphs, and equations

Equivalence: Understand that the equality sign indicates that two expressions are equivalent

- Recognize that the equation $y = mx + b$ represents a linear relationship and means that $mx + b$ is an expression equivalent to y
- Recognize that linear equations in one unknown, $k = mx + b$ or $y = m(t) + b$, where k, t, m, and b are constant numbers, are special cases of the equation $y = mx + b$
- Recognize that finding the missing value of one of the variables in a linear relationship, $y = mx + b$, is the same as finding a missing coordinate of a point (x, y) that lies on the graph of the relationship
- Solve linear equations in one variable using symbolic methods, tables, and graphs
- Recognize that a linear inequality in one unknown is associated with a linear equation
- Solve linear inequalities using graphs or symbolic reasoning
- Show that two expressions are equivalent
- Write and interpret equivalent expressions

What Do You Expect?

Experimental and Theoretical Probabilities: Understand experimental and theoretical probabilities

- Recognize that probabilities are useful for predicting what will happen over the long run
- For an event described in everyday language, identify the outcomes in a sample space that compose the event
- Interpret experimental and theoretical probabilities and the relationship between them and recognize that experimental probabilities are better estimates of theoretical probabilities when they are based on larger numbers
- Distinguish between outcomes that are equally likely or not equally likely by collecting data and analyzing experimental probabilities
- Realize that the probability of simple events is a ratio of favorable outcomes to all outcomes in the sample space
- Recognize that the probability of a chance event is a number between 0 and 1 that expresses the likelihood of the event occurring
- Approximate the probability of a chance event by collecting data on the chance process that produces it and observing its long-run relative frequency, and predict the approximate relative frequency given the probability
- Determine the fairness of a game

GRADE 7 *continued*

Reasoning With Probability: Explore and develop probability models by identifying possible outcomes and analyze probabilities to solve problems
- Develop a uniform probability model by assigning equal probability to all outcomes, and use the model to determine probabilities of events
- Develop a probability model (which may not be uniform) by observing frequencies in data generated from a chance process
- Represent sample spaces for simple and compound events and find probabilities using organized lists, tables, tree diagrams, area models, and simulation
- Realize that, just as with simple events, the probability of a compound event is a ratio of favorable outcomes to all outcomes in the sample space
- Design and use a simulation to generate frequencies for simple and compound events
- Analyze situations that involve two or more stages (or actions) called *compound events*
- Use area models to analyze the theoretical probabilities for two-stage outcomes
- Analyze situations that involve binomial outcomes
- Use probability to calculate the long-term average of a game of chance
- Determine the expected value of a probability situation
- Use probability and expected value to make a decision

Filling and Wrapping

Surface Areas and Volumes of Polygonal Prisms and Cylinders: Understand surface areas and volumes of prisms and cylinders and how they are related
- Describe prisms by using their vertices, faces, and edges
- Visualize three-dimensional shapes and the effects of slicing those shapes by planes
- Deepen understanding of volumes and surface areas of rectangular prisms
- Estimate and calculate surface areas and volumes of polygonal prisms by relating them to rectangular prisms
- Explore the relationships between the surface areas and volumes of prisms
- Relate surface areas and volumes for common figures, especially optimization of surface area for fixed volume
- Predict the effects of scaling dimensions on linear, surface area, and volume measures of prisms, cylinders, and other figures
- Investigate the relationship between volumes of prisms and volumes of cylinders as well as the relationship between surface areas of prisms and surface areas of cylinders
- Use volumes and surface areas of prisms to develop formulas for volumes and surface areas of cylinders
- Discover that volumes of prisms and cylinders can be calculated as the product of the area of the base and the height
- Solve problems involving surface areas and volumes of solid figures

Areas and Circumferences of Circles: Understand the areas and circumferences of circles and how they are related
- Relate area of a circle to covering a figure and circumference to surrounding a figure
- Estimate and calculate areas and circumferences of circles
- Explore the relationship between circle radius (or diameter) and area
- Investigate the connection of π to area calculation by estimating the number of radius squares needed to cover a circle
- Investigate the relationship between area and circumference of a circle
- Solve problems involving areas and circumferences of circles

Volumes of Spheres and Cones: Understand the relationships between the volumes of cylinders and the volumes of cones and spheres
- Relate volumes of cylinders to volumes of cones and spheres
- Estimate and calculate volumes of spheres and cones
- Solve problems involving surface areas and volumes of spheres and cones

Samples and Populations

The Process of Statistical Investigation: Deepen the understanding of the process of statistical investigation and apply this understanding to samples
- Pose questions, collect data, analyze data, and interpret data to answer questions

Analysis of Samples: Understand that data values in a sample vary and that summary statistics of samples, even same-sized samples, taken from the same population also vary
- Choose appropriate measures of center (mean, median, or mode) and spread (range, IQR, or MAD) to summarize a sample
- Choose appropriate representations to display distributions of samples
- Compare summary statistics of multiple samples drawn from either the same population or from two different populations and explain how the samples vary

Design and Use of Simulations: Understand that simulations can model real-world situations
- Design a model that relies on probability concepts to obtain a desired result
- Use the randomly generated frequencies for events to draw conclusions

Predictions and Conclusions About Populations: Understand that summary statistics of a representative sample can be used to gain information about a population
- Describe the benefits and drawbacks to various sampling plans
- Use random-sampling techniques to select representative samples
- Apply concepts from probability to select random samples from populations
- Explain how sample size influences the reliability of sample statistics and resulting conclusions and predictions
- Explain how different sampling plans influence the reliability of sample statistics and resulting conclusions and predictions
- Use statistics from representative samples to draw conclusions about populations
- Use measures of center, measures of spread, and data displays from more than one random sample to compare and draw conclusions about more than one population
- Use mean and MAD, or median and IQR, from random samples to assess whether the differences in the samples are due to natural variability or due to meaningful differences in the underlying populations

GRADE 8

Thinking With Mathematical Models

Linear and Nonlinear Relationships: Recognize and model patterns in bivariate data
- Represent data patterns using graphs, tables, word descriptions, and algebraic expressions
- Investigate the nature of linear functions in contexts
- Use mathematical models to answer questions about linear relationships
- Write linear functions from verbal, numerical, or graphical information
- Analyze and solve linear equations
- Model situations with inequalities expressed as "at most" and "at least" situations
- Investigate the nature of inverse variation in contexts
- Use mathematical models to answer questions about inverse variation relationships
- Compare inverse variation relationships with linear relationships

Data Analysis: Measure variation in data and strength of association in bivariate data
- Use data to make predictions
- Fit a line to data that show a linear trend and measure closeness of fit
- Analyze scatter plots of bivariate data to determine the strength of the linear association between the two variables
- Use correlation coefficients informally to describe the strength of the linear association illustrated by scatter plots
- Use standard deviation to measure variability in univariate distributions
- Distinguish between categorical and numerical variables
- Use two-way tables and analysis of cell frequencies and relative frequencies to decide whether two variables are related

Looking for Pythagoras

Pythagorean Theorem: Understand and apply the Pythagorean Theorem
- Develop strategies for finding the distance between two points on a coordinate grid
- Explain a proof of the Pythagorean Theorem
- Use the Pythagorean Theorem and its converse to solve a variety of problems
- Use the Pythagorean Theorem to find the equation of a circle with its center located at the origin

Real Numbers: Understand that the set of real numbers consists of rational and irrational numbers
- Interpret square roots and cube roots of numbers by making use of their related geometric representations
- Relate the area of a square to the side length of the square
- Estimate the values of square roots
- Estimate the values of cube roots
- Relate the volume of a cube to the edge length of the cube
- Compare numbers that can be represented as fractions (rational numbers) to numbers that cannot be represented as fractions (irrational numbers) and recognize that the set of real numbers consists of rational and irrational numbers
- Represent rational numbers as fractions and as terminating decimals or repeating decimals
- Recognize that irrational numbers cannot be represented as fractions and are nonterminating, nonrepeating decimals
- Recognize that the square root of a whole number that is not a square is irrational
- Locate irrational numbers on a number line
- Use and understand properties of rational and irrational numbers

Growing, Growing, Growing

Exponential Functions: Explore problem situations in which two or more variables have an exponential relationship to each other
- Identify situations that can be modeled with an exponential function
- Identify the pattern of change (growth/decay factor) between two variables that represent an exponential function in a situation, table, graph, or equation
- Represent an exponential function with a table, graph, or equation

- Make connections among the patterns of change in a table, graph, and equation of an exponential function
- Compare the growth/decay rate and growth/decay factor for an exponential function and recognize the role each plays in an exponential situation
- Identify the growth/decay factor and initial value in problem situations, tables, graphs, and equations that represent exponential functions
- Determine whether an exponential function represents a growth (increasing) or decay (decreasing) pattern, from an equation, table, or graph that represents an exponential function
- Determine the values of the independent and dependent variables from a table, graph, or equation of an exponential function
- Use an exponential equation to describe the graph and table of an exponential function
- Predict the y-intercept from an equation, graph, or table that represents an exponential function
- Interpret the information that the y-intercept of an exponential function represents
- Determine the effects of the growth (decay) factor and initial value for an exponential function on a graph of the function
- Solve problems about exponential growth and decay from a variety of different subject areas, including science and business, using an equation, table, or graph
- Observe that one exponential equation can model different contexts
- Compare exponential and linear functions

Equivalence: Develop understanding of equivalent exponential expressions
- Write and interpret exponential expressions that represent the dependent variable in an exponential function
- Develop the rules for operating with rational exponents and explain why they work
- Write, interpret, and operate with numerical expressions in scientific notation
- Write and interpret equivalent expressions using the rules for exponents and operations
- Solve problems that involve exponents, including scientific notation

Frogs, Fleas, and Painted Cubes

Quadratic Functions: Explore problem situations in which two variables are in a quadratic relationship
- Identify situations that can be modeled by quadratic functions
- Identify the pattern of change between two variables that represent a quadratic function in a situation, table, graph, or equation
- Determine values of the independent and dependent variables in a quadratic function from a table, graph, or equation
- Represent a quadratic function with a table, graph, and equation
- Make connections among the equation of a quadratic function, its graph, and the patterns of change in its table
- Use a quadratic equation to describe the characteristics of its graph and table
- Determine whether a quadratic function will have a maximum or a minimum point and predict the maximum or minimum point from its equation, graph, or table
- Predict the x- and y-intercepts from the equation, graph, or table of a quadratic function
- Predict the line of symmetry from an equation, graph, or table of a quadratic function
- Interpret the information that the x- and y-intercepts and maximum or minimum point represent
- Use an equation, graph, and table to solve problems involving quadratic relationships
- Observe that one quadratic equation can model different contexts
- Compare linear, quadratic, and exponential functions

Equivalence: Develop an understanding of equivalent quadratic expressions
- Write and interpret a quadratic expression to represent the dependent variable in a quadratic function
- Use an area model to develop an understanding of the Distributive Property
- Use the Distributive Property to write equivalent quadratic expressions in expanded or factored form
- Select and interpret the appropriate equivalent quadratic expression (in factored or expanded form) for predicting the x- and y-intercepts, maximum or minimum point, and the line of symmetry for a graph of a quadratic function

Butterflies, Pinwheels, and Wallpaper

Transformations: Describe types of transformations that relate points by the motions of reflections, rotations, and translations, and describe methods for identifying and creating symmetric plane figures
- Recognize properties of reflection, rotation, and translation transformations
- Explore techniques for using rigid motion transformations to create symmetric designs
- Use coordinate rules for basic rigid motion transformations

Congruence and Similarity: Understand congruence and similarity and explore necessary and sufficient conditions for establishing congruent and similar shapes
- Recognize that two figures are congruent if one is derived from the other by a sequence of reflection, rotation, and/or translation transformations
- Recognize that two figures are similar if one can be obtained from the other by a sequence of reflections, rotations, translations, and/or dilations
- Use transformations to describe a sequence that exhibits the congruence between figures
- Use transformations to explore minimum measurement conditions for establishing congruence of triangles
- Use transformations to explore minimum measurement conditions for establishing similarity of triangles
- Relate properties of angles formed by parallel lines and transversals, and the angle sum in any triangle, to properties of transformations
- Use properties of congruent and similar triangles to solve problems about shapes and measurements

Say It With Symbols

Equivalence: Develop understanding of equivalent expressions and equations
- Model situations with symbolic statements
- Recognize when two or more symbolic statements represent the same context
- Use the properties of real numbers, such as the Distributive Property, to write equivalent expressions
- Determine if different symbolic expressions are mathematically equivalent
- Interpret the information that equivalent expressions represent in a given context
- Determine the equivalent expression or equation that is most helpful in answering a particular question about a relationship
- Use algebraic equations to describe the relationship among the volumes of cylinders, cones and spheres that have the same height and radius
- Solve linear equations involving parentheses
- Determine if a linear equation has a finite number of solutions, an infinite number of solutions, or no solution
- Develop understanding and some fluency with factoring quadratic expressions
- Solve quadratic equations by factoring
- Recognize how and when to use symbols, rather than tables or graphs, to display relationships, generalizations, and proofs

Functions: Develop an understanding of specific functions such as linear, exponential and quadratic functions
- Develop proficiency in identifying and representing relationships expressed in problem contexts with appropriate functions and use these relationships to solve the problem
- Analyze equations to determine the patterns of change in the tables and graphs that the equations represent
- Relate parts of a symbolic statement or expression to the underlying properties of the relationship they represent and to the context of the problem
- Determine characteristics of a graph (intercepts, maxima and minima, shape, etc.) of an equation by looking at its symbolic representation

It's In the System

Linear Equations: Develop understanding of linear equations and systems of linear equations
- Recognize linear equations in two variables in standard form $Ax + By = C$
- Recognize that a linear equation in the form $Ax + By = C$ has infinitely many solutions (x, y) and the graph of those solutions is always a straight line
- Recognize that the form $Ax + By = C$ of linear equations is equivalent to the form $y = mx + b$ for linear equations
- Continue to develop skills in solving a linear equation in two variables by graphing and with algebraic methods
- Recognize that solving a system of linear equations is equivalent to finding values of the variables that will simultaneously satisfy all equations in the system
- Develop skills in solving systems of linear equations by graphing solutions of separate equations; writing the system of equations in equivalent $y = mx + b$ form; or using combinations of the system to eliminate one variable
- Recognize that systems of linear equations in the form $\begin{cases} Ax + By = C \\ Dx + Ey = F \end{cases}$ may have exactly one solution, which is the intersection point of the lines represented by the equations; infinitely many solutions, which is represented by a single line for both equations; or no solution, which is represented by two parallel lines
- Choose between graphing and symbolic methods to efficiently find the solution to a particular system of linear equations
- Gain fluency with symbol manipulation in solving systems of linear equations
- Solve problems that involve systems of linear equations

Linear Inequalities: Develop understanding of graphing and symbolic methods for solving linear inequalities with one and two variables
- Recognize differences between strict and inclusive inequalities
- Continue to develop skill in solving a linear inequality in two variables by graphing and symbolic methods.
- Develop skill in solving systems of linear inequalities by graphing solutions of each inequality and finding the region of feasible points that satisfy both inequalities; and solving inequalities to find pairs of numbers that satisfy both inequalities
- Choose between graphing and symbolic methods to efficiently find the region of feasible points to a particular system of linear inequalities
- Solve a simple system consisting of a linear equation and a quadratic equation in two variables symbolically and graphically
- Solve problems that involve linear inequalities or systems of linear inequalities

Function Junction

Functions: Understand functions
- Describe *domain* and *range* of functions
- Use $f(x)$ notation to describe and operate with functions
- Construct and interpret inverses of functions
- Analyze function rates of change using graphs
- Identify contexts and graphs of step and piecewise defined functions
- Analyze polynomial functions and their graphs
- Identify, analyze, and solve problems related to arithmetic and geometric sequences
- Compare arithmetic and geometric sequences to linear and exponential functions
- Recognize and solve problems using special kinds of functions

Equivalence: Understand equivalence of algebraic expressions and functions
- Connect expressions for functions whose graphs are related by translation and/or stretching
- Develop and use vertex form to graph quadratic functions and solve quadratic equations
- Connect polynomial expressions and graphs of the polynomial functions they define, in order to identify max/min points, intercepts, and solutions of equations
- Use completing the square to write quadratics in equivalent vertex form
- Develop the quadratic formula for solving equations
- Develop complex numbers and operations
- Develop algorithms for adding, subtracting, and multiplying polynomials

Correlation of CMP3 Content to Common Core Content Standards

GRADE 6

CMP3 Content	Standards for Mathematical Content
Prime Time: Factors and Multiples	
Building on Factors and Multiples	6.NS.B.4
Common Multiples and Common Factors	6.NS.B.4
Factorizations: Searching for Factor Strings	6.EE.A.1, 6.EE.A.2b, 6.NS.B.4
Linking Multiplication and Addition: The Distributive Property	6.EE.A.1, 6.EE.A.2b, 6.EE.A.2c, 6.NS.B.4
Comparing Bits and Pieces: Ratios, Rational Numbers, and Equivalence	
Making Comparisons	6.RP.A.1, 6.RP.A.3, 6.RP.A.2, 6.NS.C.6, 6.NS.B.4
Connecting Ratios and Rates	6.RP.A.1, 6.RP.A.2, 6.RP.A.3, 6.RP.A.3b, 6.RP.A.3a, 6.NS.B.4
Extending the Number Line	6.NS.C.5, 6.NS.C.6, 6.NS.C.6a, 6.NS.C.6c, 6.NS.C.7, 6.NS.C.7a, 6.NS.C.7b, 6.NS.C.7c, 6.NS.C.7d, 6.RP.A.1, 6.RP.A.3, 6.RP.A.2, 6.NS.B.4
Working With Percents	6.RP.A.1, 6.RP.A.2, 6.RP.A.3, 6.RP.A.3b, 6.RP.A.3c
Let's Be Rational: Understanding Fraction Operations	
Extending Addition and Subtraction of Fractions	6.NS.B.3, 6.NS.B.4
Building on Multiplication With Fractions	6.EE.A.3
Dividing With Fractions	6.EE.A.2b, 6.NS.A.1
Wrapping Up the Operations	6.EE.A.2c, 6.EE.B.6, 6.EE.B.7, 6.EE.A.2, 6.EE.A.2a, 6.EE.A.2b
Covering and Surrounding: Two-Dimensional Measurement	
Designing Bumper Cars: Extending and Building on Area and Perimeter	6.NS.C.8, 6.EE.A.2, 6.EE.A.2a, 6.EE.A.2c, 6.EE.A.3, 6.EE.B.6, 6.EE.C.9
Measuring Triangles	6.EE.A.2, 6.EE.A.2a, 6.EE.A.2c, 6.EE.B.6, 6.EE.A.3, 6.EE.A.4, 6.G.A.1
Measuring Parallelograms	6.EE.A.2, 6.EE.A.2a, 6.EE.A.2c, 6.NS.C.8, 6.EE.B.6, 6.EE.C.9, 6.G.A.1, 6.G.A.3
Measuring Surface Area and Volume	6.EE.A.2, 6.EE.A.2a, 6.EE.A.2c, 6.EE.A.4, 6.EE.B.6, 6.EE.C.9, 6.G.A.1, 6.G.A.2, 6.G.A.4

CMP3 Content	Standards for Mathematical Content
Decimal Ops: Computing With Decimals and Percents	
Decimal Operations and Estimation	6.RP.A.1, 6.RP.A.2, 6.RP.A.3, 6.RP.A.3b
Adding and Subtracting Decimals	6.EE.A.2, 6.EE.A.2a, 6.EE.B.5, 6.EE.B.6, 6.EE.B.7, 6.NS.B.3
Multiplying and Dividing Decimals	6.NS.A.1, 6.EE.B.7, 6.NS.B.2, 6.NS.B.3
Using Percents	6.RP.A.3c, 6.NS.B.3, 6.RP.A.3, 6.EE.A.3, 6.EE.B.6, 6.EE.B.7
Variables and Patterns: Focus on Algebra	
Variables, Tables, and Graphs	6.EE.C.9, 6.NS.C.6c, 6.NS.C.8, 6.RP.A.3a, 6.RP.A.3b, 6.RP.A.3d
Analyzing Relationships Among Variables	6.EE.C.9, 6.NS.C.6b, 6.NS.C.6c, 6.NS.C.8, 6.NS.C.6
Relating Variables With Equations	6.EE.A.2, 6.EE.A.2a, 6.EE.A.2c, 6.EE.B.6, 6.EE.B.7, 6.EE.C.9, 6.RP.A.2, 6.RP.A.3a, 6.RP.A.3b, 6.RP.A.3d, 6.RP.A.3, 6.EE.A.1, 6.EE.A.3, 6.EE.A.4
Expressions, Equations, and Inequalities	6.EE.A.2c, 6.EE.A.3, 6.EE.A.4, 6.EE.B.5, 6.EE.B.6, 6.EE.B.7, 6.EE.B.8, 6.EE.C.9, 6.NS.C.8, 6.RP.A.3b, 6.RP.A.3a, 6.EE.A.2a, 6.EE.A.2b
Data About Us: Statistics and Data Analysis	
What's in a Name? Organizing, Representing, and Describing Data	6.SP.A.1, 6.SP.A.2, 6.SP.A.3, 6.SP.B.4, 6.SP.B.5, 6.SP.B.5a, 6.SP.B.5c
Who's in Your Household? Using the Mean	6.SP.A.1, 6.SP.A.2, 6.SP.A.3, 6.SP.B.4, 6.SP.B.5, 6.SP.B.5a, 6.SP.B.5b, 6.SP.B.5c, 6.SP.B.5d
What Is Your Favorite …? Measuring Variability	6.RP.A.3, 6.RP.A.3a, 6.NS.C.6, 6.NS.C.7, 6.SP.A.1, 6.SP.A.2, 6.SP.B.4, 6.SP.B.5, 6.SP.A.3, 6.SP.B.5c, 6.SP.B.5d
What Numbers Describe Us? Using Graphs to Group Data	6.NS.C.6, 6.NS.C.7, 6.SP.A.1, 6.SP.A.2, 6.SP.B.4, 6.SP.B5, 6.SP.A.3, 6.SP.B.5a, 6.SP.B.5c, 6.SP.B.5d

KEY
■ Common Core Standard in Major Cluster
■ Common Core Standard in Supporting Cluster
■ Common Core Standard in Additional Cluster

PACING
A Unit that is composed of 3 Investigations (10–14 Problems): 18–24 days
A Unit that is composed of 4 Investigations (13–17 Problems): 22–28 days
A Unit that is composed of 5 Investigations (15–19 Problems): 26–32 days
(includes days dedicated to assessment)

GRADE 7

CMP3 Content	Standards for Mathematical Content
Shapes and Designs: Two-Dimensional Geometry	
The Family of Polygons	7.G.A.2
Designing Polygons: The Angle Connection	7.EE.A.2, 7.EE.B.4, 7.G.A.2
Designing Triangles and Quadrilaterals: The Side Connection	7.G.A.2, 7.G.B.5
Accentuate the Negative: Integers and Rational Numbers	
Extending the Number System	7.NS.A.1, 7.NS.A.1a, 7.NS.A.3, 7.EE.B.4, 7.EE.B.4b, 7.NS.A.1b, 7.NS.A.1c
Adding and Subtracting Rational Numbers	7.NS.A.1, 7.NS.A.1b, 7.NS.A.1c, 7.NS.A.3, 7.NS.A.1a, 7.EE.B.3
Multiplying and Dividing Rational Numbers	7.NS.A.2, 7.NS.A.2a, 7.NS.A.2b, 7.NS.A.2c, 7.NS.A.3, 7.NS.A.2d, 7.EE.B.3
Properties of Operations	7.NS.A.1, 7.NS.A.1d, 7.NS.A.2, 7.NS.A.2a, 7.NS.A.3, 7.NS.A.2c, 7.EE.B.3
Stretching and Shrinking: Understanding Similarity	
Enlarging and Reducing Shapes	7.RP.A.2, 7.RP.A.2b, 7.G.A.1, 7.G.A.2, 7.G.B.6
Similar Figures	7.RP.A.2, 7.RP.A.2a, 7.RP.A.2b, 7.G.A.1, 7.G.B.6
Scaling Perimeter and Area	7.RP.A.2, 7.RP.A.2b, 7.RP.A.2a, 7.G.A.1, 7.G.A.2, 7.G.B.6
Similarity and Ratios	7.RP.A.2, 7.RP.A.2a, 7.EE.B.4, 7.RP.A.2b, 7.RP.A.3, 7.EE.B.3, 7.G.A.1, 7.G.B.6
Comparing and Scaling: Ratios, Rates, Percents, and Proportions	
Ways of Comparing: Ratios and Proportions	7.RP.A.2, 7.RP.A.3, 7.EE.B.4
Comparing and Scaling Rates	7.RP.A.1, 7.RP.A.2, 7.RP.A.2a, 7.RP.A.2b, 7.RP.A.2c, 7.RP.A.2d, 7.RP.A.3, 7.EE.B.4, 7.EE.B.4a
Markups, Markdowns, and Measures: Using Ratios, Percents, and Proportions	7.RP.A.2, 7.RP.A.3, 7.RP.A.1, 7.RP.A.2d, 7.NS.A.3, 7.EE.B.3, 7.EE.B.4, 7.EE.B.4a
Moving Straight Ahead: Linear Relationships	
Walking Rates: Exploring Linear Relationships	7.EE.B.3, 7.EE.B.4, 7.EE.B.4a, 7.RP.A.2, 7.RP.A.2a, 7.RP.A.2b, 7.RP.A.2c
Linear Relationships: Using Graphs, Tables, and Equations	7.EE.B.3, 7.EE.B.4, 7.EE.B.4a, 7.RP.A.2b, 7.RP.A.2c, 7.RP.A.2d
Solving Equations	7.EE.A.2, 7.EE.B.4a, 7.EE.B.4b, 7.EE.A.1, 7.EE.B.3, 7.EE.B.4
Exploring Slope: Connecting Rates and Ratios	7.EE.A.1, 7.EE.A.2, 7.EE.B.4, 7.EE.B.4a, 7.RP.A.2d, 7.EE.B.3

CMP3 Content	Standards for Mathematical Content
What Do You Expect? Probability and Expected Value	
A First Look at Chance	7.RP.A.2, 7.EE.B.3, 7.SP.C.6, 7.SP.C.7a, 7.SP.C.7b
Experimental and Theoretical Probability	7.RP.A.2, 7.EE.B.3, 7.SP.C.5, 7.SP.C.6, 7.SP.C.7b, 7.SP.C.8, 7.SP.C.8a, 7.SP.C.8b, 7.SP.C.7
Making Decisions With Probability	7.RP.A.2, 7.EE.B.3, 7.SP.C.6, 7.SP.C.7, 7.SP.C.7a, 7.SP.C.7b, 7.SP.C.8, 7.SP.C.8a, 7.SP.C.5
Analyzing Compound Events Using an Area Model	7.RP.A.2, 7.EE.B.3, 7.SP.C.5, 7.SP.C.6, 7.SP.C.8, 7.SP.C.8a, 7.SP.C.8b, 7.SP.C.8c, 7.SP.C.7, 7.SP.C.7a, 7.SP.C.7b
Binomial Outcomes	7.RP.A.2, 7.EE.B.3, 7.SP.C.5, 7.SP.C.7, 7.SP.C.7a, 7.SP.C.8a, 7.SP.C.8b, 7.SP.C.8c, 7.SP.C.8
Filling and Wrapping: Three-Dimensional Measurement	
Building Smart Boxes: Rectangular Prisms	7.RP.A.2, 7.EE.A.2, 7.G.B.6, 7.G.A.1
Polygonal Prisms	7.NS.A.3, 7.G.A.3, 7.G.B.6
Area and Circumference of Circles	7.NS.A.3, 7.EE.A.1, 7.EE.A.2, 7.G.B.4, 7.G.B.6
Cylinders, Cones, and Spheres	7.NS.A.3, 7.G.B.4, 7.G.B.6
Samples and Populations: Making Comparisons and Predictions	
Making Sense of Samples	7.SP.B.4
Choosing a Sample From a Population	7.SP.A.1, 7.SP.A.2
Using Samples to Draw Conclusions	7.RP.A.2, 7.NS.A.1, 7.NS.A.1b, 7.SP.A.1, 7.SP.A.2, 7.SP.C.5, 7.SP.C.7, 7.SP.C.7a, 7.SP.B.3, 7.SP.B.4

KEY
■ Common Core Standard in Major Cluster
■ Common Core Standard in Supporting Cluster
■ Common Core Standard in Additional Cluster

PACING
A Unit that is composed of 3 Investigations (10–14 Problems): 18–24 days
A Unit that is composed of 4 Investigations (13–17 Problems): 22–28 days
A Unit that is composed of 5 Investigations (15–19 Problems): 26–32 days
(includes days dedicated to assessment)

GRADE 8

CMP3 Content	Standards for Mathematical Content
Thinking With Mathematical Models: Linear and Inverse Variation	
Exploring Data Patterns	8.F.B.5, 8.SP.A.1
Linear Models and Equations	8.EE.B.5, 8.EE.C.7, 8.EE.C.8, 8.F.B.4, 8.EE.C.7b, 8.EE.C.8a, 8.EE.C.8c, 8.F.A.1, 8.F.A.2, 8.F.A.3, 8.SP.A.2, 8.SP.A.1, 8.SP.A.3
Inverse Variation	8.EE.B.5, 8.F.B.5, 8.F.A.1, 8.F.A.3, 8.SP.A.1
Variability and Associations in Numeric Data	8.F.A.1, 8.F.A.3, 8.F.B.4, 8.F.B.5, 8.SP.A.1, 8.SP.A.3, 8.SP.A.2
Variability and Associations in Categorical Data	8.SP.A.4
Looking for Pythagoras: The Pythagorean Theorem	
Coordinate Grids	8.G.B.8
Squaring Off	8.EE.A.2, 8.NS.A.2
The Pythagorean Theorem	8.G.B.6, 8.G.B.7, 8.G.B.8
Using the Pythagorean Theorem: Understanding Real Numbers	8.EE.A.2, 8.G.B.7, 8.NS.A.1, 8.NS.A.2
Using the Pythagorean Theorem: Analyzing Triangles and Circles	8.G.A.4, 8.G.B.7, 8.G.B.8
Growing, Growing, Growing: Exponential Functions	
Exponential Growth	8.EE.A.3, 8.F.B.4, 8.F.A.1, 8.F.A.3, 8.F.B.5
Examining Growth Patterns: Exponential Functions	8.F.B.5, 8.F.A.1
Growth Factors and Growth Rates	8.F.A.1, 8.F.A.2, 8.F.A.3, 8.F.B.5
Exponential Decay Functions	8.F.A.1, 8.F.A.2, 8.F.B.5
Patterns With Exponents	8.EE.A.1, 8.EE.A.4, 8.EE.A.2, 8.EE.A.3, 8.F.A.3
Butterflies, Pinwheels, and Wallpaper: Symmetry and Transformations	
Symmetry and Transformations	8.G.A.1, 8.G.A.1a, 8.G.A.1b, 8.G.A.1c
Transformations and Congruence	8.G.A.2, 8.G.A.1a, 8.G.A.1b, 8.G.A.1
Transforming Coordinates	8.G.A.1c, 8.G.A.5, 8.G.A.1, 8.G.A.1a, 8.G.A.1b, 8.G.A.2, 8.G.A.3
Dilations and Similar Figures	8.G.A.3, 8.G.A.4, 8.G.A.5, 8.EE.B.6

CMP3 Content	Standards for Mathematical Content
Say It With Symbols: Making Sense of Symbols	
Making Sense of Symbols: Equivalent Expressions	8.EE.C.7, 8.EE.C.7b, 8.F.A.3
Combining Expressions	8.EE.C.7, 8.EE.C.7b, 8.F.A.1, 8.F.A.2, 8.F.A.3, 8.G.C.9
Solving Equations	8.EE.C.7, 8.EE.C.7b, 8.F.A.1, 8.EE.A.2, 8.EE.C.7a, 8.EE.C.8, 8.EE.C.8a, 8.EE.C.8b, 8.EE.C.8c
Looking Back at Functions	8.EE.C.7b, 8.F.A.1, 8.F.A.3, 8.F.B.4, 8.F.B.5, 8.EE.C.7
Reasoning With Symbols	8.EE.C.7b, 8.F.A.1, 8.F.A.2, 8.F.B.4
It's In the System: Systems of Linear Equations and Inequalities	
Linear Equations With Two Variables	8.EE.C.8, 8.EE.C.8a, 8.EE.C.8b, 8.EE.C.8c, 8.F.A.3
Solving Linear Systems Symbolically	8.EE.C.8a, 8.EE.C.8b, 8.EE.C.8c, 8.EE.C.8
Systems of Functions and Inequalities	8.EE.C.8c, 8.EE.C.8a
Systems of Linear Inequalities	8.EE.C.8c, 8.EE.C.8b

KEY

■ Common Core Standard in Major Cluster
■ Common Core Standard in Supporting Cluster
■ Common Core Standard in Additional Cluster

PACING

A Unit that is composed of 3 Investigations (10–14 Problems): 18–24 days
A Unit that is composed of 4 Investigations (13–17 Problems): 22–28 days
A Unit that is composed of 5 Investigations (15–19 Problems): 26–32 days
(includes days dedicated to assessment)

CMP3 Content	Standards for Mathematical Content
Thinking With Mathematical Models: Linear and Inverse Variation	
Exploring Data Patterns	8.F.B.5, 8.SP.A.1, F-IF.B.4, F-IF.B.6, N-Q.A.1, N-Q.A.2, F-IF.C.7, F-IF.C.9, F-BF.A.1a, F-LE.A.1, F-LE.A.1b
Linear Models and Equations	8.F.B.3, 8.F.B.4, 8.EE.B.5, 8.EE.C.7, 8.EE.C.8, 8.EE.C.8c, 8.F.A.1, 8.F.A.2, 8.SP.A.2, 8.SP.A.1, 8.SP.A.3, A-SSE.A.1a, A-CED.A.1, A-CED.A.2, A-REI.A.1, A-REI.B.3, F-IF.A.1, N-Q.A.1, F-BF.A.1, F-BF.A.1a, F-LE.A.2, F-LE.B.5, S-ID.B.6, S-ID.B.6a, S-ID.B.6b, S-ID.B.6c, A-REI.C.6
Inverse Variation	8.F.A.3, 8.F.B.5, 8.EE.B.5, 8.F.A.1, 8.SP.A.1, A-CED.A.2, A-CED.A.4, A-REI.A.1, F-IF.C.7e, F-IF.C.8, F-BF.A.1, F-BF.A.1a, S-ID.B.6a
Variability and Associations in Numerical Data	8.F.A.1, 8.F.A.3, 8.F.B.4, 8.F.B.5, 8.SP.A.1, 8.SPA.3, 8.SP.A.2, A-CED.A.2, S-ID.C.7, S-ID.C.8, S-ID.C.9, N-Q.A.1, S-ID.B.6, S-ID.B.6b, S-ID.A.1, S-ID.A.2, S-ID.A.3
Variability and Associations in Categorical Data	8.SP.A.4, S-ID.C.9, S-ID.B.5
Looking for Pythagoras: The Pythagorean Theorem	
Coordinate Grids	8.G.B.8
Squaring Off	8.EE.A.2, 8.NS.A.2, N-Q.A.3
The Pythagorean Theorem	8.G.B.6, 8.G.B.7, 8.G.B.8
Using the Pythagorean Theorem: Understanding Real Numbers	8.EE.A.2, 8.EE.C.7a, 8.G.B.7, 8.NS.A.1, 8.NS.A.2, A-CED.A.1, N-Q.A.3
Using the Pythagorean Theorem: Analyzing Triangles and Circles	8.G.A.4, 8.G.B.7, 8.G.B.8, A-CED.A.2, A-REI.D.10, N-Q.A.3

CMP3 Content	Standards for Mathematical Content
Growing, Growing, Growing: Exponential Functions	
Exponential Growth	8.EE.A.3, 8.F.B.4, 8.F.A.1, 8.F.A.3, 8.F.B.5, A-SSE.A.1, A-CED.A.1, A-CED.A.2, A-REI.D.10, F-IF.B.4, F-IF.C.9, F-LE.A.1a, F-LE.A.2, F-LE.A.3, F-LE.B.5
Examining Growth Patterns	8.F.B.5, 8.F.A.1, A-SSE.A.1a, A-CED.A.2, A-REI.D.10, F-IF.B.4, N-Q.A.1, N-Q.A.2, F-LE.A.2, F-LE.B.5
Growth Factors and Growth Rates	8.F.A.1, 8.F.A.2, 8.F.A.3, 8.F.B.5, A-SSE.A.1a, A-SSE.A.1b, A-CED.A.2, A-REI.D.10, F-IF.B.4, F-IF.B.6, F-LE.A.1a, F-LE.A.1c, F-LE.A.2, F-LE.B.5
Exponential Decay	8.F.A.1, 8.F.A.2, 8.F.B.5, A-SSE.A.1a, A-SSE.A.1b, A-CED.A.2, A-REI.D.10, F-IF.B.4, F-IF.B.6, N-Q.A.1, F-IF.C.9, F-LE.A.1a, F-LE.A.1c, F-LE.A.2, F-LE.B.5
Patterns with Exponents	8.EE.A.1, 8.EE.A.4, 8.EE.A.2, 8.EE.A.3, 8.F.A.3, A-SSE.A.1a, A-SSE.A.2, A-SSE.B.3c
Frogs, Fleas, and Painted Cubes: Quadratic Functions	
Introduction to Quadratic Functions	A-SSE.A.1, A-SSE.A.1b, A-CED.A.1, A-CED.A.2, A-REI.D.10, F-IF.B.4, N-Q.A.1, F-IF.C.7, F-IF.C.7a, F-IF.C.9, F-BF.A.1
Quadratic Expressions	A-SSE.A.1, A-SSE.A.1a, A-SSE.A.1b, A-SSE.A.2, A-CED.A.2, A-REI.D.10, F-IF.B.4, A-SSE.B.3, F-IF.C.7, F-IF.C.7a, F-IF.C.8, F-IF.C.8a, F-BF.A.1, F-BF.A.1a
Quadratic Patterns of Change	A-SSE.A.1b, A-SSE.A.2, A-CED.A.2, A-REI.D.10, F-IF.B.4, A-SSE.B.3, F-IF.C.7, F-IF.C.7a, F-IF.C.9, F-BF.A.1, F-BF.A.1a, F-LE.A.1, F-LE.A.1a, F-LE.A.1b
Frogs Meet Fleas On a Cube: More Applications of Quadratic Functions	A-CED.A.2, A-REI.D.10, F-IF.B.4, F-IF.C.7, F-IF.C.7a, F-IF.C.9, F-LE.A.1, F-LE.A.1a, F-LE.A.1b

CMP3 Content	Standards for Mathematical Content
Butterflies, Pinwheels, and Wallpaper: Symmetry and Transformations	
Symmetry and Transformations	8.G.A.1, 8.G.A.1a, 8.G.A.1b, 8.G.A.1c
Transformations and Congruence	8.G.A.2, 8.G.A.1a, 8.G.A.1b, 8.G.A.1
Transforming Coordinates	8.G.A.3, 8.G.A.1c, 8.G.A.5, 8.G.A.1, 8.G.A.1a, 8.G.A.1b, 8.G.A.2
Dilations and Similar Figures	8.G.A.3, 8.G.A.4, 8.G.A.5, 8.EE.B.6
Say It With Symbols: Making Sense of Symbols	
Making Sense of Symbols: Equivalent Expressions	8.EE.C.7, 8.EE.C.7b, 8.F.A.3, A-SSE.A.1, A-SSE.A.1a, A-SSE.A.1b, A-SSE.A.2, A-SSE.B.3, F-IF.C.9, F-BF.A.1a
Combining Expressions	8.EE.C.7, 8.EE.C.7b, 8.F.A.1, 8.F.A.2, 8.F.A.3, 8.G.C.9, A-SSE.A.1, A-SSE.A.1a, A-SSE.A.1b, A-SSE.A.2, A-REI.B.3, N-Q.A.1, N-Q.A.2, A-SSE.B.3, F-IF.C.9, F-BF.A.1, F-BF.A.1a
Solving Equations	8.EE.C.7, 8.EE.C.7b, 8.F.A.1, 8.EE.A.2, 8.EE.C.7a, 8.EE.C.8, 8.EE.C.8a, 8.EE.C.8b, 8.EE.C.8c, A-SSE.A.1, A-SSE.A.1a, A-SSE.A.1b, A-SSE.A.2, A-CED.A.1, A-CED.A.2, A-REI.A.1, A-REI.B.3, A-REI.B.4, A-REI.B.4b, A-REI.D.10, A-REI.D.11, N-Q.A.1, A-SSE.B.3, A-SSE.B.3a, A-REI.C.6
Looking Back at Functions	8.EE.C.7b, 8.F.A.1, 8.F.A.3, 8.F.B.4, 8.F.B.5, 8.EE.C.7, A-SSE.A.1, A-SSE.A.1a, A-SSE.A.1b, A-SSE.A.2, A-CED.A.1, A-CED.A.2, A-REI.B.3, A-REI.B.4, A-REI.B.4b, N-Q.A.1, N-Q.A.2, A-SSE.B.3, A-SSE.B.3a, F-IF.C.9, F-BF.A.1, F-BF.A.1a, F-LE.A.1, F-LE.A.2, F-LE.B.5
Reasoning With Symbols	8.EE.C.7b, 8.F.A.1, 8.F.A.2, 8.F.B.4, A-SSE.A.1, A-SSE.A.1a, A-SSE.A.1b, A-SSE.A.2, A-CED.A.1, A-CED.A.2, A-SSE.B.3, F-BF.A.1, N-RN.B.3

CMP3 Content	Standards for Mathematical Content
It's In the System: Systems of Linear Equations and Inequalities	
Linear Equations With Two Variables	8.EE.C.8, 8.EE.C.8a, 8.EE.C.8b, 8.EE.C.8c, 8.F.A.3, A-CED.A.2, A-CED.A.3, A-CED.A.4, A-REI.B.3, A-REI.D.10, A-REI.C.6
Solving Linear Systems Symbolically	8.EE.C.8a, 8.EE.C.8b, 8.EE.C.8c, 8.EE.C.8, A-CED.A.2, A-CED.A.3, A-CED.A.4, A-REI.B.3, A-REI.D.10, A-REI.C.5, A-REI.C.6
Systems of Functions and Inequalities	8.EE.C.8c, 8.EE.C.8a, A-CED.A.1, A-CED.A.2, A-CED.A.3, A-REI.B.3, A-REI.B.4, A-REI.B.4b, A-REI.D.10, A-REI.C.6
Systems of Linear Inequalities	8.EE.C.8c, 8.EE.C.8b, A-CED.A.2, A-CED.A.3, A-REI.D.10, A-REI.D.12, A-REI.C.6
Function Junction: Functions, Expressions, Equations, and Graphs	
The Families of Functions	F-IF.A.1, F-IF.A.2, F-IF.B.4, F-IF.B.5, F-IF.B.6, N-Q.A.1, N-Q.A.2, F-IF.C.7b
Arithmetic and Geometric Sequences	F-IF.A.3, F-BF.A.1a
Transforming Graphs, Expressions, and Functions	F-IF.C.7a, F-IF.C.9, F-BF.B.3
Solving Quadratic Equations Algebraically	A-REI.B.3, A-REI.B.4a, A-REI.B.4b, A-SSE.A.2, A-SSE.B.3b, A-APR.B.3, F-BF.B.3
Polynomial Expressions, Functions, and Equations	A-APR.A.1, F-IF.B.4, A-APR.B.3, F-IF.C.9

KEY

■ Common Core Standard in Major Cluster
■ Common Core Standard in Supporting Cluster
■ Common Core Standard in Additional Cluster

PACING

A Unit that is composed of 3 Investigations (10–14 Problems): 18–24 days
A Unit that is composed of 4 Investigations (13–17 Problems): 22–28 days
A Unit that is composed of 5 Investigations (15–19 Problems): 26–32 days
(includes days dedicated to assessment)

CMP3 Content	Standards for Mathematical Content
Thinking With Mathematical Models: Linear and Inverse Variation	
Exploring Data Patterns	8.F.B.5, 8.SP.A.1, F-IF.B.4, F-IF.B.6, N-Q.A.1, N-Q.A.2, F-IF.C.7, F-IF.C.9, F-BF.A.1a, F-BF.A.2, F-LE.A.1, F-LE.A.1b
Linear Models and Equations	8.F.B.3, 8.F.B.4, 8.EE.B.5, 8.EE.C.7, 8.EE.C.8, 8.EE.C.8c, 8.F.A.1, 8.F.A.2, 8.SP.A.2, 8.SP.A.1, 8.SP.A.3, A-SSE.A.1a, A-CED.A.1, A-CED.A.2, A-REI.A.1, A-REI.B.3, F-IF.A.1, N-Q.A.1, F-BF.A.1, F-BF.A.1a, F-BF.A.1b, F-LE.A.2, F-LE.B.5, S-ID.B.6, S-ID.B.6a, S-ID.B.6b, S-ID.B.6c, A-REI.C.6
Inverse Variation	8.F.A.3, 8.F.B.5, 8.EE.B.5, 8.F.A.1, 8.SP.A.1, A-CED.A.2, A-CED.A.4, A-REI.A.1, F-IF.C.7e, F-IF.C.8, F-BF.A.1, F-BF.A.1a, S-ID.B.6a
Variability and Associations in Numeric Data	8.F.A.1, 8.F.A.3, 8.F.B.4, 8.F.B.5, 8.SP.A.1, 8.SPA.3, 8.SP.A.2, A-CED.A.2, S-ID.C.7, S-ID.C.8, S-ID.C.9, N-Q.A.1, S-ID.B.6, S-ID.B.6b, S-ID.A.1, S-ID.A.2, S-ID.A.3
Variability and Associations in Categorical Data	8.SP.A.4, S-ID.C.9, S-ID.B.5
Looking for Pythagoras: The Pythagorean Theorem	
Coordinate Grids	8.G.B.8
Squaring Off	8.EE.A.2, 8.NS.A.2, N-Q.A.3
The Pythagorean Theorem	8.G.B.6, 8.G.B.7, 8.G.B.8
Using the Pythagorean Theorem: Understanding Real Numbers	8.EE.A.2, 8.EE.C.7a, 8.G.B.7, 8.NS.A.1, 8.NS.A.2, A-CED.A.1, N-Q.A.3
Using the Pythagorean Theorem: Analyzing Triangles and Circles	8.G.A.4, 8.G.B.7, 8.G.B.8, A-CED.A.2, A-REI.D.10, N-Q.A.3

CMP3 Content	Standards for Mathematical Content
Growing, Growing, Growing: Exponential Functions	
Exponential Growth	8.EE.A.3, 8.F.B.4, 8.F.A.1, 8.F.A.3, 8.F.B.5, A-SSE.A.1, A-CED.A.1, A-CED.A.2, A-REI.D.10, F-IF.B.4, F-IF.C.9, F-LE.A.1a, F-LE.A.2, F-LE.A.3, F-LE.B.5, F-IF.C.7e
Examining Growth Patterns	8.F.B.5, 8.F.A.1, A-SSE.A.1a, A-CED.A.2, A-REI.D.10, F-IF.B.4, N-Q.A.1, N-Q.A.2, F-LE.A.2, F-LE.B.5
Growth Factors and Growth Rates	8.F.A.1, 8.F.A.2, 8.F.A.3, 8.F.B.5, A-SSE.A.1a, A-SSE.A.1b, A-CED.A.2, A-REI.D.10, F-IF.B.4, F-IF.B.6, F-IF.C.8b, F-LE.A.1a, F-LE.A.1c, F-LE.A.2, F-LE.B.5
Exponential Decay	8.F.A.1, 8.F.A.2, 8.F.B.5, A-SSE.A.1a, A-SSE.A.1b, A-CED.A.2, A-REI.D.10, F-IF.B.4, F-IF.B.6, N-Q.A.1, F-IF.C.9, F-LE.A.1a, F-LE.A.1c, F-LE.A.2, F-LE.B.5, F-IF.C.7e
Patterns with Exponents	8.EE.A.1, 8.EE.A.4, 8.EE.A.2, 8.EE.A.3, 8.F.A.3, A-SSE.A.1a, A-SSE.A.2, A-SSE.B.3c, F-IF.C.8b, F-IF.C.7e, N-RN.A.1, N-RN.A.2
Frogs, Fleas, and Painted Cubes: Quadratic Functions	
Introduction to Quadratic Functions	A-SSE.A.1, A-SSE.A.1b, A-CED.A.1, A-CED.A.2, A-REI.D.10, F-IF.B.4, N-Q.A.1, F-IF.C.7, F-IF.C.7a, F-IF.C.9, F-BF.A.1
Quadratic Expressions	A-SSE.A.1, A-SSE.A.1a, A-SSE.A.1b, A-SSE.A.2, A-CED.A.2, A-REI.D.10, F-IF.B.4, A-SSE.B.3, F-IF.C.7, F-IF.C.7a, F-IF.C.8, F-IF.C.8a, F-BF.A.1, F-BF.A.1a
Quadratic Patterns of Change	A-SSE.A.1b, A-SSE.A.2, A-CED.A.2, A-REI.D.10, F-IF.B.4, A-SSE.B.3, A-SSE.B.3a, F-IF.C.7, F-IF.C.7a, F-IF.C.9, F-BF.A.1, F-BF.A.1a, F-LE.A.1, F-LE.A.1a, F-LE.A.1b
Frogs Meet Fleas On a Cube: More Applications of Quadratic	A-CED.A.2, A-REI.D.10, F-IF.B.4, F-IF.C.7, F-IF.C.7a, F-IF.C.9, F-LE.A.1, F-LE.A.1a, F-LE.A.1b

CMP3 Content	Standards for Mathematical Content
Butterflies, Pinwheels, and Wallpaper: Symmetry and Transformations	
Symmetry and Transformations	8.G.A.1, 8.G.A.1a, 8.G.A.1b, 8.G.A.1c
Transformations and Congruence	8.G.A.2, 8.G.A.1a, 8.G.A.1b, 8.G.A.1
Transforming Coordinates	8.G.A.3, 8.G.A.1c, 8.G.A.5, 8.G.A.1, 8.G.A.1a, 8.G.A.1b, 8.G.A.2
Dilations and Similar Figures	8.G.A.3, 8.G.A.4, 8.G.A.5, 8.EE.B.6
Say It With Symbols: Making Sense of Symbols	
Making Sense of Symbols: Equivalent Expressions	8.EE.C.7, 8.EE.C.7b, 8.F.A.3, A-SSE.A.1, A-SSE.A.1a, A-SSE.A.1b, A-SSE.A.2, A-SSE.B.3, F-IF.C.9, F-BF.A.1a
Combining Expressions	8.EE.C.7, 8.EE.C.7b, 8.F.A.1, 8.F.A.2, 8.F.A.3, 8.G.C.9, A-SSE.A.1, A-SSE.A.1a, A-SSE.A.1b, A-SSE.A.2, A-CED.A.1, A-REI.B.3, N-Q.A.1, N-Q.A.2, A-SSE.B.3, F-IF.C.9, F-BF.A.1, F-BF.A.1a
Solving Equations	8.EE.C.7, 8.EE.C.7b, 8.F.A.1, 8.EE.A.2, 8.EE.C.7a, 8.EE.C.8, 8.EE.C.8a, 8.EE.C.8b, 8.EE.C.8c, A-SSE.A.1, A-SSE.A.1a, A-SSE.A.1b, A-SSE.A.2, A-REI.A.1, A-REI.B.3, A-REI.B.4, A-REI.B.4b, A-REI.D.10, A-REI.D.11, N-Q.A.1, A-SSE.B.3, A-SSE.B.3a, A-CED.A.1, A-REI.C.6
Looking Back at Functions	8.EE.C.7b, 8.F.A.1, 8.F.A.3, 8.F.B.4, 8.F.B.5, 8.EE.C.7, A-SSE.A.1, A-SSE.A.1a, A-SSE.A.1b, A-SSE.A.2, A-CED.A.1, A-CED.A.2, A-REI.B.3, A-REI.B.4, A-REI.B.4b, N-Q.A.1, N-Q.A.2, A-SSE.B.3, A-SSE.B.3a, F-IF.C.9, F-BF.A.1, F-BF.A.1a, F-LE.A.1, F-LE.A.2, F-LE.B.5
Reasoning With Symbols	8.EE.B.7b, 8.F.A.1, 8.F.A.2, 8.F.B.4, A-SSE.A.1, A-SSE.A.1a, A-SSE.A.1b, A-SSE.A.2, A-CED.A.1, A-CED.A.2, A-SSE.B.3, F-BF.A.1, N-RN.B.3

CMP3 Content	Standards for Mathematical Content
It's In the System: Systems of Linear Equations and Inequalities	
Linear Equations With Two Variables	8.EE.C.8, 8.EE.C.8a, 8.EE.C.8b, 8.EE.C.8c, 8.F.A.3, A-CED.A.2, A-CED.A.3, A-CED.A.4, A-REI.B.3, A-REI.D.10, A-REI.C.6
Solving Linear Systems Symbolically	8.EE.C.8a, 8.EE.C.8b, 8.EE.C.8c, 8.EE.C.8, A-CED.A.2, A-CED.A.3, A-CED.A.4, A-REI.B.3, A-REI.D.10, A-REI.C.5, A-REI.C.6
Systems of Functions and Inequalities	8.EE.C.8c, 8.EE.C.8a, A-CED.A.1, A-CED.A.2, A-CED.A.3, A-REI.B.3, A-REI.B.4, A-REI.B.4b, A-REI.D.10, A-REI.C.6, A-REI.C.7
Systems of Linear Inequalities	8.EE.C.8c, 8.EE.C.8b, A-CED.A.2, A-CED.A.3, A-REI.D.10, A-REI.D.12, A-REI.C.6
Function Junction: Functions, Expressions, Equations, and Graphs	
The Families of Functions	F-IF.A.1, F-IF.A.2, F-IF.B.4, F-IF.B.5, F-IF.B.6, N-Q.A.1, N-Q.A.2, F-IF.C.7b, F-BF.B.4a
Arithmetic and Geometric Sequences	F-IF.A.3, F-BF.A.2, F-BF.A.1a
Transforming Graphs, Expressions, and Functions	F-IF.C.7a, F-IF.C.9, F-BF.B.3
Solving Quadratic Equations Algebraically	A-REI.B.4, A-REI.B.4a, A-REI.B.4b, A-SSE.A.2, A-SSE.B.3b, F-IF.C.8a, F-BF.B.3
Polynomial Expressions, Functions, and Equations	A-APR.A.1, F-IF.B.4, F-IF.C.9, F-BF.A.1b

KEY

■ Common Core Standard in Major Cluster
■ Common Core Standard in Supporting Cluster
■ Common Core Standard in Additional Cluster

PACING

A Unit that is composed of 3 Investigations (10–14 Problems): 18–24 days
A Unit that is composed of 4 Investigations (13–17 Problems): 22–28 days
A Unit that is composed of 5 Investigations (15–19 Problems): 26–32 days
(includes days dedicated to assessment)

Appendix D
Correlation of Common Core Content Standards to CMP3 Content

GRADE 6

Number	Standard for Mathematical Content	CMP3 Unit: Investigation
6.RP.A	**Understand ratio concepts and use ratio reasoning to solve problems.**	
6.RP.A.1	Understand the concept of a ratio and use ratio language to describe a ratio relationship between two quantities. **For example:** "The ratio of wings to beaks in the bird house at the zoo was 2:1, because for every 2 wings there was 1 beak." "For every vote candidate A received, candidate C received nearly three votes."	Comparing Bits and Pieces: Inv. 1, 2, 3, 4 Decimal Ops: Inv. 1
6.RP.A.2	Understand the concept of a unit rate a/b associated with a ratio a:b with $b \neq 0$, and use rate language in the context of a ratio relationship. **For example:** "This recipe has a ratio of 3 cups of flour to 4 cups of sugar, so there is ¾ cup of flour for each cup of sugar." "We paid $75 for 15 hamburgers, which is a rate of $5 per hamburger."	Comparing Bits and Pieces: Inv. 1, 2, 3, 4 Decimal Ops: Inv. 1 Variables and Patterns: Inv. 3
6.RP.A.3	Use ratio and rate reasoning to solve real-world and mathematical problems, e.g., by reasoning about tables of equivalent ratios, tape diagrams, double number line diagrams, or equations.	Comparing Bits and Pieces: Inv. 1, 2, 3, 4 Decimal Ops: Inv. 1, 4 Variables and Patterns: Inv. 3 Data About Us: Inv. 3
6.RP.A.3a	Make tables of equivalent ratios relating quantities with whole-number measurements, find missing values in the tables, and plot the pairs of values on the coordinate plane. Use tables to compare ratios.	Comparing Bits and Pieces: Inv. 2 Variables and Patterns: Inv. 1, 3, 4 Data About Us: Inv. 3
6.RP.A.3b	Solve unit rate problems including those involving unit pricing and constant speed. **For example:** if it took 7 hours to mow 4 lawns, then at that rate, how many lawns could be mowed in 35 hours? At what rate were lawns being mowed?	Comparing Bits and Pieces: Inv. 2, 4 Decimal Ops: Inv. 1 Variables and Patterns: Inv. 1, 3, 4
6.RP.A.3c	Find a percent of a quantity as a rate per 100 (e.g., 30% of a quantity means 30/100 times the quantity); solve problems involving finding the whole, given a part and the percent.	Comparing Bits and Pieces: Inv. 4 Decimal Ops: Inv. 4
6.RP.A.3.d	Use ratio reasoning to convert measurement units; manipulate and transform units appropriately when multiplying or dividing quantities.	Variables and Patterns: Inv. 1, 3

Number	Standard for Mathematical Content	CMP3 Unit: Investigation
6.NS.A	**Apply and extend previous understandings of multiplication and division to divide fractions by fractions.**	
6.NS.A.1	Interpret and compute quotients of fractions, and solve word problems involving division of fractions by fractions, e.g., by using visual fraction models and equations to represent the problem. **For example:** create a story context for (⅔) ÷ (¾) and use a visual fraction model to show the quotient; use the relationship between multiplication and division to explain that (⅔) ÷ (¾) = % because ¾ of % is ⅔. (In general, $(a/b) ÷ (c/d) = ad/bc$.) How much chocolate will each person get if 3 people share ½ lb of chocolate equally? How many ¾-cup servings are in ⅔ of a cup of yogurt? How wide is a rectangular strip of land with length ¾ mi and area ½ square mi?	Let's Be Rational: Inv. 3
6.NS.B	**Compute fluently with multi-digit numbers and find common factors and multiples.**	
6.NS.B.2	Fluently divide multi-digit numbers using the standard algorithm.	Let's Be Rational: Inv. 3 Decimal Ops: Inv. 3
6.NS.B.3	Fluently add, subtract, multiply, and divide multi-digit decimals using the standard algorithm for each operation.	Let's Be Rational: Inv. 1 Decimal Ops: Inv. 2, 3, 4
6.NS.B.4	Find the greatest common factor of two whole numbers less than or equal to 100 and the least common multiple of two whole numbers less than or equal to 12. Use the distributive property to express a sum of two whole numbers 1–100 with a common factor as a multiple of a sum of two whole numbers with no common factor. **For example:** express 36 + 8 as 4 (9 + 2).	Prime Time: Inv. 1, 2, 3, 4 Comparing Bits and Pieces: Inv. 1, 2, 3 Let's Be Rational: Inv. 1
6.NS.C	**Apply and extend previous understandings of numbers to the system of rational numbers.**	
6.NS.C.5	Understand that positive and negative numbers are used together to describe quantities having opposite directions or values (e.g., temperature above/below zero, elevation above/below sea level, credits/debits, positive/negative electric charge); use positive and negative numbers to represent quantities in real-world contexts, explaining the meaning of 0 in each situation.	Comparing Bits and Pieces: Inv. 3
6.NS.C.6	Understand a rational number as a point on the number line. Extend number line diagrams and coordinate axes familiar from previous grades to represent points on the line and in the plane with negative number coordinates.	Comparing Bits and Pieces: Inv. 1, 3 Variables and Patterns: Inv. 2 Data About Us: Inv. 2, 3, 4

Grade 6 *continued*

Number	Standard for Mathematical Content	CMP3 Unit: Investigation
6.NS.C6a	Recognize opposite signs of numbers as indicating locations on opposite sides of 0 on the number line; recognize that the opposite of the opposite of a number is the number itself, e.g., $-(-3) = 3$, and that 0 is its own opposite.	Comparing Bits and Pieces: Inv. 3
6.NS.C.6b	Understand signs of numbers in ordered pairs as indicating locations in quadrants of the coordinate plane; recognize that when two ordered pairs differ only by signs, the locations of the points are related by reflections across one or both axes.	Variables and Patterns: Inv. 2
6.NS.C.6c	Find and position integers and other rational numbers on a horizontal or vertical number line diagram; find and position pairs of integers and other rational numbers on a coordinate plane.	Comparing Bits and Pieces: Inv. 3 Variables and Patterns: Inv. 1, 2
6.NS.C.7	Understand ordering and absolute value of rational numbers.	Comparing Bits and Pieces: Inv. 3 Data About Us: Inv. 2, 3, 4
6.NS.C.7a	Interpret statements of inequality as statements about the relative position of two numbers on a number line diagram. **For example:** interpret $-3 > -7$ as a statement that -3 is located to the right of -7 on a number line oriented from left to right.	Comparing Bits and Pieces: Inv. 3
6.NS.C.7b	Write, interpret, and explain statements of order for rational numbers in real-world contexts. **For example:** write $-3°C > -7°C$ to express the fact that $-3°C$ is warmer than $-7°C$.	
6.NS.C.7c	Understand the absolute value of a rational number as its distance from 0 on the number line; interpret absolute value as magnitude for a positive or negative quantity in a real-world situation. **For example:** for an account balance of -30 dollars, write $|-30| = 30$ to describe the size of the debt in dollars.	
6.NS.C.7d	Distinguish comparisons of absolute value from statements about order. **For example:** recognize that an account balance less than -30 dollars represents a debt greater than 30 dollars.	
6.NS.C.8	Solve real-world and mathematical problems by graphing points in all four quadrants of the coordinate plane. Include use of coordinates and absolute value to find distances between points with the same first coordinate or the same second coordinate.	Covering and Surrounding: Inv. 1, 3 Variables and Patterns: Inv. 1, 2, 4
6.EE.A	**Apply and extend previous understandings of arithmetic to algebraic expressions.**	
6.EE.A.1	Write and evaluate numerical expressions involving whole-number exponents.	Prime Time: Inv. 3, 4 Variables and Patterns: Inv. 3
6.EE.A.2	Write, read, and evaluate expressions in which letters stand for numbers.	Let's Be Rational: Inv 4 Covering and Surrounding: Inv. 1, 2, 3, 4 Decimal Ops: Inv. 2 Variables and Patterns: Inv. 3
6.EE.A.2a	Write expressions that record operations with numbers and with letters standing for numbers. **For example:** express the calculation "Subtract y from 5" as $5 - y$.	Let's Be Rational: Inv. 4 Covering and Surrounding: Inv. 1, 2, 3, 4 Decimal Ops: Inv. 2 Variables and Patterns: Inv. 3, 4

Number	Standard for Mathematical Content	CMP3 Unit: Investigation
6.EE.A.2b	Identify parts of an expression using mathematical terms (sum, term, product, factor, quotient, coefficient); view one or more parts of an expression as a single entity. **For example:** describe the expression 2 (8 + 7) as a product of two factors; view (8 + 7) as both a single entity and a sum of two terms.	Prime Time: Inv. 3, 4 Let's Be Rational: Inv. 3, 4 Variables and Patterns: Inv. 4
6.EE.A.2c	Evaluate expressions at specific values of their variables. Include expressions that arise from formulas used in real-world problems. Perform arithmetic operations, including those involving whole-number exponents, in the conventional order when there are no parentheses to specify a particular order (Order of Operations). **For example:** use the formulas $V = s^3$ and $A = 6 s^2$ to find the volume and surface area of a cube with sides of length $s = \frac{1}{2}$.	Let's Be Rational: Inv. 4 Covering and Surrounding: Inv. 1, 2, 3, 4 Variables and Patterns: Inv. 3, 4
6.EE.A.3	Apply the properties of operations to generate equivalent expressions. **For example:** apply the distributive property to the expression 3 (2 + x) to produce the equivalent expression 6 + 3x; apply the distributive property to the expression 24x + 18y to produce the equivalent expression 6 (4x + 3y); apply properties of operations to y + y + y to produce the equivalent expression 3y.	Let's Be Rational: Inv. 2 Covering and Surrounding: Inv. 1, 2 Decimal Ops: Inv. 4 Variables and Patterns: Inv. 3, 4
6.EE.A.4	Identify when two expressions are equivalent (i.e., when the two expressions name the same number regardless of which value is substituted into them). **For example:** the expressions y + y + y and 3y are equivalent because they name the same number regardless of which number y stands for.	Covering and Surrounding: Inv. 2, 4 Variables and Patterns: Inv. 3, 4
6.EE.B.	**Reason about and solve one-variable equations and inequalities.**	
6.EE.B.5	Understand solving an equation or inequality as a process of answering a question: which values from a specified set, if any, make the equation or inequality true? Use substitution to determine whether a given number in a specified set makes an equation or inequality true.	Decimal Ops: Inv. 2 Variables and Patterns: Inv. 4
6.EE.B.6	Use variables to represent numbers and write expressions when solving a real-world or mathematical problem; understand that a variable can represent an unknown number, or, depending on the purpose at hand, any number in a specified set.	Let's Be Rational: Inv. 4 Covering and Surrounding: Inv. 1, 2, 3, 4 Decimal Ops: Inv. 2, 4 Variables and Patterns: Inv. 3, 4
6.EE.B.7	Solve real-world and mathematical problems by writing and solving equations of the form $x + p = q$ and $px = q$ for cases in which p, q and x are all nonnegative rational numbers.	Let's Be Rational: Inv. 4 Decimal Ops: Inv. 2, 3, 4 Variables and Patterns: Inv. 3, 4

Number	Standard for Mathematical Content	CMP3 Unit: Investigation
6.EE.B.8	Write an inequality of the form $x > c$ or $x < c$ to represent a constraint or condition in a real-world or mathematical problem. Recognize that inequalities of the form $x > c$ or $x < c$ have infinitely many solutions; represent solutions of such inequalities on number line diagrams.	Variables and Patterns: Inv. 4
6.EE.C	**Represent and analyze quantitative relationships between dependent and independent variables.**	
6.EE.C.9	Use variables to represent two quantities in a real-world problem that change in relationship to one another; write an equation to express one quantity, thought of as the dependent variable, in terms of the other quantity, thought of as the independent variable. Analyze the relationship between the dependent and independent variables using graphs and tables, and relate these to the equation. **For example:** in a problem involving motion at constant speed, list and graph ordered pairs of distances and times, and write the equation $d = 65t$ to represent the relationship between distance and time.	Covering and Surrounding: Inv. 1, 2, 3, 4 Variables and Patterns: Inv. 1, 2, 3, 4
6.G.A	**Solve real-world and mathematical problems involving area, surface area, and volume.**	
6.G.A.1	Find the area of right triangles, other triangles, special quadrilaterals, and polygons by composing into rectangles or decomposing into triangles and other shapes; apply these techniques in the context of solving real-world and mathematical problems.	Covering and Surrounding: Inv. 2, 3, 4
6.G.A.2	Find the volume of a right rectangular prism with fractional edge lengths by packing it with unit cubes of the appropriate unit fraction edge lengths, and show that the volume is the same as would be found by multiplying the edge lengths of the prism. Apply the formulas $V = l\,w\,h$ and $V = b\,h$ to find volumes of right rectangular prisms with fractional edge lengths in the context of solving real-world and mathematical problems.	Covering and Surrounding: Inv. 4
6.G.A.3	Draw polygons in the coordinate plane given coordinates for the vertices; use coordinates to find the length of a side joining points with the same first coordinate or the same second coordinate. Apply these techniques in the context of solving real-world and mathematical problems.	Covering and Surrounding: Inv. 3
6.G.A.4	Represent three-dimensional figures using nets made up of rectangles and triangles, and use the nets to find the surface area of these figures. Apply these techniques in the context of solving real-world and mathematical problems.	Covering and Surrounding: Inv. 4

Number	Standard for Mathematical Content	CMP3 Unit: Investigation
6.SP.A	**Develop understanding of statistical variability.**	
6.SP.A.1	Recognize a statistical question as one that anticipates variability in the data related to the question and accounts for it in the answers. **For example:** "How old am I?" is not a statistical question, but "How old are the students in my school?" is a statistical question because one anticipates variability in students' ages.	Data About Us: Inv. 1, 2, 3, 4
6.SP.A.2	Understand that a set of data collected to answer a statistical question has a distribution which can be described by its center, spread, and overall shape.	Data About Us: Inv. 1, 2, 3, 4
6.SP.A.3	Recognize that a measure of center for a numerical data set summarizes all of its values with a single number, while a measure of variation describes how its values vary with a single number.	Data About Us: Inv. 1, 2, 3, 4
6.SP.B	**Summarize and describe distributions.**	
6.SP.B.4	Display numerical data in plots on a number line, including dot plots, histograms, and box plots.	Data About Us: Inv. 1, 2, 3, 4
6.SP.B.5	Summarize numerical data sets in relation to their context, such as by:	
6.SP.B.5a	Reporting the number of observations.	Data About Us: Inv. 1, 2, 4
6.SP.B.5b	Describing the nature of the attribute under investigation, including how it was measured and its units of measurement.	Data About Us: Inv. 2
6.SP.B.5c	Giving quantitative measures of center (median and/or mean) and variability (interquartile range and/or mean absolute deviation), as well as describing any overall pattern and any striking deviations from the overall pattern with reference to the context in which the data were gathered.	Data About Us: Inv. 1, 2, 3, 4
6.SP.B.5d	Relating the choice of measures of center and variability to the shape of the data distribution and the context in which the data were gathered.	Data About Us: Inv. 2, 3, 4

Grade 7

Number	Standard for Mathematical Content	CMP3 Unit: Investigation
7.RP.A	Analyze proportional relationships and use them to solve real-world and mathematical problems.	
7.RP.A.1	Compute unit rates associated with ratios of fractions, including ratios of lengths, areas and other quantities measured in like or different units. **For example:** if a person walks ½ mile in each ¼ hour, compute the unit rate as the complex fraction ½/¼ miles per hour, equivalently 2 miles per hour.	Comparing and Scaling: Inv. 2
7.RP.A.2	Recognize and represent proportional relationships between quantities.	Stretching and Shrinking: Inv. 1, 2, 3, 4 Comparing and Scaling: Inv. 1, 2, 3 Moving Straight Ahead: Inv. 1 What Do You Expect?: Inv. 1, 2, 3, 4, 5 Filling and Wrapping: Inv. 1 Samples and Populations: Inv. 3
7.RP.A.2a	Decide whether two quantities are in a proportional relationship, e.g., by testing for equivalent ratios in a table or graphing on a coordinate plane and observing whether the graph is a straight line through the origin.	Stretching and Shrinking: Inv. 2, 3, 4 Comparing and Scaling: Inv. 2 Moving Straight Ahead: Inv. 1
7.RP.A.2b	Identify the constant of proportionality (unit rate) in tables, graphs, equations, diagrams, and verbal descriptions of proportional relationships.	Stretching and Shrinking: Inv. 1, 2, 3, 4 Comparing and Scaling: Inv. 2 Moving Straight Ahead: Inv. 1, 2
7.RP.A.2c	Represent proportional relationships by equations. **For example:** if total cost t is proportional to the number n of items purchased at a constant price p, the relationship between the total cost and the number of items can be expressed as $t = pn$.	Comparing and Scaling: Inv. 2 Moving Straight Ahead: Inv. 1, 2
7.RP.A.2d	Explain what a point (x, y) on the graph of a proportional relationship means in terms of the situation, with special attention to the points (0, 0) and (1, r) where r is the unit rate.	Comparing and Scaling: Inv. 2, 3 Moving Straight Ahead: Inv. 2, 4
7.RP.A.3	Use proportional relationships to solve multistep ratio and percent problems. Examples: simple interest, tax, markups and markdowns, gratuities and commissions, fees, percent increase and decrease, percent error.	Stretching and Shrinking: Inv. 4 Comparing and Scaling: Inv. 1, 2, 3

Number	Standard for Mathematical Content	CMP3 Unit: Investigation
7.NS.A	**Apply and extend previous understandings of operations with fractions to add, subtract, multiply, and divide rational numbers.**	
7.NS.A.1	Apply and extend previous understandings of addition and subtraction to add and subtract rational numbers; represent addition and subtraction on a horizontal or vertical number line diagram.	Accentuate the Negative: Inv. 1, 2, 4 Samples and Populations: Inv. 3
7.NS.A.1a	Describe situations in which opposite quantities combine to make 0. **For example:** a hydrogen atom has 0 charge because its two constituents are oppositely charged.	Acentuate the Negative: Inv. 1, 2
7.NS.A.1b	Understand $p + q$ as the number located a distance $|q|$ from p, in the positive or negative direction depending on whether q is positive or negative. Show that a number and its opposite have a sum of 0 (are additive inverses). Interpret sums of rational numbers by describing real-world contexts.	Accentuate the Negative: Inv. 1, 2 Samples and Populations: Inv. 3
7.NS.A.1c	Understand subtraction of rational numbers as adding the additive inverse, $p - q = p + (-q)$. Show that the distance between two rational numbers on the number line is the absolute value of their difference, and apply this principle in real-world contexts.	Accentuate the Negative: Inv. 1, 2
7.NS.A.1d	Apply properties of operations as strategies to add and subtract rational numbers.	Accentuate the Negative: Inv. 4
7.NS.A.2	Apply and extend previous understandings of multiplication and division and of fractions to multiply and divide rational numbers.	Accentuate the Negative: Inv. 3, 4
7.NS.A.2a	Understand that multiplication is extended from fractions to rational numbers by requiring that operations continue to satisfy the properties of operations, particularly the distributive property, leading to products such as $(-1)(-1) = 1$ and the rules for multiplying signed numbers. Interpret products of rational numbers by describing real-world contexts.	Accentuate the Negative: Inv. 3, 4
7.NS.A.2b	Understand that integers can be divided, provided that the divisor is not zero, and every quotient of integers (with non-zero divisor) is a rational number. If p and q are integers, then $-(p/q) = (-p)/q = p/(-q)$. Interpret quotients of rational numbers by describing real world contexts.	Accentuate the Negative: Inv. 3
7.NS.A.2c	Apply properties of operations as strategies to multiply and divide rational numbers.	Accentuate the Negative: Inv. 3, 4
7.NS.A.2d	Convert a rational number to a decimal using long division; know that the decimal form of a rational number terminates in 0s or eventually repeats.	Accentuate the Negative: Inv. 3, 4
7.NS.A.3	Solve real-world and mathematical problems involving the four operations with rational numbers.	Accentuate the Negative: Inv. 1, 2, 3, 4 Comparing and Scaling: Inv. 3 Filling and Wrapping: Inv 2, 3, 4

Grade 7 *continued*

Number	Standard for Mathematical Content	CMP3 Unit: Investigation
7.EE.A	**Use properties of operations to generate equivalent expressions.**	
7.EE.A.1	Apply properties of operations as strategies to add, subtract, factor, and expand linear expressions with rational coefficients.	Moving Straight Ahead: Inv. 3, 4 Filling and Wrapping: Inv. 3
7.EE.A.2	Understand that rewriting an expression in different forms in a problem context can shed light on the problem and how the quantities in it are related. **For example:** $a + 0.05a = 1.05a$ means that "increase by 5%" is the same as "multiply by 1.05."	Shapes and Designs: Inv. 2 Moving Straight Ahead: Inv. 3, 4 Filling and Wrapping: Inv. 1, 3
7.EE.B	**Solve real-life and mathematical problems using numerical and algebraic expressions and equations.**	
7.EE.B.3	Solve multi-step real-life and mathematical problems posed with positive and negative rational numbers in any form (whole numbers, fractions, and decimals), using tools strategically. Apply properties of operations to calculate with numbers in any form; convert between forms as appropriate; and assess the reasonableness of answers using mental computation and estimation strategies. **For example,** If a woman making $25 an hour gets a 10% raise, she will make an additional $\frac{1}{10}$ of her salary an hour, or $2.50, for a new salary of $27.50. If you want to place a towel bar 9¾ inches long in the center of a door that is 27½ inches wide, you will need to place the bar about 9 inches from each edge; this estimate can be used as a check on the exact computation.	Accentuate the Negative: Inv. 2, 3, 4 Stretching and Shrinking: Inv. 4 Comparing and Scaling: Inv. 3 Moving Straight Ahead: Inv. 1, 2, 3, 4
7.EE.B.4	Use variables to represent quantities in a real-world or mathematical problem, and construct simple equations and inequalities to solve problems by reasoning about the quantities.	Shapes and Designs: Inv. 2 Accentuate the Negative: Inv. 1 Stretching and Shrinking: Inv. 4 Comparing and Scaling: Inv. 1, 2, 3 Moving Straight Ahead: Inv. 1, 2, 3, 4
7.EE.B.4a	Solve word problems leading to equations of the form $px + q = r$ and $p(x + q) = r$, where p, q, and r are specific rational numbers. Solve equations of these forms fluently. Compare an algebraic solution to an arithmetic solution, identifying the sequence of the operations used in each approach. **For example:** the perimeter of a rectangle is 54 cm. Its length is 6 cm. What is its width?	Comparing and Scaling: Inv. 2, 3 Moving Straight Ahead: Inv. 1, 2, 3, 4
7.EE.B.4b	Solve word problems leading to inequalities of the form $px + q > r$ or $px + q < r$, where p, q, and r are specific rational numbers. Graph the solution set of the inequality and interpret it in the context of the problem. **For example:** As a salesperson, you are paid $50 per week plus $3 per sale. This week you want your pay to be at least $100. Write an inequality for the number of sales you need to make, and describe the solutions.	Accentuate the Negative: Inv. 1 Moving Straight Ahead: Inv. 3

Number	Standard for Mathematical Content	CMP3 Unit: Investigation
7.G.A	**Draw, construct, and describe geometrical figures and describe the relationships between them.**	
7.G.A.1	Solve problems involving scale drawings of geometric figures, including computing actual lengths and areas from a scale drawing and reproducing a scale drawing at a different scale.	Stretching and Shrinking: Inv. 1, 2, 3, 4 Filling and Wrapping: Inv. 1
7.G.A.2	Draw (freehand, with ruler and protractor, and with technology) geometric shapes with given conditions. Focus on constructing triangles from three measures of angles or sides, noticing when the conditions determine a unique triangle, more than one triangle, or no triangle.	Shapes and Designs: Inv. 1, 2, 3 Stretching and Shrinking: Inv. 1, 3
7.G.A.3	Describe the two-dimensional figures that result from slicing three dimensional figures, as in plane sections of right rectangular prisms and right rectangular pyramids.	Filling and Wrapping: Inv. 2
7.G.B	**Solve real-life and mathematical problems involving angle measure, area, surface area, and volume.**	
7.G.B.4	Know the formulas for the area and circumference of a circle and use them to solve problems; give an informal derivation of the relationship between the circumference and area of a circle.	Filling and Wrapping: Inv. 3, 4
7.G.B.5	Use facts about supplementary, complementary, vertical, and adjacent angles in a multi-step problem to write and solve simple equations for an unknown angle in a figure.	Shapes and Designs: Inv. 3
7.G.B.6	Solve real-world and mathematical problems involving area, volume and surface area of two- and three-dimensional objects composed of triangles, quadrilaterals, polygons, cubes, and right prisms.	Stretching and Shrinking: Inv. 1, 2, 3, 4 Filling and Wrapping: Inv. 1, 2, 3, 4
7.SP.A	**Use random sampling to draw inferences about a population.**	
7.SP.A.1	Understand that statistics can be used to gain information about a population by examining a sample of the population; generalizations about a population from a sample are valid only if the sample is representative of that population. Understand that random sampling tends to produce representative samples and support valid inferences.	
7.SP.A.2	Use data from a random sample to draw inferences about a population with an unknown characteristic of interest. Generate multiple samples (or simulated samples) of the same size to gauge the variation in estimates or predictions. **For example:** estimate the mean word length in a book by randomly sampling words from the book; predict the winner of a school election based on randomly sampled survey data. Gauge how far off the estimate or prediction might be.	Samples and Populations: Inv. 2, 3

Grade 7 *continued*

Number	Standard for Mathematical Content	CMP3 Unit: Investigation
7.SP.B	**Draw informal comparative inferences about two populations.**	
7.SP.B.3	Informally assess the degree of visual overlap of two numerical data distributions with similar variabilities, measuring the difference between the centers by expressing it as a multiple of a measure of variability. **For example:** the mean height of players on the basketball team is 10 cm greater than the mean height of players on the soccer team, about twice the variability (mean absolute deviation) on either team; on a dot plot, the separation between the two distributions of heights is noticeable.	Samples and Populations: Inv. 3
7.SP.B.4	Use measures of center and measures of variability for numerical data from random samples to draw informal comparative inferences about two populations. **For example:** decide whether the words in a chapter of a seventh-grade science book are generally longer than the words in a chapter of a fourth-grade science book.	Samples and Populations: Inv. 1, 3
7.SP.C	**Investigate chance processes and develop, use, and evaluate probability models.**	
7.SP.C.5	Understand that the probability of a chance event is a number between 0 and 1 that expresses the likelihood of the event occurring. Larger numbers indicate greater likelihood. A probability near 0 indicates an unlikely event, a probability around ½ indicates an event that is neither unlikely nor likely, and a probability near 1 indicates a likely event.	What Do You Expect?: Inv. 2, 3, 4, 5 Samples and Populations: Inv. 3
7.SP.C.6	Approximate the probability of a chance event by collecting data on the chance process that produces it and observing its long-run relative frequency, and predict the approximate relative frequency given the probability. **For example:** when rolling a number cube 600 times, predict that a 3 or 6 would be rolled roughly 200 times, but probably not exactly 200 times.	What Do You Expect?: Inv. 1, 2, 3, 4
7.SP.C.7	Develop a probability model and use it to find probabilities of events. Compare probabilities from a model to observed frequencies; if the agreement is not good, explain possible sources of the discrepancy.	What Do You Expect?: Inv. 2, 3, 4, 5 Samples and Populations: Inv. 3
7.SP.C.7a	Develop a uniform probability model by assigning equal probability to all outcomes, and use the model to determine probabilities of events. **For example:** if a student is selected at random from a class, find the probability that Jane will be selected and the probability that a girl will be selected.	What Do You Expect?: Inv. 1, 3, 4, 5 Samples and Populations: Inv. 3

Number	Standard for Mathematical Content	CMP3 Unit: Investigation
7.SP.C.7b	Develop a probability model (which may not be uniform) by observing frequencies in data generated from a chance process. **For example:** find the approximate probability that a spinning penny will land heads up or that a tossed paper cup will land open-end down. Do the outcomes for the spinning penny appear to be equally likely based on the observed frequencies?	What Do You Expect?: Inv. 1, 2, 3, 4
7.SP.C.8	Find probabilities of compound events using organized lists, tables, tree diagrams, and simulation.	What Do You Expect?: Inv. 2, 3, 4, 5
7.SP.C.8a	Understand that, just as with simple events, the probability of a compound event is the fraction of outcomes in the sample space for which the compound event occurs.	What Do You Expect?: Inv. 2, 3, 4, 5
7.SP.C.8b	Represent sample spaces for compound events using methods such as organized lists, tables and tree diagrams. For an event described in everyday language (e.g., "rolling double sixes"), identify the outcomes in the sample space which compose the event.	What Do You Expect?: Inv. 2, 4, 5
7.SP.C.8c	Design and use a simulation to generate frequencies for compound events. **For example:** use random digits as a simulation tool to approximate the answer to the question: If 40% of donors have type A blood, what is the probability that it will take at least 4 donors to find one with type A blood?	What Do You Expect?: Inv. 4, 5

Grade 8

Number	Standard for Mathematical Content	CMP3 Unit: Investigation
8.NS.A	**Know that there are numbers that are not rational, and approximate them by rational numbers.**	
8.NS.A.1	Understand informally that every number has a decimal expansion; the rational numbers are those with decimal expansions that terminate in 0s or eventually repeat. Know that other numbers are called irrational.	Looking for Pythagoras: Inv. 4
8.NS.A.2	Use rational approximations of irrational numbers to compare the size of irrational numbers, locate them approximately on a number line diagram, and estimate the value of expressions (e.g., π^2). For example, by truncating the decimal expansion of $\sqrt{2}$, show that $\sqrt{2}$ is between 1 and 2, then between 1.4 and 1.5, and explain how to continue on to get better approximations.	Looking for Pythagoras: Inv. 2, 4
8.EE.A	**Work with radicals and integer exponents.**	
8.EE.A.1	Know and apply the properties of integer exponents to generate equivalent numerical expressions. For example, $3^2 \times 3^{-5} = 3^{-3} = (1/3)^3 = 1/27$.	Growing, Growing, Growing: Inv. 5
8.EE.A.2	Use square root and cube root symbols to represent solutions to equations of the form $x^2 = p$ and $x^3 = p$, where p is a positive rational number. Evaluate square roots of small perfect squares and cube roots of small perfect cubes. Know that $\sqrt{2}$ is irrational.	Looking for Pythagoras: Inv. 2, 4 Growing, Growing, Growing: Inv. 5 Say It With Symbols: Inv. 3
8.EE.A.3	Use numbers expressed in the form of a single digit times an integer power of 10 to estimate very large or very small quantities, and to express how many times as much one is than the other. For example, estimate the population of the United States as 3 × 108 and the population of the world as 7 × 109, and determine that the world population is more than 20 times larger.	Growing, Growing, Growing: Inv. 1, 5
8.EE.A.4	Perform operations with numbers expressed in scientific notation, including problems where both decimal and scientific notation are used. Use scientific notation and choose units of appropriate size for measurements of very large or very small quantities (e.g., use millimeters per year for seafloor spreading). Interpret scientific notation that has been generated by technology.	Growing, Growing, Growing: Inv. 5

Number	Standard for Mathematical Content	CMP3 Unit: Investigation
8.EE.B	**Understand the connections between proportional relationships, lines, and linear equations.**	
8.EE.B.5	Graph proportional relationships, interpreting the unit rate as the slope of the graph. Compare two different proportional relationships represented in different ways. For example, compare a distance-time graph to a distance-time equation to determine which of two moving objects has greater speed.	Thinking With Mathematical Models: Inv. 2, 3
8.EE.B.6	Use similar triangles to explain why the slope m is the same between any two distinct points on a non-vertical line in the coordinate plane; derive the equation $y = mx$ for a line through the origin and the equation $y = mx + b$ for a line intercepting the vertical axis at b.	Butterflies, Pinwheels, and Wallpaper: Inv. 4
8.EE.C	**Analyze and solve linear equations and pairs of simultaneous linear equations.**	
8.EE.C.7	Solve linear equations in one variable.	Thinking With Mathematical Models: Inv. 2 Say It With Symbols: Inv. 1, 2, 3, 4
8.EE.C.7a	Give examples of linear equations in one variable with one solution, infinitely many solutions, or no solutions. Show which of these possibilities is the case by successively transforming the given equation into simpler forms, until an equivalent equation of the form $x = a$, $a = a$, or $a = b$ results (where a and b are different numbers).	Looking for Pythagoras: Inv. 4 Say It With Symbols: Inv. 3
8.EE.C.7b	Solve linear equations with rational number coefficients, including equations whose solutions require expanding expressions using the distributive property and collecting like terms.	Thinking With Mathematical Models: Inv. 2 Say It With Symbols: Inv. 1, 2, 3, 4, 5
8.EE.C.8	Analyze and solve pairs of simultaneous linear equations.	Thinking With Mathematical Models: Inv. 2 Say It With Symbols: Inv. 3 It's In the System: Inv. 1, 2
8.EE.C.8a	Understand that solutions to a system of two linear equations in two variables correspond to points of intersection of their graphs, because points of intersection satisfy both equations simultaneously.	Thinking With Mathematical Models: Inv. 2 Say It With Symbols: Inv. 3 It's In the System: Inv. 1, 2, 3

Number	Standard for Mathematical Content	CMP3 Unit: Investigation
8.EE.C.8b	Solve systems of two linear equations in two variables algebraically, and estimate solutions by graphing the equations. Solve simple cases by inspection. For example, $3x + 2y = 5$ and $3x + 2y = 6$ have no solution because $3x + 2y$ cannot simultaneously be 5 and 6.	Say It With Symbols: Inv. 3 It's In the System: Inv. 1, 2, 4
8.EE.C.8c	Solve real-world and mathematical problems leading to two linear equations in two variables. For example, given coordinates for two pairs of points, determine whether the line through the first pair of points intersects the line through the second pair.	Thinking With Mathematical Models: Inv. 2 Say It With Symbols: Inv. 3 It's In the System: Inv. 1, 2, 3, 4
8.F.A	**Define, evaluate, and compare functions.**	
8.F.A.1	Understand that a function is a rule that assigns to each input exactly one output. The graph of a function is the set of ordered pairs consisting of an input and the corresponding output.	Thinking With Mathematical Models: Inv. 2, 3, 4 Growing, Growing, Growing: Inv. 1, 2, 3, 4 Say It With Symbols: Inv. 2, 3, 4, 5
8.F.A.2	Compare properties of two functions each represented in a different way (algebraically, graphically, numerically in tables, or by verbal descriptions). For example, given a linear function represented by a table of values and a linear function represented by an algebraic expression, determine which function has the greater rate of change.	Thinking With Mathematical Models: Inv. 2 Growing, Growing, Growing: Inv. 3, 4 Say It With Symbols: Inv. 2, 5
8.F.A.3	Interpret the equation $y = mx + b$ as defining a linear function, whose graph is a straight line; give examples of functions that are not linear. For example, the function $A = s^2$ giving the area of a square as a function of its side length is not linear because its graph contains the points (1, 1), (2, 4) and (3, 9), which are not on a straight line.	Thinking With Mathematical Models: Inv. 2, 3 Growing, Growing, Growing: Inv. 1, 3, 5 Say It With Symbols: Inv. 1, 2, 4 It's In the System: Inv. 1
8.F.B	**Use functions to model relationships between quantities.**	
8.F.B.4	Construct a function to model a linear relationship between two quantities. Determine the rate of change and initial value of the function from a description of a relationship or from two (x, y) values, including reading these from a table or from a graph. Interpret the rate of change and initial value of a linear function in terms of the situation it models, and in terms of its graph or a table of values.	Thinking With Mathematical Models: Inv. 2, 4 Growing, Growing, Growing: Inv. 1 Say It With Symbols: Inv. 4, 5
8.F.B.5	Describe qualitatively the functional relationship between two quantities by analyzing a graph (e.g., where the function is increasing or decreasing, linear or nonlinear). Sketch a graph that exhibits the qualitative features of a function that has been described verbally.	Thinking With Mathematical Models: Inv. 1, 3, 4 Growing, Growing, Growing: Inv. 1, 2, 3, 4 Say It With Symbols: Inv. 4

Number	Standard for Mathematical Content	CMP3 Unit: Investigation
8.G.A	**Understand congruence and similarity using physical models, transparencies, or geometry software.**	
8.G.A.1	Verify experimentally the properties of rotations, reflections, and translations:	Butterflies, Pinwheels, and Wallpaper: Inv. 1, 2, 3
8.G.A.1a	Lines are taken to lines, and line segments to line segments of the same length.	Butterflies, Pinwheels, and Wallpaper: Inv. 1, 2, 3
8.G.A.1b	Angles are taken to angles of the same measure.	Butterflies, Pinwheels, and Wallpaper: Inv. 1, 2, 3
8.G.A.1c	Parallel lines are taken to parallel lines.	Butterflies, Pinwheels, and Wallpaper: Inv. 1, 3
8.G.A.2	Understand that a two-dimensional figure is congruent to another if the second can be obtained from the first by a sequence of rotations, reflections, and translations; given two congruent figures, describe a sequence that exhibits the congruence between them.	Butterflies, Pinwheels, and Wallpaper: Inv. 2, 3
8.G.A.3	Describe the effect of dilations, translations, rotations, and reflections on two-dimensional figures using coordinates.	Butterflies, Pinwheels, and Wallpaper: Inv. 3, 4
8.G.A.4	Understand that a two-dimensional figure is similar to another if the second can be obtained from the first by a sequence of rotations, reflections, translations, and dilations; given two similar twodimensional figures, describe a sequence that exhibits the similarity between them.	Looking for Pythagoras: Inv. 5 Butterflies, Pinwheels, and Wallpaper: Inv. 4
8.G.A.5	Use informal arguments to establish facts about the angle sum and exterior angle of triangles, about the angles created when parallel lines are cut by a transversal, and the angle-angle criterion for similarity of triangles. For example, arrange three copies of the same triangle so that the sum of the three angles appears to form a line, and give an argument in terms of transversals why this is so.	Butterflies, Pinwheels, and Wallpaper: Inv. 3, 4
8.G.B	**Understand and apply the Pythagorean Theorem.**	
8.G.B.6	Explain a proof of the Pythagorean Theorem and its converse.	Looking for Pythagoras: Inv. 3
8.G.B.7	Apply the Pythagorean Theorem to determine unknown side lengths in right triangles in real-world and mathematical problems in two and three dimensions.	Looking for Pythagoras: Inv. 3, 4, 5
8.G.B.8	Apply the Pythagorean Theorem to find the distance between two points in a coordinate system.	Looking for Pythagoras: Inv. 3, 5

Number	Standard for Mathematical Content	CMP3 Unit: Investigation
8.G.C	**Solve real-world and mathematical problems involving volume of cylinders, cones, and spheres.**	
8.G.C.9	Know the formulas for the volumes of cones, cylinders, and spheres and use them to solve real-world and mathematical problems.	Say It With Symbols: Inv. 2
8.SP.A	**Investigate patterns of association in bivariate data.**	
8.SP.A.1	Construct and interpret scatter plots for bivariate measurement data to investigate patterns of association between two quantities. Describe patterns such as clustering, outliers, positive or negative association, linear association, and nonlinear association.	Thinking With Mathematical Models: Inv. 1, 2, 3, 4
8.SP.A.2	Know that straight lines are widely used to model relationships between two quantitative variables. For scatter plots that suggest a linear association, informally fit a straight line, and informally assess the model fit by judging the closeness of the data points to the line.	Thinking With Mathematical Models: Inv. 2, 4
8.SP.A.3	Use the equation of a linear model to solve problems in the context of bivariate measurement data, interpreting the slope and intercept. For example, in a linear model for a biology experiment, interpret a slope of 1.5 cm/hr as meaning that an additional hour of sunlight each day is associated with an additional 1.5 cm in mature plant height.	Thinking With Mathematical Models: Inv. 2, 4
8.SP.A.4	Understand that patterns of association can also be seen in bivariate categorical data by displaying frequencies and relative frequencies in a two-way table. Construct and interpret a two-way table summarizing data on two categorical variables collected from the same subjects. Use relative frequencies calculated for rows or columns to describe possible association between the two variables. For example, collect data from students in your class on whether or not they have a curfew on school nights and whether or not they have assigned chores at home. Is there evidence that those who have a curfew also tend to have chores?	Thinking With Mathematical Models: Inv. 5

Grade 8 / Algebra 1

Number	Standard for Mathematical Content	CMP3 Unit: Investigation
8.NS.A	**Know that there are numbers that are not rational, and approximate them by rational numbers.**	
8.NS.A.1	Understand informally that every number has a decimal expansion; the rational numbers are those with decimal expansions that terminate in 0s or eventually repeat. Know that other numbers are called irrational.	Looking for Pythagoras: Inv. 4
8.NS.A.2	Use rational approximations of irrational numbers to compare the size of irrational numbers, locate them approximately on a number line diagram, and estimate the value of expressions (e.g., π^2). For example, by truncating the decimal expansion of $\sqrt{2}$, show that $\sqrt{2}$ is between 1 and 2, then between 1.4 and 1.5, and explain how to continue on to get better approximations.	Looking for Pythagoras: Inv. 2, 4
8.EE.A	**Work with radicals and integer exponents.**	
8.EE.A.1	Know and apply the properties of integer exponents to generate equivalent numerical expressions. For example, $3^2 \times 3^{-5} = 3^{-3} = (\frac{1}{3})^3 = \frac{1}{27}$.	Growing, Growing, Growing: Inv. 5
8.EE.A.2	Use square root and cube root symbols to represent solutions to equations of the form $x^2 = p$ and $x^3 = p$, where p is a positive rational number. Evaluate square roots of small perfect squares and cube roots of small perfect cubes. Know that $\sqrt{2}$ is irrational.	Looking for Pythagoras: Inv. 2, 4 Growing, Growing, Growing: Inv. 5 Say It With Symbols: Inv. 3
8.EE.A.3	Use numbers expressed in the form of a single digit times an integer power of 10 to estimate very large or very small quantities, and to express how many times as much one is than the other. For example, estimate the population of the United States as 3 × 108 and the population of the world as 7 × 109, and determine that the world population is more than 20 times larger.	Growing, Growing, Growing: Inv. 1, 5
8.EE.A.4	Perform operations with numbers expressed in scientific notation, including problems where both decimal and scientific notation are used. Use scientific notation and choose units of appropriate size for measurements of very large or very small quantities (e.g., use millimeters per year for seafloor spreading). Interpret scientific notation that has been generated by technology.	Growing, Growing, Growing: Inv. 5

Number	Standard for Mathematical Content	CMP3 Unit: Investigation
8.EE.B	**Understand the connections between proportional relationships, lines, and linear equations.**	
8.EE.B.5	Graph proportional relationships, interpreting the unit rate as the slope of the graph. Compare two different proportional relationships represented in different ways. For example, compare a distance-time graph to a distance-time equation to determine which of two moving objects has greater speed.	Thinking With Mathematical Models: Inv. 2, 3
8.EE.B.6	Use similar triangles to explain why the slope m is the same between any two distinct points on a non-vertical line in the coordinate plane; derive the equation $y = mx$ for a line through the origin and the equation $y = mx + b$ for a line intercepting the vertical axis at b.	Butterflies, Pinwheels, and Wallpaper: Inv. 4
8.EE.C	**Analyze and solve linear equations and pairs of simultaneous linear equations.**	
8.EE.C.7	Solve linear equations in one variable.	Thinking With Mathematical Models: Inv. 2 Say It With Symbols: Inv. 1, 2, 3, 4
8.EE.C.7a	Give examples of linear equations in one variable with one solution, infinitely many solutions, or no solutions. Show which of these possibilities is the case by successively transforming the given equation into simpler forms, until an equivalent equation of the form $x = a$, $a = a$, or $a = b$ results (where a and b are different numbers).	Looking for Pythagoras: Inv. 4 Say It With Symbols: Inv. 3
8.EE.C.7b	Solve linear equations with rational number coefficients, including equations whose solutions require expanding expressions using the distributive property and collecting like terms.	Thinking With Mathematical Models: Inv. 2 Say It With Symbols: Inv. 1, 2, 3, 4, 5
8.EE.C.8	Analyze and solve pairs of simultaneous linear equations.	Thinking With Mathematical Models: Inv. 2 Say It With Symbols: Inv. 3 It's In the System: Inv. 1, 2
8.EE.C.8a	Understand that solutions to a system of two linear equations in two variables correspond to points of intersection of their graphs, because points of intersection satisfy both equations simultaneously.	Thinking With Mathematical Models: Inv. 2 Say It With Symbols: Inv. 3 It's In the System: Inv. 1, 2, 3
8.EE.C.8b	Solve systems of two linear equations in two variables algebraically, and estimate solutions by graphing the equations. Solve simple cases by inspection. For example, $3x + 2y = 5$ and $3x + 2y = 6$ have no solution because $3x + 2y$ cannot simultaneously be 5 and 6.	Say It With Symbols: Inv. 3 It's In the System: Inv. 1, 2, 4
8.EE.C.8c	Solve real-world and mathematical problems leading to two linear equations in two variables. For example, given coordinates for two pairs of points, determine whether the line through the first pair of points intersects the line through the second pair.	Thinking With Mathematical Models: Inv. 2 Say It With Symbols: Inv. 3 It's In the System: Inv. 1, 2, 3, 4

Number	Standard for Mathematical Content	CMP3 Unit: Investigation
8.F.A	**Define, evaluate, and compare functions.**	
8.F.A.1	Understand that a function is a rule that assigns to each input exactly one output. The graph of a function is the set of ordered pairs consisting of an input and the corresponding output.	Thinking With Mathematical Models: Inv. 2, 3, 4 Growing, Growing, Growing: Inv. 1, 2, 3, 4 Say It With Symbols: Inv. 2, 3, 4, 5
8.F.A.2	Compare properties of two functions each represented in a different way (algebraically, graphically, numerically in tables, or by verbal descriptions). For example, given a linear function represented by a table of values and a linear function represented by an algebraic expression, determine which function has the greater rate of change.	Thinking With Mathematical Models: Inv. 2 Growing, Growing, Growing: Inv. 3, 4 Say It With Symbols: Inv. 2, 5
8.F.A.3	Interpret the equation $y = mx + b$ as defining a linear function, whose graph is a straight line; give examples of functions that are not linear. For example, the function $A = s^2$ giving the area of a square as a function of its side length is not linear because its graph contains the points (1, 1), (2, 4) and (3, 9), which are not on a straight line.	Thinking With Mathematical Models: Inv. 2, 3, 4 Growing, Growing, Growing: Inv. 1, 3, 5 Say It With Symbols: Inv. 1, 2, 4 It's In the System: Inv. 1
8.F.B	**Use functions to model relationships between quantities.**	
8.F.B.4	Construct a function to model a linear relationship between two quantities. Determine the rate of change and initial value of the function from a description of a relationship or from two (x, y) values, including reading these from a table or from a graph. Interpret the rate of change and initial value of a linear function in terms of the situation it models, and in terms of its graph or a table of values.	Thinking With Mathematical Models: Inv. 2, 4 Growing, Growing, Growing: Inv. 1 Say It With Symbols: Inv. 4, 5
8.F.B.5	Describe qualitatively the functional relationship between two quantities by analyzing a graph (e.g., where the function is increasing or decreasing, linear or nonlinear). Sketch a graph that exhibits the qualitative features of a function that has been described verbally.	Thinking With Mathematical Models: Inv. 1, 3, 4 Growing, Growing, Growing: Inv. 1, 2, 3, 4 Say It With Symbols: Inv. 4

Grade 8 / Algebra 1 *continued*

As Identified by PARCC

Number	Standard for Mathematical Content	CMP3 Unit: Investigation
8.G.A	**Understand congruence and similarity using physical models, transparencies, or geometry software.**	
8.G.A.1	Verify experimentally the properties of rotations, reflections, and translations:	Butterflies, Pinwheels, and Wallpaper: Inv. 1, 2, 3
8.G.A.1a	Lines are taken to lines, and line segments to line segments of the same length.	Butterflies, Pinwheels, and Wallpaper: Inv. 1, 2, 3
8.G.A.1b	Angles are taken to angles of the same measure.	Butterflies, Pinwheels, and Wallpaper: Inv. 1, 2, 3
8.G.A.1c	Parallel lines are taken to parallel lines.	Butterflies, Pinwheels, and Wallpaper: Inv. 1, 3
8.G.A.2	Understand that a two-dimensional figure is congruent to another if the second can be obtained from the first by a sequence of rotations, reflections, and translations; given two congruent figures, describe a sequence that exhibits the congruence between them.	Butterflies, Pinwheels, and Wallpaper: Inv. 2, 3
8.G.A.3	Describe the effect of dilations, translations, rotations, and reflections on two-dimensional figures using coordinates.	Butterflies, Pinwheels, and Wallpaper: Inv. 3, 4
8.G.A.4	Understand that a two-dimensional figure is similar to another if the second can be obtained from the first by a sequence of rotations, reflections, translations, and dilations; given two similar twodimensional figures, describe a sequence that exhibits the similarity between them.	Looking for Pythagoras: Inv. 5 Butterflies, Pinwheels, and Wallpaper: Inv. 4
8.G.A.5	Use informal arguments to establish facts about the angle sum and exterior angle of triangles, about the angles created when parallel lines are cut by a transversal, and the angle-angle criterion for similarity of triangles. For example, arrange three copies of the same triangle so that the sum of the three angles appears to form a line, and give an argument in terms of transversals why this is so.	Butterflies, Pinwheels, and Wallpaper: Inv. 3, 4
8.G.B	**Understand and apply the Pythagorean Theorem.**	
8.G.B.6	Explain a proof of the Pythagorean Theorem and its converse.	Looking for Pythagoras: Inv. 3
8.G.B.7	Apply the Pythagorean Theorem to determine unknown side lengths in right triangles in real-world and mathematical problems in two and three dimensions.	Looking for Pythagoras: Inv. 3, 4, 5
8.G.B.8	Apply the Pythagorean Theorem to find the distance between two points in a coordinate system.	Looking for Pythagoras: Inv. 3, 5

A51 Implementing and Teaching CMP3

Number	Standard for Mathematical Content	CMP3 Unit: Investigation
8.G.C	**Solve real-world and mathematical problems involving volume of cylinders, cones, and spheres.**	
8.G.C.9	Know the formulas for the volumes of cones, cylinders, and spheres and use them to solve real-world and mathematical problems.	Say It With Symbols: Inv. 2
8.SP.A	**Investigate patterns of association in bivariate data.**	
8.SP.A.1	Construct and interpret scatter plots for bivariate measurement data to investigate patterns of association between two quantities. Describe patterns such as clustering, outliers, positive or negative association, linear association, and nonlinear association.	Thinking With Mathematical Models: Inv. 1, 2, 3, 4
8.SP.A.2	Know that straight lines are widely used to model relationships between two quantitative variables. For scatter plots that suggest a linear association, informally fit a straight line, and informally assess the model fit by judging the closeness of the data points to the line.	Thinking With Mathematical Models: Inv. 2, 4
8.SP.A.3	Use the equation of a linear model to solve problems in the context of bivariate measurement data, interpreting the slope and intercept. For example, in a linear model for a biology experiment, interpret a slope of 1.5 cm/hr as meaning that an additional hour of sunlight each day is associated with an additional 1.5 cm in mature plant height.	Thinking With Mathematical Models: Inv. 2, 4
8.SP.A.4	Understand that patterns of association can also be seen in bivariate categorical data by displaying frequencies and relative frequencies in a two-way table. Construct and interpret a two-way table summarizing data on two categorical variables collected from the same subjects. Use relative frequencies calculated for rows or columns to describe possible association between the two variables. For example, collect data from students in your class on whether or not they have a curfew on school nights and whether or not they have assigned chores at home. Is there evidence that those who have a curfew also tend to have chores?	Thinking With Mathematical Models: Inv. 5

Number	Standard for Mathematical Content	CMP3 Unit: Investigation
N-Q.A	**Reason quantitatively and use units to solve problems.**	
N-Q.A.1	Use units as a way to understand problems and to guide the solution of multi-step problems; choose and interpret units consistently in formulas; choose and interpret the scale and the origin in graphs and data displays.	Thinking With Mathematical Models: Inv. 1, 2, 4 Growing, Growing, Growing: Inv. 2, 4 Frogs, Fleas, and Painted Cubes: Inv. 1 Say It With Symbols: Inv. 2, 3, 4 Function Junction: Inv. 1
N-Q.A.2	Define appropriate quantities for the purpose of descriptive modeling.	Thinking With Mathematical Models: Inv. 1 Growing, Growing, Growing: Inv. 2, 4 Say It With Symbols: Inv. 2, 4 Function Junction: Inv. 1
N-Q.A.3	Choose a level of accuracy appropriate to limitations on measurement when reporting quantities.	Looking for Pythagoras: Inv. 2, 4, 5
N-RN.B	**Use properties of rational and irrational numbers.**	
N-RN.B.3	Explain why the sum or product of two rational numbers is rational; that the sum of a rational number and an irrational number is irrational; and that the product of a nonzero rational number and an irrational number is irrational.	Say It With Symbols: Inv. 5
A-SSE.A	**Interpret the structure of expressions**	
A-SSE.A.1	Interpret expressions that represent a quantity in terms of its context.	
A-SSE.A.1a	Interpret parts of an expression, such as terms, factors, and coefficients.	Thinking With Mathematical Models: Inv. 2 Growing, Growing, Growing: Inv. 1, 2, 3, 4, 5 Frogs, Fleas, and Painted Cubes: Inv. 2 Say It With Symbols: Inv. 1, 2, 3, 4, 5
A-SSE.A.1b	Interpret complicated expressions by viewing one or more of their parts as a single entity. For example, interpret $P(1+r)n$ as the product of P and a factor not depending on P.	Growing, Growing, Growing: Inv. 3, 4 Frogs, Fleas, and Painted Cubes: Inv. 1, 2, 3 Say It With Symbols: Inv. 1, 2, 3, 4, 5
A-SSE.A.2	Use the structure of an expression to identify ways to rewrite it. For example, see $x^4 - y^4$ as $(x^2)^2 - (y^2)^2$, thus recognizing it as a difference of squares that can be factored as $(x^2 - y^2)(x^2 + y^2)$.	Growing, Growing, Growing: Inv. 5 Frogs, Fleas, and Painted Cubes: Inv. 2, 3 Say It With Symbols: Inv. 1, 2, 3, 4, 5 Function Junction: Inv. 4

Number	Standard for Mathematical Content	CMP3 Unit: Investigation
A-SSE.B	**Write expressions in equivalent forms to solve problems**	
A-SSE.B.3	Choose and produce an equivalent form of an expression to reveal and explain properties of the quantity represented by the expression.	
A-SSE.B.3a	Factor a quadratic expression to reveal the zeros of the function it defines.	Say It With Symbols: Inv. 3, 4
A-SSE.B.3b	Complete the square in a quadratic expression to reveal the maximum or minimum value of the function it defines.	Function Junction: Inv. 4
A-SSE.B.3c	Use the properties of exponents to transform expressions for exponential functions. For example the expression $1.15t$ can be rewritten as $(^{1.15}\!/_{12})12t \approx 1.01212t$ to reveal the approximate equivalent monthly interest rate if the annual rate is 15%.	Growing, Growing, Growing: Inv. 5
A-APR.A	**Perform arithmetic operations on polynomials**	
A-APR.A.1	Understand that polynomials form a system analogous to the integers, namely, they are closed under the operations of addition, subtraction, and multiplication; add, subtract, and multiply polynomials.	Function Junction: Inv. 5
A-APR.B	**Understand the relationship between zeros and factors of polynomials**	
A-APR.B.3	Identify zeros of polynomials when suitable factorizations are available, and use the zeros to construct a rough graph of the function defined by the polynomial.	Function Junction: Inv. 4, 5
A-CED.A	**Create equations that describe numbers or relationships**	
A-CED.A.1	Create equations and inequalities in one variable and use them to solve problems. Include equations arising from linear and quadratic functions, and simple rational and exponential functions.	Thinking With Mathematical Models: Inv. 2 Looking for Pythagoras: Inv. 4 Growing, Growing, Growing: Inv. 1 Frogs, Fleas, and Painted Cubes: Inv. 1 Say It With Symbols: Inv. 2, 3, 4, 5 It's In the System: Inv. 3

A-CED.A.2	Create equations in two or more variables to represent relationships between quantities; graph equations on coordinate axes with labels and scales.	Thinking With Mathematical Models:
		  Inv. 2, 3, 4
		Looking for Pythagoras: Inv. 5
		Growing, Growing, Growing: Inv. 1, 2, 3, 4
		Frogs, Fleas, and Painted Cubes:
		  Inv. 1, 2, 3, 4
		Say It With Symbols: Inv. 3, 4, 5
		It's In the System: Inv. 1, 2, 3, 4

A-CED.A.3	Represent constraints by equations or inequalities, and by systems of equations and/or inequalities, and interpret solutions as viable or nonviable options in a modeling context. For example, represent inequalities describing nutritional and cost constraints on combinations of different foods.	It's In the System: Inv. 1, 2, 3, 4
A-CED.A.4	Rearrange formulas to highlight a quantity of interest, using the same reasoning as in solving equations. For example, rearrange Ohm's law $V = IR$ to highlight resistance R.	Thinking With Mathematical Models: Inv. 3 It's In the System: Inv. 1, 2

Number	Standard for Mathematical Content	CMP3 Unit: Investigation
A-REI.A	**Understand solving equations as a process of reasoning and explain the reasoning**	
A-REI.A.1	Explain each step in solving a simple equation as following from the equality of numbers asserted at the previous step, starting from the assumption that the original equation has a solution. Construct a viable argument to justify a solution method.	Thinking With Mathematical Models: Inv. 2 Say It With Symbols: Inv. 3
A-REI.B	**Solve equations and inequalities in one variable**	
A-REI.B.3	Solve linear equations and inequalities in one variable, including equations with coefficients represented by letters.	Thinking With Mathematical Models: Inv. 2 Say It With Symbols: Inv. 2, 3, 4 It's In the System: Inv. 1, 2, 3
A-REI.B.4	Solve quadratic equations in one variable.	
A-REI.B.4a	Use the method of completing the square to transform any quadratic equation in x into an equation of the form $(x - p)^2 = q$ that has the same solutions. Derive the quadratic formula from this form.	Function Junction: Inv. 4
A-REI.B.4b	Solve quadratic equations by inspection (e.g., for $x^2 = 49$), taking square roots, completing the square, the quadratic formula and factoring, as appropriate to the initial form of the equation. Recognize when the quadratic formula gives complex solutions and write them as $a \pm bi$ for real numbers a and b.	Say It With Symbols: Inv. 3, 4 It's In the System: Inv. 3 Function Junction: Inv. 4
A-REI.C	**Solve systems of equations**	
A-REI.C.5	Prove that, given a system of two equations in two variables, replacing one equation by the sum of that equation and a multiple of the other produces a system with the same solutions.	It's In the System: Inv. 2
A-REI.C.6	Solve systems of linear equations exactly and approximately (e.g., with graphs), focusing on pairs of linear equations in two variables.	Thinking With Mathematical Models: Inv. 2 Say It With Symbols: Inv. 3 It's In the System: Inv. 1, 2, 4
A-REI.D	**Represent and solve equations and inequalities graphically**	
A-REI.D.10	Understand that the graph of an equation in two variables is the set of all its solutions plotted in the coordinate plane, often forming a curve (which could be a line).	Looking for Pythagoras: Inv. 5 Growing, Growing, Growing: Inv. 1, 2, 3, 4 Frogs, Fleas, and Painted Cubes: Inv. 1, 2, 3, 4 Say It With Symbols: Inv. 3 It's In the System: Inv. 1, 2, 3, 4
A-REI.D.11	Explain why the x-coordinates of the points where the graphs of the equations $y = f(x)$ and $y = g(x)$ intersect are the solutions of the equation $f(x) = g(x)$; find the solutions approximately, e.g., using technology to graph the functions, make tables of values, or find successive approximations. Include cases where $f(x)$ and/or $g(x)$ are linear, polynomial, rational, absolute value, exponential, and logarithmic functions.	Say It With Symbols: Inv. 3

Number	Standard for Mathematical Content	CMP3 Unit: Investigation
A-REI.D.12	Graph the solutions to a linear inequality in two variables as a halfplane (excluding the boundary in the case of a strict inequality), and graph the solution set to a system of linear inequalities in two variables as the intersection of the corresponding half-planes.	It's In the System: Inv. 4
F-IF.A	**Understand the concept of a function and use function notation**	
F-IF.A.1	Understand that a function from one set (called the domain) to another set (called the range) assigns to each element of the domain exactly one element of the range. If f is a function and x is an element of its domain, then $f(x)$ denotes the output of f corresponding to the input x. The graph of f is the graph of the equation $y = f(x)$.	Thinking With Mathematical Models: Inv. 2 Function Junction: Inv. 1
F-IF.A.2	Use function notation, evaluate functions for inputs in their domains, and interpret statements that use function notation in terms of a context.	Function Junction: Inv. 1
F-IF.A.3	Recognize that sequences are functions, sometimes defined recursively, whose domain is a subset of the integers. For example, the Fibonacci sequence is defined recursively by $f(0) = f(1) = 1$, $f(n + 1) = f(n) + f(n - 1)$ for $n \geq 1$.	Function Junction: Inv. 2
F-IF.B	**Interpret functions that arise in applications in terms of the context**	
F-IF.B.4	For a function that models a relationship between two quantities, interpret key features of graphs and tables in terms of the quantities, and sketch graphs showing key features given a verbal description of the relationship. Key features include: intercepts; intervals where the function is increasing, decreasing, positive, or negative; relative maximums and minimums; symmetries; end behavior; and periodicity.	Thinking With Mathematical Models: Inv. 1 Growing, Growing, Growing: Inv. 1, 2, 3, 4 Frogs, Fleas, and Painted Cubes: Inv. 1, 2, 3, 4 Function Junction: Inv. 1, 5
F-IF.B.5	Relate the domain of a function to its graph and, where applicable, to the quantitative relationship it describes. For example, if the function $h(n)$ gives the number of person-hours it takes to assemble n engines in a factory, then the positive integers would be an appropriate domain for the function.	Function Junction: Inv. 1
F-IF.B.6	Calculate and interpret the average rate of change of a function (presented symbolically or as a table) over a specified interval. Estimate the rate of change from a graph.	Thinking With Mathematical Models: Inv. 1 Growing, Growing, Growing: Inv. 3, 4 Function Junction: Inv. 1

Number	Standard for Mathematical Content	CMP3 Unit: Investigation
F-IF.C	**Analyze functions using different representations**	
F-IF.C.7	Graph functions expressed symbolically and show key features of the graph, by hand in simple cases and using technology for more complicated cases.	
F-IF.C.7a	Graph linear and quadratic functions and show intercepts, maxima, and minima.	Frogs, Fleas, and Painted Cubes: Inv. 1, 2, 3, 4 Function Junction: Inv. 3
F-IF.C.7b	Graph square root, cube root, and piecewise-defined functions, including step functions and absolute value functions.	Function Junction: Inv. 1
F-IF.C.8	Write a function defined by an expression in different but equivalent forms to reveal and explain different properties of the function.	
F-IF.C.8a	Use the process of factoring and completing the square in a quadratic function to show zeros, extreme values, and symmetry of the graph, and interpret these in terms of a context.	Frogs, Fleas, and Painted Cubes: Inv. 2 Function Junction: Inv. 4
F-IF.C.9	Compare properties of two functions each represented in a different way (algebraically, graphically, numerically in tables, or by verbal descriptions). For example, given a graph of one quadratic function and an algebraic expression for another, say which has the larger maximum.	Thinking With Mathematical Models: Inv. 1 Growing, Growing, Growing: Inv. 1, 4 Frogs, Fleas, and Painted Cubes: Inv. 1, 3, 4 Say It With Symbols: Inv. 1, 2, 4 Function Junction: Inv. 3, 5
F-BF.A	**Build a function that models a relationship between two quantities**	
F-BF.A.1	Write a function that describes a relationship between two quantities.	
F-BF.A.1a	Determine an explicit expression, a recursive process, or steps for calculation from a context.	Thinking With Mathematical Models: Inv. 1, 2, 3 Frogs, Fleas, and Painted Cubes: Inv. 2, 3 Say It With Symbols: Inv. 1, 2, 4 Function Junction: Inv. 2

Number	Standard for Mathematical Content	CMP3 Unit: Investigation
F-BF.B	**Build new functions from existing functions**	
F-BF.B.3	Identify the effect on the graph of replacing $f(x)$ by $f(x) + k$, $k\,f(x)$, $f(kx)$, and $f(x + k)$ for specific values of k (both positive and negative); find the value of k given the graphs. Experiment with cases and illustrate an explanation of the effects on the graph using technology. Include recognizing even and odd functions from their graphs and algebraic expressions for them.	Function Junction: Inv. 3
F-LE.A	**Construct and compare linear and exponential models and solve problems**	
F-LE.A.1	Distinguish between situations that can be modeled with linear functions and with exponential functions.	
F-LE.A.1a	Prove that linear functions grow by equal differences over equal intervals, and that exponential functions grow by equal factors over equal intervals.	Growing, Growing, Growing: Inv. 1, 3, 4 Frogs, Fleas, and Painted Cubes: Inv. 3, 4
F-LE.A.1b	Recognize situations in which one quantity changes at a constant rate per unit interval relative to another.	Thinking With Mathematical Models: Inv. 1 Frogs, Fleas, and Painted Cubes: Inv. 3, 4
F-LE.A.1c	Recognize situations in which a quantity grows or decays by a constant percent rate per unit interval relative to another.	Growing, Growing, Growing: Inv. 3, 4
F-LE.A.2	Construct linear and exponential functions, including arithmetic and geometric sequences, given a graph, a description of a relationship, or two input-output pairs (include reading these from a table).	Thinking With Mathematical Models: Inv. 2 Growing, Growing, Growing: Inv. 1, 2, 3, 4 Say It With Symbols: Inv. 4
F-LE.A.3	Observe using graphs and tables that a quantity increasing exponentially eventually exceeds a quantity increasing linearly, quadratically, or (more generally) as a polynomial function.	Growing, Growing, Growing: Inv. 1
F-LE.B	**Interpret expressions for functions in terms of the situation they model**	
F-LE.B.5	Interpret the parameters in a linear or exponential function in terms of a context.	Thinking With Mathematical Models: Inv. 2 Growing, Growing, Growing: Inv. 1, 2, 3, 4 Say It With Symbols: Inv. 4

Number	Standard for Mathematical Content	CMP3 Unit: Investigation
S-ID.A	**Summarize, represent, and interpret data on a single count or measurement variable**	
S-ID.A.1	Represent data with plots on the real number line (dot plots, histograms, and box plots).	Thinking With Mathematical Models: Inv. 4
S-ID.A.2	Use statistics appropriate to the shape of the data distribution to compare center (median, mean) and spread (interquartile range, standard deviation) of two or more different data sets.	Thinking With Mathematical Models: Inv. 4
S-ID.A.3	Interpret differences in shape, center, and spread in the context of the data sets, accounting for possible effects of extreme data points (outliers).	Thinking With Mathematical Models: Inv. 4
S-ID.B	**Summarize, represent, and interpret data on two categorical and quantitative variables**	
S-ID.B.5	Summarize categorical data for two categories in two-way frequency tables. Interpret relative frequencies in the context of the data (including joint, marginal, and conditional relative frequencies). Recognize possible associations and trends in the data.	Thinking With Mathematical Models: Inv. 5
S-ID.B.6	Represent data on two quantitative variables on a scatter plot, and describe how the variables are related.	
S-ID.B.6a	Fit a function to the data; use functions fitted to data to solve problems in the context of the data. Use given functions or choose a function suggested by the context. Emphasize linear and exponential models.	Thinking With Mathematical Models: Inv. 2, 3
S-ID.B.6b	Informally assess the fit of a function by plotting and analyzing residuals.	Thinking With Mathematical Models: Inv. 2, 4
S-ID.B.6c	Fit a linear function for a scatter plot that suggests a linear association.	Thinking With Mathematical Models: Inv. 2
S-ID.C	**Interpret linear models**	
S-ID.C.7	Interpret the slope (rate of change) and the intercept (constant term) of a linear model in the context of the data.	Thinking With Mathematical Models: Inv. 4
S-ID.C.8	Compute (using technology) and interpret the correlation coefficient of a linear fit.	Thinking With Mathematical Models: Inv. 4
S-ID.C.9	Distinguish between correlation and causation.	Thinking With Mathematical Models: Inv. 4, 5

Grade 8 / Algebra 1

Number	Standard for Mathematical Content	CMP3 Unit: Investigation
8.NS.A	**Know that there are numbers that are not rational, and approximate them by rational numbers.**	
8.NS.A.1	Understand informally that every number has a decimal expansion; the rational numbers are those with decimal expansions that terminate in 0s or eventually repeat. Know that other numbers are called irrational.	Looking for Pythagoras: Inv. 4
8.NS.A.2	Use rational approximations of irrational numbers to compare the size of irrational numbers, locate them approximately on a number line diagram, and estimate the value of expressions (e.g., π^2). For example, by truncating the decimal expansion of $\sqrt2$, show that $\sqrt2$ is between 1 and 2, then between 1.4 and 1.5, and explain how to continue on to get better approximations.	Looking for Pythagoras: Inv. 2, 4
8.EE.A	**Work with radicals and integer exponents.**	
8.EE.A.1	Know and apply the properties of integer exponents to generate equivalent numerical expressions. For example, $3^2 \times 3^{-5} = 3^{-3} = (1/3)^3 = 1/27$.	Growing, Growing, Growing: Inv. 5
8.EE.A.2	Use square root and cube root symbols to represent solutions to equations of the form $x^2 = p$ and $x^3 = p$, where p is a positive rational number. Evaluate square roots of small perfect squares and cube roots of small perfect cubes. Know that $\sqrt2$ is irrational.	Looking for Pythagoras: Inv. 2, 4 Growing, Growing, Growing: Inv. 5 Say It With Symbols: Inv. 3
8.EE.A.3	Use numbers expressed in the form of a single digit times an integer power of 10 to estimate very large or very small quantities, and to express how many times as much one is than the other. For example, estimate the population of the United States as 3×108 and the population of the world as 7×109, and determine that the world population is more than 20 times larger.	Growing, Growing, Growing: Inv. 1, 5
8.EE.A.4	Perform operations with numbers expressed in scientific notation, including problems where both decimal and scientific notation are used. Use scientific notation and choose units of appropriate size for measurements of very large or very small quantities (e.g., use millimeters per year for seafloor spreading). Interpret scientific notation that has been generated by technology.	Growing, Growing, Growing: Inv. 5

Number	Standard for Mathematical Content	CMP3 Unit: Investigation
8.EE.B	**Understand the connections between proportional relationships, lines, and linear equations.**	
8.EE.B.5	Graph proportional relationships, interpreting the unit rate as the slope of the graph. Compare two different proportional relationships represented in different ways. For example, compare a distance-time graph to a distance-time equation to determine which of two moving objects has greater speed.	Thinking With Mathematical Models: Inv. 2, 3
8.EE.B.6	Use similar triangles to explain why the slope m is the same between any two distinct points on a non-vertical line in the coordinate plane; derive the equation $y = mx$ for a line through the origin and the equation $y = mx + b$ for a line intercepting the vertical axis at b.	Butterflies, Pinwheels, and Wallpaper: Inv. 4
8.EE.C	**Analyze and solve linear equations and pairs of simultaneous linear equations.**	
8.EE.C.7	Solve linear equations in one variable.	Thinking With Mathematical Models: Inv. 2 Say It With Symbols: Inv. 1, 2, 3, 4
8.EE.C.7a	Give examples of linear equations in one variable with one solution, infinitely many solutions, or no solutions. Show which of these possibilities is the case by successively transforming the given equation into simpler forms, until an equivalent equation of the form $x = a$, $a = a$, or $a = b$ results (where a and b are different numbers).	Looking for Pythagoras: Inv. 4 Say It With Symbols: Inv. 3
8.EE.C.7b	Solve linear equations with rational number coefficients, including equations whose solutions require expanding expressions using the distributive property and collecting like terms.	Thinking With Mathematical Models: Inv. 2 Say It With Symbols: Inv. 1, 2, 3, 4, 5
8.EE.C.8	Analyze and solve pairs of simultaneous linear equations.	Thinking With Mathematical Models: Inv. 2 Say It With Symbols: Inv. 3 It's In the System: Inv. 1, 2
8.EE.C.8a	Understand that solutions to a system of two linear equations in two variables correspond to points of intersection of their graphs, because points of intersection satisfy both equations simultaneously.	Thinking With Mathematical Models: Inv. 2 Say It With Symbols: Inv. 3 It's In the System: Inv. 1, 2, 3
8.EE.C.8b	Solve systems of two linear equations in two variables algebraically, and estimate solutions by graphing the equations. Solve simple cases by inspection. For example, $3x + 2y = 5$ and $3x + 2y = 6$ have no solution because $3x + 2y$ cannot simultaneously be 5 and 6.	Say It With Symbols: Inv. 3 It's In the System: Inv. 1, 2, 4
8.EE.C.8c	Solve real-world and mathematical problems leading to two linear equations in two variables. For example, given coordinates for two pairs of points, determine whether the line through the first pair of points intersects the line through the second pair.	Thinking With Mathematical Models: Inv. 2 Say It With Symbols: Inv. 3 It's In the System: Inv. 1, 2, 3, 4

Number	Standard for Mathematical Content	CMP3 Unit: Investigation
8.F.A	**Define, evaluate, and compare functions.**	
8.F.A.1	Understand that a function is a rule that assigns to each input exactly one output. The graph of a function is the set of ordered pairs consisting of an input and the corresponding output.	Thinking With Mathematical Models: Inv. 2, 3, 4 Growing, Growing, Growing: Inv. 1, 2, 3, 4 Say It With Symbols: Inv. 2, 3, 4, 5
8.F.A.2	Compare properties of two functions each represented in a different way (algebraically, graphically, numerically in tables, or by verbal descriptions). For example, given a linear function represented by a table of values and a linear function represented by an algebraic expression, determine which function has the greater rate of change.	Thinking With Mathematical Models: Inv. 2 Growing, Growing, Growing: Inv. 3, 4 Say It With Symbols: Inv. 2, 5
8.F.A.3	Interpret the equation $y = mx + b$ as defining a linear function, whose graph is a straight line; give examples of functions that are not linear. For example, the function $A = s^2$ giving the area of a square as a function of its side length is not linear because its graph contains the points (1, 1), (2, 4) and (3, 9), which are not on a straight line.	Thinking With Mathematical Models: Inv. 2, 3 Growing, Growing, Growing: Inv. 1, 3, 5 Say It With Symbols: Inv. 1, 2, 4 It's In the System: Inv. 1
8.F.B	**Use functions to model relationships between quantities.**	
8.F.B.4	Construct a function to model a linear relationship between two quantities. Determine the rate of change and initial value of the function from a description of a relationship or from two (x, y) values, including reading these from a table or from a graph. Interpret the rate of change and initial value of a linear function in terms of the situation it models, and in terms of its graph or a table of values.	Thinking With Mathematical Models: Inv. 2, 4 Growing, Growing, Growing: Inv. 1 Say It With Symbols: Inv. 4, 5
8.F.B.5	Describe qualitatively the functional relationship between two quantities by analyzing a graph (e.g., where the function is increasing or decreasing, linear or nonlinear). Sketch a graph that exhibits the qualitative features of a function that has been described verbally.	Thinking With Mathematical Models: Inv. 1, 3, 4 Growing, Growing, Growing: Inv. 1, 2, 3, 4 Say It With Symbols: Inv. 4

Number	Standard for Mathematical Content	CMP3 Unit: Investigation
8.G.A	**Understand congruence and similarity using physical models, transparencies, or geometry software.**	
8.G.A.1	Verify experimentally the properties of rotations, reflections, and translations:	Butterflies, Pinwheels, and Wallpaper: Inv. 1, 2, 3
8.G.A.1a	Lines are taken to lines, and line segments to line segments of the same length.	Butterflies, Pinwheels, and Wallpaper: Inv. 1, 2, 3
8.G.A.1b	Angles are taken to angles of the same measure.	Butterflies, Pinwheels, and Wallpaper: Inv. 1, 2, 3
8.G.A.1c	Parallel lines are taken to parallel lines.	Butterflies, Pinwheels, and Wallpaper: Inv. 1, 3
8.G.A.2	Understand that a two-dimensional figure is congruent to another if the second can be obtained from the first by a sequence of rotations, reflections, and translations; given two congruent figures, describe a sequence that exhibits the congruence between them.	Butterflies, Pinwheels, and Wallpaper: Inv. 2, 3
8.G.A.3	Describe the effect of dilations, translations, rotations, and reflections on two-dimensional figures using coordinates.	Butterflies, Pinwheels, and Wallpaper: Inv. 3, 4
8.G.A.4	Understand that a two-dimensional figure is similar to another if the second can be obtained from the first by a sequence of rotations, reflections, translations, and dilations; given two similar twodimensional figures, describe a sequence that exhibits the similarity between them.	Looking for Pythagoras: Inv. 5 Butterflies, Pinwheels, and Wallpaper: Inv. 4
8.G.A.5	Use informal arguments to establish facts about the angle sum and exterior angle of triangles, about the angles created when parallel lines are cut by a transversal, and the angle-angle criterion for similarity of triangles. For example, arrange three copies of the same triangle so that the sum of the three angles appears to form a line, and give an argument in terms of transversals why this is so.	Butterflies, Pinwheels, and Wallpaper: Inv. 3, 4
8.G.B	**Understand and apply the Pythagorean Theorem.**	
8.G.B.6	Explain a proof of the Pythagorean Theorem and its converse.	Looking for Pythagoras: Inv. 3
8.G.B.7	Apply the Pythagorean Theorem to determine unknown side lengths in right triangles in real-world and mathematical problems in two and three dimensions.	Looking for Pythagoras: Inv. 3, 4, 5
8.G.B.8	Apply the Pythagorean Theorem to find the distance between two points in a coordinate system.	Looking for Pythagoras: Inv. 3, 5

Number	Standard for Mathematical Content	CMP3 Unit: Investigation
8.G.C	**Solve real-world and mathematical problems involving volume of cylinders, cones, and spheres.**	
8.G.C.9	Know the formulas for the volumes of cones, cylinders, and spheres and use them to solve real-world and mathematical problems.	Say It With Symbols: Inv. 2
8.SP.A	**Investigate patterns of association in bivariate data.**	
8.SP.A.1	Construct and interpret scatter plots for bivariate measurement data to investigate patterns of association between two quantities. Describe patterns such as clustering, outliers, positive or negative association, linear association, and nonlinear association.	Thinking With Mathematical Models: Inv. 1, 2, 3, 4
8.SP.A.2	Know that straight lines are widely used to model relationships between two quantitative variables. For scatter plots that suggest a linear association, informally fit a straight line, and informally assess the model fit by judging the closeness of the data points to the line.	Thinking With Mathematical Models: Inv. 2, 4
8.SP.A.3	Use the equation of a linear model to solve problems in the context of bivariate measurement data, interpreting the slope and intercept. For example, in a linear model for a biology experiment, interpret a slope of 1.5 cm/hr as meaning that an additional hour of sunlight each day is associated with an additional 1.5 cm in mature plant height.	Thinking With Mathematical Models: Inv. 2, 4
8.SP.A.4	Understand that patterns of association can also be seen in bivariate categorical data by displaying frequencies and relative frequencies in a two-way table. Construct and interpret a two-way table summarizing data on two categorical variables collected from the same subjects. Use relative frequencies calculated for rows or columns to describe possible association between the two variables. For example, collect data from students in your class on whether or not they have a curfew on school nights and whether or not they have assigned chores at home. Is there evidence that those who have a curfew also tend to have chores?	Thinking With Mathematical Models: Inv. 5

Number	Standard for Mathematical Content	CMP3 Unit: Investigation
N-Q.A	**Reason quantitatively and use units to solve problems.**	
N-Q.A.1	Use units as a way to understand problems and to guide the solution of multi-step problems; choose and interpret units consistently in formulas; choose and interpret the scale and the origin in graphs and data displays.	Thinking With Mathematical Models: Inv. 1, 2, 4 Growing, Growing, Growing: Inv. 2, 4 Frogs, Fleas, and Painted Cubes: Inv. 1 Say It With Symbols: Inv. 2, 3, 4 Function Junction: Inv. 1
N-Q.A.2	Define appropriate quantities for the purpose of descriptive modeling.	Thinking With Mathematical Models: Inv. 1 Growing, Growing, Growing: Inv. 2 Say It With Symbols: Inv. 2, 4 Function Junction: Inv. 1
N-Q.A.3	Choose a level of accuracy appropriate to limitations on measurement when reporting quantities.	Looking for Pythagoras: Inv. 2, 4, 5
N-RN.A	**Extend the properties of exponents to rational exponents.**	
N-RN.A.1	Explain how the definition of the meaning of rational exponents follows from extending the properties of integer exponents to those values, allowing for a notation for radicals in terms of rational exponents. For example, we define $5^{1/3}$ to be the cube root of 5 because we want $(5^{1/3})^3 = 5^{(1/3)3}$ to hold, so $(5^{1/3})^3$ must equal 5.	Growing, Growing, Growing: Inv. 5
N-RN.A.2	Rewrite expressions involving radicals and rational exponents using the properties of exponents.	Growing, Growing, Growing: Inv. 5
N-RN.B	**Use properties of rational and irrational numbers.**	
N-RN.B.3	Explain why the sum or product of two rational numbers is rational; that the sum of a rational number and an irrational number is irrational; and that the product of a nonzero rational number and an irrational number is irrational.	Say It With Symbols: Inv. 5
A-SSE.A	**Interpret the structure of expressions**	
A-SSE.A.1	Interpret expressions that represent a quantity in terms of its context.	
A-SSE.A.1a	Interpret parts of an expression, such as terms, factors, and coefficients.	Thinking With Mathematical Models: Inv. 2 Growing, Growing, Growing: Inv. 1, 2, 3, 4, 5 Frogs, Fleas, and Painted Cubes: Inv. 2 Say It With Symbols: Inv. 1, 2, 3, 4, 5
A-SSE.A.1b	Interpret complicated expressions by viewing one or more of their parts as a single entity. For example, interpret $P(1+r)n$ as the product of P and a factor not depending on P.	Growing, Growing, Growing: Inv. 3, 4 Frogs, Fleas, and Painted Cubes: Inv. 1, 2, 3 Say It With Symbols: Inv. 1, 2, 3, 4, 5

Number	Standard for Mathematical Content	CMP3 Unit: Investigation
A-SSE.A.2	Use the structure of an expression to identify ways to rewrite it. For example, see $x^4 - y^4$ as $(x^2)^2 - (y^2)^2$, thus recognizing it as a difference of squares that can be factored as $(x^2 - y^2)(x^2 + y^2)$.	Growing, Growing, Growing: Inv. 5 Frogs, Fleas, and Painted Cubes: Inv. 2, 3 Say It With Symbols: Inv. 1, 2, 3, 4, 5 Function Junction: Inv. 4
A-SSE.B	**Write expressions in equivalent forms to solve problems**	
A-SSE.B.3	Choose and produce an equivalent form of an expression to reveal and explain properties of the quantity represented by the expression.	
A-SSE.B.3a	Factor a quadratic expression to reveal the zeros of the function it defines.	Say It With Symbols: Inv. 3, 4
A-SSE.B.3b	Complete the square in a quadratic expression to reveal the maximum or minimum value of the function it defines.	Function Junction: Inv. 4
A-SSE.B.3c	Use the properties of exponents to transform expressions for exponential functions. For example the expression $1.15t$ can be rewritten as $(1.15^{1/12})12t \approx 1.01212t$ to reveal the approximate equivalent monthly interest rate if the annual rate is 15%.	Growing, Growing, Growing: Inv. 5
A-APR.A	**Perform arithmetic operations on polynomials**	
A-APR.A.1	Understand that polynomials form a system analogous to the integers, namely, they are closed under the operations of addition, subtraction, and multiplication; add, subtract, and multiply polynomials.	Function Junction: Inv. 5
A-CED.A	**Create equations that describe numbers or relationships**	
A-CED.A.1	Create equations and inequalities in one variable and use them to solve problems. Include equations arising from linear and quadratic functions, and simple rational and exponential functions.	Thinking With Mathematical Models: Inv. 2 Looking for Pythagoras: Inv. 4 Growing, Growing, Growing: Inv. 1 Frogs, Fleas, and Painted Cubes: Inv. 1 Say It With Symbols: Inv. 2, 3, 4, 5 It's In the System: Inv. 3
A-CED.A.2	Create equations in two or more variables to represent relationships between quantities; graph equations on coordinate axes with labels and scales.	Thinking With Mathematical Models: Inv. 2, 3, 4 Looking for Pythagoras: Inv. 5 Growing, Growing, Growing: Inv. 1, 2, 3, 4 Frogs, Fleas, and Painted Cubes: Inv. 1, 2, 3, 4 Say It With Symbols: Inv. 3, 4, 5 It's In the System: Inv. 1, 2, 3, 4
A-CED.A.3	Represent constraints by equations or inequalities, and by systems of equations and/or inequalities, and interpret solutions as viable or nonviable options in a modeling context. For example, represent inequalities describing nutritional and cost constraints on combinations of different foods.	It's In the System: Inv. 1, 2, 3, 4
A-CED.A.4	Rearrange formulas to highlight a quantity of interest, using the same reasoning as in solving equations. For example, rearrange Ohm's law $V = IR$ to highlight resistance R.	Thinking With Mathematical Models: Inv. 3 It's In the System: Inv. 1, 2

Number	Standard for Mathematical Content	CMP3 Unit: Investigation
A-REI.A	**Understand solving equations as a process of reasoning and explain the reasoning**	
A-REI.A.1	Explain each step in solving a simple equation as following from the equality of numbers asserted at the previous step, starting from the assumption that the original equation has a solution. Construct a viable argument to justify a solution method.	Thinking With Mathematical Models: Inv. 2 Say It With Symbols: Inv. 3
A-REI.B	**Solve equations and inequalities in one variable**	
A-REI.B.3	Solve linear equations and inequalities in one variable, including equations with coefficients represented by letters.	Thinking With Mathematical Models: Inv. 2 Say It With Symbols: Inv. 2, 3, 4 It's In the System: Inv. 1, 2, 3
A-REI.B.4	Solve quadratic equations in one variable.	
A-REI.B.4a	Use the method of completing the square to transform any quadratic equation in x into an equation of the form $(x - p)^2 = q$ that has the same solutions. Derive the quadratic formula from this form.	Function Junction: Inv. 4
A-REI.B.4b	Solve quadratic equations by inspection (e.g., for $x^2 = 49$), taking square roots, completing the square, the quadratic formula and factoring, as appropriate to the initial form of the equation. Recognize when the quadratic formula gives complex solutions and write them as $a \pm bi$ for real numbers a and b.	Say It With Symbols: Inv. 3, 4 It's In the System: Inv. 3 Function Junction: Inv. 4
A-REI.C	**Solve systems of equations**	
A-REI.C.5	Prove that, given a system of two equations in two variables, replacing one equation by the sum of that equation and a multiple of the other produces a system with the same solutions.	It's In the System: Inv. 2
A-REI.C.6	Solve systems of linear equations exactly and approximately (e.g., with graphs), focusing on pairs of linear equations in two variables.	Thinking With Mathematical Models: Inv. 2 Say It With Symbols: Inv. 3 It's In the System: Inv. 1, 2, 4
A-REI.C.7	Solve a simple system consisting of a linear equation and a quadratic equation in two variables algebraically and graphically. For example, find the points of intersection between the line $y = -3x$ and the circle $x^2 + y^2 = 3$.	It's In the System: Inv. 3

Number	Standard for Mathematical Content	CMP3 Unit: Investigation
A-REI.D	**Represent and solve equations and inequalities graphically**	
A-REI.D.10	Understand that the graph of an equation in two variables is the set of all its solutions plotted in the coordinate plane, often forming a curve (which could be a line).	Looking for Pythagoras: Inv. 5 Growing, Growing, Growing: Inv. 1, 2, 3, 4 Frogs, Fleas, and Painted Cubes: Inv. 1, 2, 3, 4 Say It With Symbols: Inv. 3 It's In the System: Inv. 1, 2, 3, 4
A-REI.D.11	Explain why the x-coordinates of the points where the graphs of the equations $y = f(x)$ and $y = g(x)$ intersect are the solutions of the equation $f(x) = g(x)$; find the solutions approximately, e.g., using technology to graph the functions, make tables of values, or find successive approximations. Include cases where $f(x)$ and/or $g(x)$ are linear, polynomial, rational, absolute value, exponential, and logarithmic functions.	Say It With Symbols: Inv. 3
A-REI.D.12	Graph the solutions to a linear inequality in two variables as a halfplane (excluding the boundary in the case of a strict inequality), and graph the solution set to a system of linear inequalities in two variables as the intersection of the corresponding half-planes.	It's In the System: Inv. 4
F-IF.A	**Understand the concept of a function and use function notation**	
F-IF.A.1	Understand that a function from one set (called the domain) to another set (called the range) assigns to each element of the domain exactly one element of the range. If f is a function and x is an element of its domain, then $f(x)$ denotes the output of f corresponding to the input x. The graph of f is the graph of the equation $y = f(x)$.	Thinking With Mathematical Models: Inv. 2 Function Junction: Inv. 1
F-IF.A.2	Use function notation, evaluate functions for inputs in their domains, and interpret statements that use function notation in terms of a context.	Function Junction: Inv. 1
F-IF.A.3	Recognize that sequences are functions, sometimes defined recursively, whose domain is a subset of the integers. For example, the Fibonacci sequence is defined recursively by $f(0) = f(1) = 1$, $f(n + 1) = f(n) + f(n - 1)$ for $n \geq 1$.	Function Junction: Inv. 2

Number	Standard for Mathematical Content	CMP3 Unit: Investigation
F-IF.B	**Interpret functions that arise in applications in terms of the context**	
F-IF.B.4	For a function that models a relationship between two quantities, interpret key features of graphs and tables in terms of the quantities, and sketch graphs showing key features given a verbal description of the relationship. Key features include: intercepts; intervals where the function is increasing, decreasing, positive, or negative; relative maximums and minimums; symmetries; end behavior; and periodicity.	Thinking With Mathematical Models: Inv. 1 Growing, Growing, Growing: Inv. 1, 2, 3, 4 Frogs, Fleas, and Painted Cubes: Inv. 1, 2, 3, 4 Function Junction: Inv. 1, 5
F-IF.B.5	Relate the domain of a function to its graph and, where applicable, to the quantitative relationship it describes. For example, if the function $h(n)$ gives the number of person-hours it takes to assemble n engines in a factory, then the positive integers would be an appropriate domain for the function.	Function Junction: Inv. 1
F-IF.B.6	Calculate and interpret the average rate of change of a function (presented symbolically or as a table) over a specified interval. Estimate the rate of change from a graph.	Thinking With Mathematical Models: Inv. 1 Growing, Growing, Growing: Inv. 3, 4 Function Junction: Inv. 1
F-IF.C	**Analyze functions using different representations**	
F-IF.C.7	Graph functions expressed symbolically and show key features of the graph, by hand in simple cases and using technology for more complicated cases.	
F-IF.C.7a	Graph linear and quadratic functions and show intercepts, maxima, and minima.	Frogs, Fleas, and Painted Cubes: Inv. 1, 2, 3, 4 Function Junction: Inv. 3
F-IF.C.7b	Graph square root, cube root, and piecewise-defined functions, including step functions and absolute value functions.	Function Junction: Inv. 1
F-IF.C.7e	Graph exponential and logarithmic functions, showing intercepts and end behavior, and trigonometric functions, showing period, midline, and amplitude.	Growing, Growing, Growing: Inv. 1, 2, 3, 4, 5

Number	Standard for Mathematical Content	CMP3 Unit: Investigation
F-IF.C.8	Write a function defined by an expression in different but equivalent forms to reveal and explain different properties of the function.	
F-IF.C.8a	Use the process of factoring and completing the square in a quadratic function to show zeros, extreme values, and symmetry of the graph, and interpret these in terms of a context.	Frogs, Fleas, and Painted Cubes: Inv. 2 Function Junction: Inv. 4
F-IF.C.8b	Use the properties of exponents to interpret expressions for exponential functions. For example, identify percent rate of change in functions such as $y = (1.02)^t$, $y = (0.97)^t$, $y = (1.01)^{12t}$, $y = (1.2)^{t/10}$, and classify them as representing exponential growth or decay.	Growing, Growing, Growing: Inv. 3, 5
F-IF.C.9	Compare properties of two functions each represented in a different way (algebraically, graphically, numerically in tables, or by verbal descriptions). For example, given a graph of one quadratic function and an algebraic expression for another, say which has the larger maximum.	Thinking With Mathematical Models: Inv. 1 Growing, Growing, Growing: Inv. 1, 4 Frogs, Fleas, and Painted Cubes: Inv. 1, 3, 4 Say It With Symbols: Inv. 1, 2, 4 Function Junction: Inv. 3, 5
F-BF.A	**Build a function that models a relationship between two quantities**	
F-BF.A.1	Write a function that describes a relationship between two quantities.	
F-BF.A.1a	Determine an explicit expression, a recursive process, or steps for calculation from a context.	Thinking With Mathematical Models: Inv. 1, 2, 3 Frogs, Fleas, and Painted Cubes: Inv. 2, 3 Say It With Symbols: Inv. 1, 2, 4 Function Junction: Inv. 2
F-BF.A.1b	Combine standard function types using arithmetic operations. For example, build a function that models the temperature of a cooling body by adding a constant function to a decaying exponential, and relate these functions to the model.	Thinking With Mathematical Models: Inv. 2 Function Junction: Inv. 5
F-BF.A.2	Write arithmetic and geometric sequences both recursively and with an explicit formula, use them to model situations, and translate between the two forms.	Thinking With Mathematical Models: Inv. 1 Function Junction: Inv. 2

Number	Standard for Mathematical Content	CMP3 Unit: Investigation
F-BF.B	**Build new functions from existing functions**	
F-BF.B.3	Identify the effect on the graph of replacing $f(x)$ by $f(x) + k$, $k\,f(x)$, $f(kx)$, and $f(x + k)$ for specific values of k (both positive and negative); find the value of k given the graphs. Experiment with cases and illustrate an explanation of the effects on the graph using technology. Include recognizing even and odd functions from their graphs and algebraic expressions for them.	Function Junction: Inv. 3
F-BF.B.4	Find inverse functions.	
F-BF.B.4a	Solve an equation of the form $f(x) = c$ for a simple function f that has an inverse and write an expression for the inverse. For example, $f(x) = 2x^3$ for $x > 0$ or $f(x) = (x+1)/(x-1)$ for $x \neq 1$.	Function Junction: Inv. 1
F-LE.A	**Construct and compare linear and exponential models and solve problems**	
F-LE.A.1	Distinguish between situations that can be modeled with linear functions and with exponential functions.	
F-LE.A.1a	Prove that linear functions grow by equal differences over equal intervals, and that exponential functions grow by equal factors over equal intervals.	Growing, Growing, Growing: Inv. 1, 3, 4 Frogs, Fleas, and Painted Cubes: Inv. 3, 4
F-LE.A.1b	Recognize situations in which one quantity changes at a constant rate per unit interval relative to another.	Thinking With Mathematical Models: Inv. 1 Frogs, Fleas, and Painted Cubes: Inv. 3, 4
F-LE.A.1c	Recognize situations in which a quantity grows or decays by a constant percent rate per unit interval relative to another.	Growing, Growing, Growing: Inv. 3, 4
F-LE.A.2	Construct linear and exponential functions, including arithmetic and geometric sequences, given a graph, a description of a relationship, or two input-output pairs (include reading these from a table).	Thinking With Mathematical Models: Inv. 2 Growing, Growing, Growing: Inv. 1, 2, 3, 4 Say It With Symbols: Inv. 4
F-LE.A.3	Observe using graphs and tables that a quantity increasing exponentially eventually exceeds a quantity increasing linearly, quadratically, or (more generally) as a polynomial function.	Growing, Growing, Growing: Inv. 1
F-LE.B	**Interpret expressions for functions in terms of the situation they model**	
F-LE.B.5	Interpret the parameters in a linear or exponential function in terms of a context.	Thinking With Mathematical Models: Inv. 2 Growing, Growing, Growing: Inv. 1, 2, 3, 4 Say It With Symbols: Inv. 4

Number	Standard for Mathematical Content	CMP3 Unit: Investigation
S-ID.A	**Summarize, represent, and interpret data on a single count or measurement variable**	
S-ID.A.1	Represent data with plots on the real number line (dot plots, histograms, and box plots).	Thinking With Mathematical Models: Inv. 4
S-ID.A.2	Use statistics appropriate to the shape of the data distribution to compare center (median, mean) and spread (interquartile range, standard deviation) of two or more different data sets.	Thinking With Mathematical Models: Inv. 4
S-ID.A.3	Interpret differences in shape, center, and spread in the context of the data sets, accounting for possible effects of extreme data points (outliers).	Thinking With Mathematical Models: Inv. 4
S-ID.B	**Summarize, represent, and interpret data on two categorical and quantitative variables**	
S-ID.B.5	Summarize categorical data for two categories in two-way frequency tables. Interpret relative frequencies in the context of the data (including joint, marginal, and conditional relative frequencies). Recognize possible associations and trends in the data.	Thinking With Mathematical Models: Inv. 5
S-ID.B.6	Represent data on two quantitative variables on a scatter plot, and describe how the variables are related.	
S-ID.B.6a	Fit a function to the data; use functions fitted to data to solve problems in the context of the data. Use given functions or choose a function suggested by the context. Emphasize linear and exponential models.	Thinking With Mathematical Models: Inv. 2, 3
S-ID.B.6b	Informally assess the fit of a function by plotting and analyzing residuals.	Thinking With Mathematical Models: Inv. 2, 4
S-ID.B.6c	Fit a linear function for a scatter plot that suggests a linear association.	Thinking With Mathematical Models: Inv. 2
S-ID.C	**Interpret linear models**	
S-ID.C.7	Interpret the slope (rate of change) and the intercept (constant term) of a linear model in the context of the data.	Thinking With Mathematical Models: Inv. 4
S-ID.C.8	Compute (using technology) and interpret the correlation coefficient of a linear fit.	Thinking With Mathematical Models: Inv. 4
S-ID.C.9	Distinguish between correlation and causation.	Thinking With Mathematical Models: Inv. 4, 5

Changes from CMP2 to CMP3

GRADE 6

Grade 6 Before	Grade 6 After
• Prime Time	• Prime Time
• Bits and Pieces I	• Comparing Bits and Pieces
• Shapes and Designs	• Let's Be Rational
• Bits and Pieces II	• Covering and Surrounding
• Covering and Surrounding	• Decimal Operations
• Bits and Pieces III	• Variables and Patterns
• How Likely Is It?	• Data About Us
• Data About Us	

What Changed for Grade 6?

- *Prime Time* contains new content on properties, including the Distributive Property.

- The CCSS emphasis on the concept of ratio at Grade 6 led to reworking *Bits and Pieces I* into *Comparing Bits and Pieces.*

- *Let's Be Rational* is based on *Bits and Pieces II,* with the removal of some content and additional development of division of fractions, including emphasis on estimation. A new Investigation provides algebraic support on properties of operations.

- Changes to *Covering and Surrounding* include cutting back on area of rectangles and moving Investigation of circles to Grade 7. Additional content includes nets and surface area of three-dimensional figures, and volume of prisms with fractional side lengths.

- *Decimal Ops* is a mostly new unit that addresses the decimal fluency standards.

- *How Likely Is It?* has been removed to reflect the elimination of probability at Grade 6 in the CCSS.

- The CCSS calls for the introduction of algebra and graphing at Grade 6, so *Variables and Patterns* has been moved to Grade 6.

- *Data About Us* has been revised to include the statistical analysis of graphs and to include some content from *Samples and Populations.*

GRADE 7

Grade 7 Before	Grade 7 After
• Variables and Patterns	• Shapes and Designs
• Stretching and Shrinking	• Accentuate the Negative
• Comparing and Scaling	• Stretching and Shrinking
• Accentuate the Negative	• Comparing and Scaling
• Moving Straight Ahead	• Moving Straight Ahead
• Filling and Wrapping	• What Do You Expect?
• What Do You Expect?	• Filling and Wrapping
• Data Distributions	• Samples and Populations

What Changed for Grade 7?

- Because of the de-emphasis of Geometry in Grade 6, *Shapes and Designs* has been moved to the beginning of Grade 7.

- *Accentuate the Negative* includes new content on rational numbers. Throughout the unit, students perform operations with fractions, decimals, and integers.

- *Comparing and Scaling* has been revised to develop more completely the ideas and strategies introduced in *Stretching and Shrinking*. Students use proportional reasoning in contexts other than Geometry and develop additional strategies for solving proportions, including efficient scaling and common denominators. More time is spent on developing proportional reasoning and connections among rates, ratios, rate tables, and proportions. The constant of proportionality is introduced and provides connections to the next unit, *Moving Straight Ahead*.

- Some of the content from CMP2's *How Likely Is It?* has been added to the Grade 7 probability unit *What Do You Expect?*

- Some of the data unit *Samples and Populations* has been moved from Grade 8 to Grade 7, with new material added.

- *Filling and Wrapping* picks up circles from *Covering and Surrounding* and adds volume and surface area of cylinders, cones, and spheres.

GRADE 8

Grade 8 Before	Grade 8 After
• Thinking With Mathematical Models	• Thinking With Mathematical Models
• Looking for Pythagoras	• Looking for Pythagoras
• Growing, Growing, Growing	• Growing, Growing, Growing
• Frogs, Fleas, and Painted Cubes	• Frogs, Fleas, and Painted Cubes
• Kaleidoscopes, Hubcaps, and Mirrors	• Butterflies, Pinwheels, and Wallpaper
• Say It With Symbols	• Say It With Symbols
• The Shapes of Algebra	• It's in the System
• Samples and Populations	• Function Junction

What Changed for Grade 8?

- Correlation and two-way-table analysis of *Samples and Populations* is now addressed at the end of *Thinking With Mathematical Models*.

- *Looking for Pythagoras* has been revised to include cube roots, repeating decimals, terminating decimals, and irrational numbers.

- In *Growing, Growing, Growing,* scientific notation is introduced. Content has been added to focus on the rules of exponents and equivalent expressions using exponents. The unit ends with an exploration of the effects of growth rates and *y*-intercepts on the graphs of exponential functions.

- *Butterflies, Pinwheels, and Wallpaper* is a revision of *Kaleidoscopes, Hubcaps, and Mirror*s corresponding to the Grade 8 standards on congruence and similarity.

- A new unit, *It's in the System,* addresses the CCSSM standards on systems of equations.

- Two units are for teachers who want to teach Algebra 1 at Grade 8: *Frogs, Fleas, and Painted Cubes* and *Function Junction.*

Appendix F
Observing a CMP Classroom

"How do you know IT when you see IT?"
Observation Protocol for CMP Classrooms

Overview

This Observation Protocol is designed as a guide for teachers, coaches, administrators, and other support personnel. The protocol provides a general overview of aspects of the classroom on which to concentrate to achieve fidelity of implementation of CMP. These aspects include students' learning practices, discourse, written and oral work, and other actions.

CMP is a problem-centered curriculum that promotes an inquiry-based teaching-learning classroom environment, in which the CCSSM Standards for Mathematical Practice come alive as students pursue solutions to Problems. Implementing a coherent student-centered investigation of mathematics presents a challenge to teachers; they need support and guidance in order to engage and sustain high-level thinking with diverse groups of students.

Many classroom observations focus on the teacher. However, it is the student engagement with mathematics that enhances learning. Thus, one must focus on the learner. Observing students' engagement, through both verbal and written statements, allows for some assessment of the learning potential of a lesson as it is being enacted. Since effective teachers have unique styles for producing rich classroom environments, it is also important to examine what the teacher does to produce such an environment. Moving the mathematical learning forward should always be the main focus.

Use of the Protocol

The intent of the protocol is to inspire rich conversations among teachers, coaches, and administrators about the learning and teaching of mathematics in a productive classroom environment. The rating scale on the protocol is not meant as a way to evaluate teachers; rather, it is provided as a tool for assessing implementation.

Keeping track of every portion of the observation may present difficulties for an observer. One way to use the protocol would be to observe the lesson and record notes using a blank observation sheet, such as Appendix G. Then, while conferencing about the lesson, the teacher and colleague can use those notes to fill in this form. Another option would be to choose a few items on which to focus. So, rather than trying to keep track of all 14 items during the lesson, the observer can focus and document evidence for a few.

A lower score on a particular item may help indicate areas of focus for district or school professional development. You will find creative ways to use the protocol as you consider its benefits.

....

Observing CMP Classrooms was originally developed for the Show-Me Center, an NSF-funded project (2003).
Yvonne Grant, Susan Friel, Glenda Lappan, Elizabeth Phillips, Sandra Wilcox

STUDENT OBSERVATION

1. Students are engaged in important mathematical tasks.

5	4	3	2	1
Most students are engaged in mathematical tasks most of the time.		Some students are engaged in mathematical tasks; others are off task much of the time.		Few students are engaged in mathematical tasks for much of the time.

2. Students communicate using mathematical language.

5	4	3	2	1
Students use mathematical language regularly and correctly to describe and clarify.		Students occasionally use mathematical language; usage is generally correct.		Students use mathematical language in superficial ways; they rely on isolated terms or phrases.

3. Students make connections related to the goals of the lesson.

5	4	3	2	1
Students make connections within mathematics and/or other subject areas.		Teacher tends to state the connections within mathematics and/or other subject areas.		Students make no connections within mathematics and/or other subject areas.

4. Students summarize.

5	4	3	2	1
Students are involved in the process of summarizing the mathematics in a lesson.		Teacher tends to summarize the mathematics in a lesson with little student involvement.		There is no summarizing at the end of the lesson.

5. Students use elements of abstraction (i.e., symbolic representations, theory building, generalizations), if appropriate.

5	4	3	2	1
Students generalize and symbolize ideas beyond the context of the specific Problem.		Students generalize using the context of the Problem.		Students do not generalize; they focus only on specific cases within the context.